McGRAW-HILL PUBLICATIONS IN THE
ZOOLOGICAL SCIENCES
A. FRANKLIN SHULL, Consulting Editor

ANIMAL ECOLOGY

ANIMAL ECOLOGY

BY

A. S. PEARSE

Professor of Zoology, Duke University

First Edition
Second Impression

McGRAW-HILL BOOK COMPANY, Inc.
NEW YORK: 370 SEVENTH AVENUE
LONDON: 6 & 8 BOUVERIE ST., E. C. 4
1926

THE MAPLE PRESS COMPANY, YORK, PA.

TO

VICTOR E. SHELFORD

PREFACE

One who writes a book that pretends to be a general survey of even a limited field of science is continually impressed with his own limitations. The writer is sure that there are many ecologists who could have done this work better. He claims no credit except that of doing the work, which is needed. This book is a very small beginning in a very large field and future developments should make better books possible.

The writer is glad to express his appreciation to certain of his colleagues. Dr. L. E. Noland and Dr. E. S. Hathaway read and criticized the whole manuscript. Dr. E. J. Kraus made valuable suggestions in connection with Chapters I, II, and VII; Mr. Chancey Juday did the same for Chapters V and VI. Dr. A. F. Shull made many useful comments in editing the manuscript. These gentlemen have saved the writer from many errors, but are, of course, not responsible for those that doubtless remain.

A. S. PEARSE.

UNIVERSITY OF WISCONSIN,
  MADISON, WIS.,
    February, 1926.

CONTENTS

ANIMAL ECOLOGY

CHAPTER I

INTRODUCTION

Ecology is the branch of biological science that deals with the relations of organisms to their surroundings. It is concerned with the adjustments and responses of whole organisms, or groups of organisms. Though many of its methods are physiological, and though it often advances through physiological experiments, it differs from physiology in that it is concerned with the responses of complete organisms, rather than those of parts. Ecology is the science of the responses of organisms to the factors in their environment.

THE RELATIONS OF ANIMALS TO ENVIRONMENT

Animal ecology may be said to have three chief aspects: (1) descriptive, (2) quantitative, (3) analytic and synthetic. *Descriptive* ecology is concerned with knowledge relating to the mode of life of animals—their habits and habitat preferences, the conditions under which they live, the association of different species together, the characteristics of animal societies, the dominance of certain societies over others, the origins and successions of societies. *Quantitative* ecology deals with information relating to the measurement of the environmental requirements and of the "vital limits" (extreme limits of toleration in the fluctuation of environmental factors) of animals, the demands that animals make upon the environment for their own maintenance and increase, the number and variety of species that can exist in particular habitats. *Analytic* and *synthetic* ecology attempts to analyze the environment and its effects by varying particular factors under controlled conditions, to reconstruct the past and predict the future, to examine into the causes of the adjustments of animals—why animals have specific habitats; why societies originate, attain success, and become extinct; why

1

animals become adapted (acquire new limits of toleration for factors in the environment).

Animals.—An animal is a coordinated, individualized "system of activities" (Wheeler, 1911) that, though it consists of matter in the form of chemical compounds and conforms to physical laws, has its individuality in the peculiar type of its activities, which are ever changing, yet maintain a certain characteristic average condition. It has been defined as "a dynamic agency acting in an unstable environment," and as a "system in dynamic equilibrium." The substances which make up the bodies of animals are chiefly those found in the atmosphere: carbon, oxygen, hydrogen, nitrogen—or, as they commonly occur in nature: carbon dioxide, oxygen, water, nitrogen, ammonia. In one sense carbon dioxide is the basis of all living substance. Some affirm that there is more to an animal than matter energized by a specific and peculiar system of activities—*i.e.*, that there is something necessary to complete an animal besides matter and physical energy. Science has not yet been able to show that there is anything else. There are two possible reasons for this failure: (1) there is nothing save matter and energy, but the nature of living substance is such that it has as yet defied complete scientific analysis, perhaps on account of its extreme complexity; (2) there is something else; something that has not been, and perhaps never can be, described or measured. Until one of these possibilities is established, there can be no conclusion. The writer, while he recognizes that either possibility may sometime be proved to be correct, feels that it is more scientific to accept the first point of view until the second is proved. Otherwise there appears to be little hope for the ultimate solution of biological problems. Again, there is perhaps no possibility of knowing all about living things, but those who have been trained in science cannot refrain from trying to go farther into the unknown—they would be unscientific if they did.

An animal, then, is a highly complex system of activities that take place under certain specific conditions in peculiar, highly complex bodies of matter. An animal must continue to maintain its system of activities or its individuality ceases to be and its protoplasm disintegrates into simpler, non-living substances that do not have the peculiarities of animals. It "maintains itself" by acquiring matter and energy from the environment, and by giving back matter and energy to the environment in the form of waste products. The common needs of an animal are air, water, organic food, cleanliness or freedom from wastes and substances that will interfere with the system of activities; at times also exercise, protection, conditions for propagation, freedom from competition, and other things.

Each animal has a peculiar constitution, or behavior pattern (Child, 1921), that makes it unique among living things. Animals of the same species, of course, show more similarity of patterns than do those of different species, but each animal has certain characteristic peculiarities. This constitution or behavior pattern limits the style of response that may take place in order to maintain an animal system of activities. A bass does not pull earthworms out of lawns; nor does a robin hunt for insects among aquatic plants. One terrier barks and runs; another terrier comes forward and bites an intruder. Each animal must meet the environment on its own terms or it is "like a fish out of water." Animals are adapted to a high degree for particular habitats, largely because they possess certain characteristics that are inherited from preexisting animals.

Plants Compared with Animals.—Plants are like animals in that their living substance appears to be much the same, but the representatives of each kingdom show certain specificities of response to the environment. Plants are generally sessile. They acquire from the earth and atmosphere inorganic materials which they make into organic substances. They respond in readily observable ways to various conditions in the environment by assuming particular forms of growth, and, of course, may also undergo various internal changes which adapt them better to varying external conditions. Animals generally are motile, and stimuli often cause them to move; when they live in different habitats there is usually no pronounced change in form, but their bodies vary physiologically. Though there are many exceptions, it may be said that plants usually grow attached in one spot where they may acquire food from the soil, water, and atmosphere, where they can secure energy from the sun, and where they grow into a form adapted to the surroundings. Animals depend largely on organic food for their body-building substances and for more or less of their energy. Stimuli usually cause them to respond by movement and they may thus migrate to places that are favorable for existence.

Environment.—Environment that has relation to animals is at or near the surface of the earth. It consists of matter and energy that are continually interacting, so that continual change is as characteristic of environment as it is of animals. The earth is subjected to various forces which act from outside. It is illuminated by light that has traveled from stars millions of miles away, it receives radiant energy from the sun and moon; all bodies outside the earth act upon it through gravitation; the atmosphere is stirred up by various forces; winds move the waters, thus creating currents which wear down land surfaces and carry sediments to the sea. The rotation of the earth about the sun brings seasonal changes; the rotation about the earth's own axis causes alternating day and night, and, with the gravitational pull of the moon and sun, is the chief factor in producing the tides and ocean currents. Many changes are taking place within the earth itself—circulation of water and other fluids, shifting of solids, chemical reactions, and various rearrangements of forces.

The environment is complex and changeful. One factor does not change without influencing others—water cannot be warmed without losing some of its power to absorb gases; air cannot be cooled without losing some of its power to hold water vapor. Some changes are sudden and erratic, like tornadoes and earthquakes; others occur slowly in an orderly manner; and some are rhythmic. A hill will always be worn down in time by erosion, an isolated lake will after a long period fill up with sediment. The present always depends upon the past, and what occurs today is, in part at least, the result of what happened yesterday. If a hill is formed, it is reasonable to suppose that it will wear down at a certain rate, which may be predicted through a knowledge of the erosive forces, the resistance of particular materials, etc. Rhythmical changes, like those associated with the seasons, months, tides, and days, may be depended upon to recur with reasonable regularity.

Habitats.—Somewhere at or near the surface of the earth each animal has a *habitat*. That is, there is some place where an animal system of activities can find an environmental system of activities in which it can maintain a reasonable condition of stability and continue to exist. Clements (1905) says: "The habitat is the sum of all the forces or factors present in a given area." If all is most favorable for the activities of an animal, conditions are said to be optimum. An animal can stand a certain range of variation in environmental conditions, but if any factor varies beyond its maximum or minimum limit of toleration, it must cease to exist or migrate to a favorable place. Warming (1909) says: "Every species must be in harmony, as regards both its external and internal construction, with the natural conditions under which it lives." If a species continues to find the environmental favorable, it may take possession of it, perhaps expelling other species, and becomes a climax formation for a certain area of the earth. A *climax formation* is a species, or group of species, that is better fitted for a particular habitat than any other. It will usually continue to occupy an area until the environment undergoes a marked change, or until some other system of organic activities is present that can reach more harmonious relations with the environment. Up to the time when a climax formation is reached there is a succession of formations, but such a formation may continue indefinitely after becoming established.

Adaptation.—An animal is successful when it fits the environment. This means that its inherited system of activities can find a place where it can establish harmonious relations with the environment. The total earth environment is so diverse that no animal can live in all the conditions present. Each species shows *adaptation* to a certain habitat, or group of habitats. Plants, in general, have wide ranges of adaptability, but if a plant does not begin its life in a suitable habitat, it ceases to exist. Most animals are able to move about somewhat and thus have a means for seeking out the most favorable habitat. The behavior of animals also maintains them in appropriate habitats after these have been discovered. Adaptation is perhaps more characteristic of the organism than of the environment. Henderson (1917) has pointed out that the particular character of earth environment made the existence of life possible, life depending on complex compounds built up largely from carbon dioxide, water, and simple nitrogenous compounds. The degree of diversity in the adjustments that living systems of activities have made in the past to conditions that probably existed before they even came into being makes the meaning of adaptation apparent—living systems are adjusted to a wonderful variety of diverse conditions in the earth environment.

Perhaps the most important relation of an animal to environment is a natural, given, or hereditary adaptability to a particular habitat. If the habitat changes a little, most animals can, through slight adjustments in their internal activities, reach a new and slightly different condition of comparative stability. If the habitat changes to such a degree, however, that the activities of an animal cannot be adjusted, then it becomes one to which the animal is not "adapted." An animal is continually making adjustments in response to stimuli. The stimuli may come from the outside or from changes in the internal physiological state of the animal itself. A successful animal must gain material and energy from the environment without being injured by it. To a considerable degree the environment controls the animal, for most of the activities of the animal system are due to changes in it. To be sure, all organisms belonging to a single species have about the same inherent capacity for expression in their reactions with environment and, being alive, they must continually undergo internal metabolic adjustments, but what they do at any particular moment is usually determined by environment. The organism and the environment are both more or less unstable, and if the latter changes, the former must undergo adjustments that tend toward conditions of greater stability. Pike and Scott (1915) have pointed out that organisms have two methods of attaining stability: (1) by making internal adjustments so that the body becomes changed and thus attuned to conditions outside, and (2) by making adjustments that serve to keep the interior of the body unchanging, regardless of conditions without. By the first method, the organism changes to fit the environment; by the second, the organism is more or less independent of environmental changes and its internal reactions usually remain fairly uniform as long as it lives.

The peculiar system or range of activities that fits each species for a particular habitat appears to be inherited with great fidelity in each succeeding generation. The specificity of adaptation in structure, function, and behavior and its relation to ecology are problems of evolution, which will be discussed in the next section.

ECOLOGY AND EVOLUTION

An animal cannot exist without environment. "The organism and the environment interpenetrate one another all through" (Sumner, 1921); and Bather (1921) remarks:

For the evolutionary biologist a species contains in itself and its environment the possibility of producing its successor. The words "its environment" are necessary because an organism cannot be conceived apart from its environment.

Adjustment to Environment.—The palæontologists agree that progressive evolutionary changes in the past have generally been correlated with striking environmental changes, and that wide diversity of particular types came about during prolonged periods of comparative stability.

The great upward steps in evolution are primarily determined by environmental changes which operate to diminish the quantity of life and work toward the extinction of ancient types. On the other hand, in the splitting of a family into various subfamilies, genera, and species, the leading rôle would seem to be taken by a tendency toward organic change, the environment remaining in the meantime nearly constant (Barrell, 1917).

According to Barrell's view, the great steps in evolution are not a consequence of life, but are forced by climatic change. The species that have persisted unchanged during the longest periods of time have been those that were in most perfect adjustment with the environment. During periods of environmental stress and change new types appeared, and during the favorable conditions afforded by long periods of stable environment, competition and perhaps other factors caused the differentiation of established types. There is no question that, in a general way, evolutionary transformations in animals have been correlated with environmental changes.

Limits to Adjustment.—In relation to powers of adjustment, animals have two types of characters: (1) those that may change during the life of an individual, and (2) those that may be modified only after long periods of time. In order that evolution may take place, it is necessary that species change. It is, therefore, necessary that modifications of systems of activities be transmitted in some way from one generation to another. The great questions of evolution at the present time are: (1) What causes animals to vary? and (2) How do modified characters become a part of the system of activities that passes on from one generation of animals to the next? For an ecologist, the important question is: How do animals become adapted?

Animals continually become adapted to minor changes in environment. The amount of perspiration given off from a man's body is correlated with variations in air temperature; the lengths of the terminal spine and the helmet on the body of the little crustacean, *Daphnia longispina*, are correlated with the temperature and viscosity of the water in which the animal lives and are also markedly influenced by the character of available food (Woltereck, 1909); drug addicts become tolerant to doses of poisons that would be fatal to those unaccustomed to the use of drugs; a person who has survived an attack of smallpox is immune to the disease.   Everywhere that animals live there are instances of adaptation to environment.   But adjustments made during the life of an individual are rarely, if ever, transmitted.   The children of a drug addict do not have unusual toleration for drugs and those who have had smallpox do not transmit immunity to their offspring.   While every animal system of activities is free to make many minor adjustments, the main features and limitations are hereditary.   Even the selection of peculiarly "adapted" individuals through a number of generations does not essentially change the hereditary pattern that is characteristic of each species.   The stock reverts to the original conditions as soon as the selection of peculiar individuals ceases—unless a mutant, or an animal that has already acquired a new range of variation, is accidentally selected.

The details of animal response are free from hereditary restraint and depend more or less upon the varying physiological states of the animal, but the main features of behavior cannot be changed from the hereditary species pattern.   The range of activities is hereditary.   The difference between readily adaptable and comparatively stable adaptations is apparently merely one of degree, but the latter to some extent rather inflexibly hold species in the parental groove.   Adaptation does not mean that an animal by striving to reach a certain state can do so, but that it has certain given characteristics that happen to fit the environment in which it lives.   It may have certain characteristics that do not fit the environment, but it can continue to live if these have no vital bearing on the adjustment of its activities.

Ecologically, limitations can be seen in the powers that animals have of adjusting themselves to changes in the environment. Some animals, like *Daphnia longispina*, assume different forms that appear better to correlate their activities with various environmental conditions. Other animals show striking instances of adjustments to regularly recurring states in the environment—there are adaptations to daily, monthly, and seasonal cycles. There are some orderly processes, however, to which animals are apparently unable to adjust themselves. For example, when a pond is physiographically young, it furnishes a habitat for many species of animals. As mud and aquatic vegetation accumulate and fill the pond, there is, after many years, a succession of species, and in its old age the pond has a different fauna from that present in the beginning. Shelford (1911) studied the fishes in ponds along the shore of Lake Michigan. He found that the young ponds contained several species of sunfishes, but in the older ponds such fishes were entirely absent and the dominant species were bullheads and mud-minnows. In this instance the members of the sunfish family doubtless possessed the usual powers of adjustment, but their hereditary patterns made them unable to go far enough to keep pace with the physiographic changes; hence they were succeeded by other species with different hereditary patterns that permitted them to flourish under the new conditions.

Variation and Environment.—Some evolutionists doubt if any adjustment to environment that is modifiable during the life of an individual can exert an influence on hereditary qualities. They hold that animals are produced with a certain range of adjustment that cannot be changed by any factor of the environment. From this point of view adaptation to environment is, in a sense, accidental. Characteristics are present; if they fit the environment, an animal may exist; if they do not, the animal cannot exist. With this point of view in mind it may be well to examine some of the views concerning the causes and factors of evolution, with particular reference to their applications to ecology.

Variation and Evolution.—To understand evolution, it is essential to account for genotypic variations in animals—and this has not as yet been done satisfactorily. It is known that each species consists of a mixture of diverse strains which breed reasonably true to type if selected and kept segregated. Such selection of strains has been made among protozoans by Jennings (1920), and among domestic animals by many persons. Among many animals conjugation changes the range of variation, either by the recombination of characters already present or through the intensification or weakening of characters in some other way. Dedifferentiation in one direction apparently precludes return to a generalized condition, and evolution is, therefore, orthogenetic. It is known that parts developed to an extraordinary degree are apt to be more variable than those that are not. It is also recognized that wide-ranging species are ordinarily more variable than those with restricted ranges. But all these and other known facts do not solve the problems of variation. Hereditary changes are produced, and no one knows exactly how or why.

Though there is little or no *evidence* that adaptive characteristics acquired during the life of an individual are transmitted to the next generation, Semon (1904) insists that heredity is racial memory; Davenport (1908) believes that individual attunement initiates racial attunement; and Child (1915), that an animal's threshold of stimulation can be gradually increased and that this condition may be inherited. Jennings (1911) states that:

The gradual formation of developmental habits seems to be the only form of the idea of the inheritance of acquired characters that is not opposed by any of the experimental facts, that helps us to understand why so many characters are not inherited—since they are not produced by the developmental processes of the organism—that fits all the recent cases that give positive evidence for the inheritance of acquired characters, and that is based on law actually known to hold for those organic processes that are most favorable for study with relation to such laws.

Until there is more evidence, it must be held that, though hereditary characters must change if evolution is to take place, environment apparently has little importance as a direct causative agent in producing such changes. Shull (1917) expresses the opinion of many modern biologists when he says that evolution is due to chemical changes in chromosomes and that the inheritance of such changes is "usually, if not always, independent of the environment."

Selection and Environment.—After species change, and new hereditary characters have actually come into existence, natural selection appears to be the most important agency for preserving such new ranges of adjustment. Davenport (1903) has pointed out the importance of the environment in selection and advanced a "theory of segregation in the fittest environment" which supplements Darwin's natural selection theory. According to his view, unadaptive variations may become adaptive, "if they can find their proper place in nature." "Suitable" structures may appear before they find proper environments.

Environment and Evolution.—Altogether, environment has played an important rôle in evolution. It has furnished a culture medium for the incubation of variations, has limited the line of development that could take place, and has even exercised control over the rate and extent of evolutionary changes. There has, however, been no general conformity when diverse animals made adjustments toward a condition of stability in a particular environment. Animals have attained similar ends by very diverse means; structure and classification are not closely related to habitat. At times slight structural differences between species are correlated with differences in habits; at other times species having almost identical structural patterns show radically different responses to environment. These facts indicate that environmental variations are not the direct cause of evolutionary variations. Variation does not match environment closely enough—it makes too many detours into blind alleys. Perhaps the evolution of habits has usually preceded the evolution of structures. Robertson (1906) believes that new species arise through an overpopulated condition, which forces certain individuals to take on new ranges of adjustment to the environment. Natural selection then operates in favor of individuals that change their habits. Robertson claims that the ecological basis for an hereditary morphological change is in the taking on of a new use for a structure. The evidence to support this rather attractive view is still to be found.

Osborn (1917) has advanced an "energy conception of life" which depends on "action and interaction," and he claims that organisms have developed according to law rather than chance. According to his view there has been, since life began, a continual interaction between environment, organism, germ plasm, and life environment (that made up of living organisms). His discussion is of value in directing attention to the fact that organisms have never been separated from environment, but does not furnish the needed *evidence* on the causes of variation.

ECOLOGY AND ZOÖGEOGRAPHY

The surface of the earth is made up of land and water. The area of the land surface is 28 per cent of that of the earth and its average height above sea level is about 2250 feet. The area of the water is 72 per cent and it has an average depth of 13,860 feet. *A priori,* one would perhaps expect to find more species of aquatic than of terrestrial animals and, were it not for the marvelous variety of adjustments that insects have made to various environmental conditions, this expectation would be fulfilled. There is more water to be inhabited than land. Water is a more stable habitat, and palæontological evidence indicates that life existed there first— the early animals were apparently all marine. If variation in animals is due to variation in environment, then the water should support fewer types of animals because it is, and has been, more stable. Perhaps little variation has permitted more types to occupy the same region of the environment in water. More offshoots of generalized types of animal structure exist in the ocean then elsewhere, however, and some whole groups of animals (like the echinoderms, brachiopods, and cephalopods) have never been able to establish residence in freshwater or on land. While the ocean remains the home of many established, archaic types, some of the more progressive animals have, during the long periods since life began, migrated to freshwater and land habitats.

Present Distribution of Animals.—The present distribution of animals is not only the result of conditions as they exist today, but also depends upon the distribution and the evolution of habitats and species in the past. The existing environment promotes or limits the distribution of animals over the earth by furnishing suitable or unsuitable habitats, but present conditions do not furnish a sufficient explanation for the present distribution of animals. Certain types have originated in particular parts of the earth and each locality has a more or less peculiar aspect that results from the presence of the types of animals that came into existence there. Though more or less similar environments exist in different parts of the earth, the animals inhabiting them are not always of the same types. Australia is, and for a long time has been, the home of most of the marsupials; Madagascar furnishes an abiding place for the majority of the species of lemurs; antelopes are characteristic of Africa; sloths of South America.

Zoögeography.—Zoögeography, like all other branches of science, is made up from facts and their interpretations. It is not complete, and perhaps never will be. Its knowledge is being extended constantly by observations, experiment, and new interpretations of facts. Zoögeography, however, has progressed to such a degree that its students have been able to divide the earth up into a number of regions and subregions. In limiting such regional areas, it has been necessary to consider the ranges of types and species of animals and the existing conditions of environment—present and past. It is generally agreed that in the land environment temperature is the most potent factor which limits the ranges of animals; that water perhaps ranks second; and that many other factors may be important under various circumstances. Water habitats are reasonably stable in regard to temperature; the salts and gases are here often more important. Sometimes closely related species have practically identical ranges, sometimes they occupy different areas which have different environmental characteristics. In general, wide-ranging species are spread over an area of monotonous environment or they are able to live in a variety of habitats. Species of narrow range are often limited to particular or local habitats.

Centers of Origin and Dispersal.—Animals as species are believed to have originated in particular regions on the earth and to have spread through contiguous areas as far as the environment permitted. Each species thus has a *center of origin*. New species may also have originated in two or more places from a preexisting species, and would then have more than one center of origin. Regions where environmental factors make it particularly easy for a species to spread constitute *highways*, and areas where some environmental factor or factors vary beyond the limit of toleration for the species are *barriers*. Means of dispersal into new regions are found in active migrations; currents; winds; land necks; mountain ranges; shallows; floating objects; the epidermis, feet, crops, and excreta of birds, insects, and other migratory animals; railway trains; ships; etc. Highways are often along mountain ranges or lowland coastal strips, in currents or prevailing winds, etc. Barriers may be related to mountains, valleys, regions where food is lacking, currents, winds, vegetation, salt, aridity, etc. Somewhere within the range of any species there is usually an area where environmental factors are better for this species than elsewhere, and this region, where the optimum is most nearly attained, may be a *center of dispersal* from which the species spreads. The center of dispersal may, or may not, occupy the same area as the center of origin.

The ranges of particular species may be extended or contracted—gradually through long periods of time; periodically, as in the seasonal migrations of many birds; sporadically, as in the migrations of the Scandinavian lemming; or through human agency. The success of the mongoose, gipsy moth, English sparrow, rabbit, and other animals in regions where they had been previously unknown indicates that many species might occupy larger areas if they could gain access to new favorable localities. The changefulness of environment and the evolution of animal species have set some hard problems for the zoögeographer. For example, a species may be extinct at its center of origin and spreading from some far-distant center of dispersal. In attempting to unravel such tangles Adams (1909) found it expedient to formulate certain criteria for the determination of centers of dispersal and origin. These criteria were intended to apply to North American beetles, but may be utilized for determining centers for any species. They are as follows:

1. Location of great or maximum taxonomic differentiation of a type or types.
2. Location of synthetic, primitive, or closely allied taxonomic forms or groups possessing convergent affinities.
3. Location of maximum size of taxonomic forms or groups.
4. Continuity and convergence of lines of dispersal.
5. Direction indicated by seasonal appearance; vernal suggesting boreal or montane origin, and æstival, austral or lowland derivation.
6. Direction indicated by continuity and directness of individual variations or modifications along highways of dispersal.
7. Location where the succession of beetle associations or societies reaches the relative equilibrium of a climax association or formation.
8. Location of dominance and great abundance of individuals.
9. Direction indicated by biographical or ecological affinities.
10. Location of least dependence upon a restricted habitat, except humid types in arid regions, and analogous cases.
11. Location (when both center of origin and dispersal) of maximum ecological differentiation in habits, habitats, food, etc.

About half of Adams' criteria deal with relations to environment. Such dependence of zoögeography on ecology is usual. From the point of view of zoögeography, existing, spreading, and disappearing are the most important attributes of animals. Animals cannot exist without an environment; the direction and speed of spreading are limited by environment; when environment is not suitable, animals decline and become extinct.

Zoögeography represents the more or less stable results of ecology—the distributional relations of animals that environment has permitted to remain for a considerable period of time. Dahl (1921) has recently published an excellent discussion of the relations of ecology to the geographic distribution of animals.

CLASSIFICATION OF HABITATS

It is possible to look at the relations of animals to environment from two points of view: (1) that of the animals or groups of animals that live in available habitats, and (2) that of the habitats as situations in which animals may live. From the view point of ecology, the unit of classification is a *mores* (Shelford, 1912). A terminology for the chief groups used in ecological classification is given in Table I.

Ecological Groups.—*Mores* are

. . . groups of organisms in full agreement as to physiological life histories shown by the details of habitat preference, time of reproduction, reactions to physical factors of the environment, etc. The organisms constituting a mores usually belong to a single species but may include more than one species as specificities of behavior are not primarily significant. *Consocies* are groups of mores usually dominated by one or two of the mores concerned and in agreement as to the main features of habitat preference, reaction to physical factors, time of reproduction, etc. . . . *Strata* are groups of consocies occupying recognizable vertical divisions of a uniform area. Strata are in agreement as to materials for abode and general physical conditions, but in less detail than the consocies which constitute them . . . *Associations* are groups of strata uniform over a considerable area. The majority of mores, consocies, and strata are different in different associations. A minority of the strata may be similar though rarely identical . . . *Formations* are groups of associations. Formations differ from one another in all the strata, no two being closely similar. The number of species common to two formations is usually small (*e.g.*, 5 per cent). Migrations of individuals from one formation to another are relatively rare.

Provinces are groups of formations that extend over large areas. *Realms* are groups of provinces and constitute the largest unitary areas of the earth. The chief ecological groups on the earth are the following:

SUPERREALM α. AQUATIC ANIMALS

REALM I. Marine Animals

   PROVINCE A. Littoral Animals

    Formation 1. Animals of Hard Beaches

     ASSOCIATION *a.* Animals of Rock Walls
      Stratum 1. Animals in Zone above High Tide
      Stratum 2. Animals in Intertidal Zone
      Stratum 3. Animals in Laminarian Zone
      Stratum 4. Animals in Shorewater

     ASSOCIATION *b.* Animals of Pebbly Beaches
      Stratum 1. Animals in Zone above High Tide
      Stratum 2. Animals in Intertidal Zone
      Stratum 3. Animals in Laminarian Zone
      Stratum 4. Animals in Shorewater

     ASSOCIATION *c.* Animals of Piles, Wharves, and Ships
      Stratum 1. Surface Animals
      Stratum 2. Boring Animals

    Formation 2. Animals of Shifting Beaches

     ASSOCIATION *a.* Animals of Clay Beaches
      Stratum 1. Animals of Drift Line
      Stratum 2. Animals of Intertidal Zone
      Stratum 3. Animals below Low Tide
      Stratum 4. Animals of Shorewater

     ASSOCIATION *b.* Animals of Sand Beaches
      Stratum 1. Animals of Drift Line
      Stratum 2. Animals of Intertidal Zone
      Stratum 3. Animals below Low Tide
      Stratum 4. Animals of Shorewater

     ASSOCIATION *c.* Animals of Mud Beaches
      Stratum 1. Animals of Drift Line
      Stratum 2. Animals of Intertidal, Exposed Mud Flats
      Stratum 3. Animals among or under Plants
      Stratum 4. Animals of Lagoons
      Stratum 5. Animals of Shorewater

     ASSOCIATION *d.* Animals of Estuaries
      Stratum 1. Freshwater Animals
      Stratum 2. Brackishwater Animals
      Stratum 3. Marine Animals

     ASSOCIATION *e.* Marsh Animals
      Stratum 1. Freshwater Animals
      Stratum 2. Brackishwater Animals
      Stratum 3. Marine Animals

   PROVINCE B. Animals of Open Ocean

    Formation 1. Shorewater Animals

     ASSOCIATION *a.* Animals Living above Depths of 150 Meters
      Stratum 1. Floating Animals
      Stratum 2. Swimming Animals

ASSOCIATION *b.*   Animals Living between Depths of 150 to 500
Meters
Stratum 1.   Floating Animals
Stratum 2.   Swimming Animals

Formation 2.   Oceanic Animals
ASSOCIATION *a.*   Pelagic Animals Living above Depths of 150
Meters
Stratum 1.   Floating Animals
Stratum 2.   Swimming Animals
ASSOCIATION *b.*   Animals Living between Depths of 150 and 1500
Meters
Stratum 1.   Floating Animals
Stratum 2.   Swimming Animals
ASSOCIATION *c.*   Pelagic Animals Living below Depths of 1500
Meters
Stratum 1.   Floating Animals
Stratum 2.   Swimming Animals

PROVINCE C.   Bottom Animals

Formation 1.   Bottom Animals on Continental Shelves
ASSOCIATION *a.*   Animals on Terrigenous Deposits
Stratum 1.   Burrowing and Sessile Animals
Stratum 2.   Swimming and Crawling Animals
ASSOCIATION *b.*   Animals on Calcareous Oozes
Stratum 1.   Burrowing and Sessile Animals
Stratum 2.   Swimming and Crawling Animals

Formation 2.   Abyssal Bottom Animals
ASSOCIATION *a.*   Animals on Calcareous Oozes
Stratum 1.   Burrowing and Sessile Animals
Stratum 2.   Swimming and Crawling Animals
ASSOCIATION *b.*   Animals on Siliceous Oozes
Stratum 1.   Burrowing and Sessile Animals
Stratum 2.   Swimming and Crawling Animals
ASSOCIATION *c.*   Animals on Red Clay
Stratum 1.   Burrowing and Sessile Animals
Stratum 2.   Swimming and Crawling Animals

REALM II.   FRESHWATER ANIMALS

PROVINCE A.   Animals of Flowing Water
Formation 1.   Animals of Rapidly Flowing Streams
ASSOCIATION *a.*   Animals of Springs
Stratum 1.   Animals on Surface
Stratum 2.   Swimming and Crawling Animals
Stratum 3.   Sessile Animals
Stratum 4.   Plant-inhabiting Animals
Stratum 5.   Animals in Pools
Stratum 6.   Burrowing Animals

ASSOCIATION *b*.   Animals of Brooks
   Stratum 1.   Animals on Surface
   Stratum 2.   Swimming Animals
   Stratum 3.   Plankton Animals
   Stratum 4.   Sessile Animals
   Stratum 5.   Plant-inhabiting Animals
   Stratum 6.   Animals in Pools
   Stratum 7.   Burrowing Animals

Formation 2.   Animals of Slowly Flowing Streams

ASSOCIATION *a*.   Animals of Creeks
   Stratum 1.   Animals above Surface
   Stratum 2.   Swimming Animals
   Stratum 3.   Plankton Animals
   Stratum 4.   Animals of Vegetation
   Stratum 5.   Bottom Animals

ASSOCIATION *b*.   Animals of Rivers
   Stratum 1.   Animals of Bottom Lands
   Stratum 2.   Shore Animals
   Stratum 3.   Animals on Surface of Water
   Stratum 4.   Plankton Animals
   Stratum 5.   Swimming Animals
   Stratum 6.   Bottom Animals

PROVINCE B.   Animals of Standing Water

SUBPROVINCE B(a).   Lacustrine Animals

Formation 1.   Littoral Animals

ASSOCIATION *a*.   Animals of Hard Beaches
   Stratum 1.   Animals of Beach above Water
   Stratum 2.   Animals along Shoreline
   Stratum 3.   Animals of Rachion
   Stratum 4.   Animals of Vegetation
   Stratum 5.   Animals of Sublittoral Zone
   Stratum 6.   Animals of Shorewater

ASSOCIATION *b*.   Animals of Sandy Beaches
   Stratum 1.   Animals of Beach above Water
   Stratum 2.   Animals of Shoreline
   Stratum 3.   Animals of Rachion
   Stratum 4.   Animals of Submerged Beach below Rachion
   Stratum 5.   Animals of Sublittoral Zone
   Stratum 6.   Animals of Shorewater

ASSOCIATION *c*.   Animals of Muddy Beaches
   Stratum 1.   Animals of Beach above Water
   Stratum 2.   Animals on Surface of Water
   Stratum 3.   Animals of Shoreline
   Stratum 4.   Animals of Rachion
   Stratum 5.   Animals of Vegetation Zone

Stratum 6.   Animals of Sublittoral Zone
Stratum 7.   Animals of Shorewater

ASSOCIATION *d.*   Animals of Lagoons
Stratum 1.   Animals of Beach above Water
Stratum 2.   Animals of Surface of Water
Stratum 3.   Animals of Shoreline
Stratum 4.   Animals of Rachion
Stratum 5.   Animals of Vegetation
Stratum 6.   Animals of Shorewater

ASSOCIATION *e.*   Animals of Estuaries
Stratum 1.   River Animals of Water
Stratum 2.   River Animals of Vegetation
Stratum 3.   River Animals of Bottom
Stratum 4.   Littoral Lake Animals

Formation 2.   Limnetic Animals

ASSOCIATION *a.*   Animals of Epilimnion
Stratum 1.   Floating Animals
Stratum 2.   Swimming Animals
ASSOCIATION *b.*   Animals of Hypolimnion
Stratum 1.   Floating Animals
Stratum 2.   Swimming Animals

Formation 3.   Bottom Animals of Deep Water

ASSOCIATION *a.*   Bottom Animals of Moderately Deep Lakes
Having Variable Bottom Temperatures
Stratum 1.   Burrowing and Sessile Animals
Stratum 2.   Crawling and Swimming Animals

ASSOCIATION *b.*   Bottom Animals of Deep Lakes Having Cool
Bottom Temperatures
Stratum 1.   Burrowing and Sessile Animals
Stratum 2.   Crawling and Swimming Animals

SUBPROVINCE B(b).   Pond Animals
Formation 1.   Littoral Animals

ASSOCIATION *a.*   Animals of Ponds with Bare Bottoms
Stratum 1.   Animals of Beach above Water
Stratum 2.   Animals on Surface
Stratum 3.   Animals along Shoreline
Stratum 4.   Animals of Shorewater
Stratum 5.   Bottom Animals

ASSOCIATION *b.*   Animals of Ponds Containing Vegetation
Stratum 1.   Animals of Beach above Water
Stratum 2.   Animals on Surface
Stratum 3.   Animals along Shoreline
Stratum 4.   Animals of Vegetation
Stratum 5.   Animals of Shorewater
Stratum 6.   Bottom Animals

SUBPROVINCE B(c). Swamp and Pool Animals

Formation 1. Swamp and Bog Animals

ASSOCIATION *a*. Animals of Swamps
 Stratum 1. Animals of Vegetation above Water
 Stratum 2. Animals of Surface
 Stratum 3. Animals of Submerged Vegetation
 Stratum 4. Animals of Swamp Water
 Stratum 5. Bottom Animals

ASSOCIATION *b*. Animals of Bogs
 Stratum 1. Animals of Vegetation above Water
 Stratum 2. Animals of Surface Vegetation
 Stratum 3. Animals on Surface
 Stratum 4. Animals in Water

Formation 2. Pool Animals

ASSOCIATION *a*. Animals of Pools with Hard Bottoms
 Stratum 1. Surface Animals
 Stratum 2. Animals in Water
 Stratum 3. Bottom Animals

ASSOCIATION *b*. Animals of Pools with Muddy Bottoms
 Stratum 1. Surface Animals
 Stratum 2. Animals in Water
 Stratum 3. Bottom Animals

PROVINCE C. Aquatic Cave Animals of Flowing Water

Formation 1. Animals of Rapidly Flowing Streams

ASSOCIATION *a*. Animals of Springs and Brooks
 Stratum 1. Animals in Flowing Water
 Stratum 2. Animals of Bottom

Formation 2. Animals of Slowly Flowing Streams

ASSOCIATION *a*. Animals of Creeks and Rivers
 Stratum 1. Animals of Flowing Water
 Stratum 2. Animals of Bottom

PROVINCE D. Aquatic Cave Animals of Standing Water

Formation 1. Animals of Lakes and Pools

ASSOCIATION *a*. Littoral Animals
 Stratum 1. Animals of Open Water
 Stratum 2. Animals of Bottom

PROVINCE E. Animals of Ground Waters

Formation 1. Animals of Ground Waters

ASSOCIATION *a*. Animals of Ground Waters
 Stratum 1. Burrowing Animals
 Stratum 2. Animals of Crevices

SUPERREALM β.   TERRESTRIAL ANIMALS

REALM I.   Terrestrial Animals

PROVINCE A.   Subterranean Animals

Formation 1.   Animals Living in Soil

ASSOCIATION *a.*   Animals in Clay Soils
Stratum 1.   Animals Visiting Surface
Stratum 2.   Animals Not Visiting Surface

ASSOCIATION *b.*   Animals in Humus
Stratum 1.   Animals Visiting Surface
Stratum 2.   Animals Not Visiting Surface

ASSOCIATION *c.*   Animals in Sandy Soils
Stratum 1.   Animals Visiting Surface
Stratum 2.   Animals Not Visiting Surface

ASSOCIATION *d.*   Animals in Rocks
Stratum 1.   Animals in Surface

Formation 2.   Cave Animals

ASSOCIATION *a.*   Transient Cave Animals
Stratum 1.   Animals Moving on Solid or Liquid Substrata
Stratum 2.   Flying Animals

ASSOCIATION *b.*   Permanent Residents in Caves
Stratum 1.   Animals Moving on Solid or Liquid Substrata
Stratum 2.   Flying Animals

PROVINCE B.   Animals above Surface of Soil

Formation 1.   Surface Animals

ASSOCIATION *a.*   Animals on Wet Ground
Stratum 1.   Animals Properly Subterranean
Stratum 2.   Surface Animals
Stratum 3.   Animals Properly above the Surface

ASSOCIATION *b.*   Animals on Medium-dry Ground
Stratum 1.   Animals Properly Subterranean
Stratum 2.   Surface Animals
Stratum 3.   Animals Properly above the Surface

ASSOCIATION *c.*   Animals on Dry Sand
Stratum 1.   Animals Properly Subterranean
Stratum 2.   Surface Animals
Stratum 3.   Animals Properly above the Surface

ASSOCIATION *d.*   Animals on Rock
Stratum 1.   Animals of Crevices
Stratum 2.   Surface Animals
Stratum 3.   Animals Properly above the Surface

Formation 2. Animals Associated with Terrestrial Plants

ASSOCIATION *a.* Animals of Forests

SUBASSOCIATION *a*(1). Animals of Coniferous Forests
Stratum 1. Animals Associated with Leaves, Twigs, and Fruits
Stratum 2. Animals on Trunks and Branches
Stratum 3. Animals Living in Wood

SUBASSOCIATION *a*(2). Animals of Deciduous Dicotyledonous Forests
Stratum 1. Animals Associated with Leaves, Twigs, and Fruits
Stratum 2. Animals on Trunks and Branches
Stratum 3. Animals Living in Wood

SUBASSOCIATION *a*(3). Animals of Evergreen Dicotyledonous Forests
Stratum 1. Animals Associated with Leaves, Twigs, and Fruits
Stratum 2. Animals on Trunks and Branches
Stratum 3. Animals Living in Wood

ASSOCIATION *b.* Animals Associated with Shrubs
Stratum 1. Animals Associated with Leaves, Twigs, and Fruits
Stratum 2. Animals on Trunks and Branches
Stratum 3. Animals Living in Wood

ASSOCIATION *c.* Animals Associated with Low (1- to 6-foot) Plants
Stratum 1. Animals Associated with Leaves, Twigs, and Fruits
Stratum 2. Animals Living within Plants

ASSOCIATION *d.* Desert Animals
Stratum 1. Animals Associated with Leaves, Twigs, and Fruits
Stratum 2. Animals Living within Plants

Formation 3. Aerial Animals

ASSOCIATION *a.* Ballooning and Gliding Animals
Stratum 1. Ballooning Animals
Stratum 2. Gliding Animals

ASSOCIATION *b.* Flying Animals
Stratum 1. Animals Associated with Water or Vegetation
Stratum 2. Animals Habitually Flying in the Air

APPENDIX I. Animals of Islands

APPENDIX II. Animals Frequenting Structures Made by Man

From the point of view of the habitats that are available, as distinguished from the groups of animals that live in them, the terminology given in the last column of Table I is proposed. The *universe* furnishes a great variety of conditions of matter and forms of energy. The *earth* (biosphere) is influenced more or

less by forces outside itself, but is the largest unit of environment
that has direct relation to ecology. It is divided roughly into
three great regions (*hydrosal*) by the relations between water and
solid earth. The earth proper consists largely of undissolved
minerals; freshwaters contain comparatively little mineral
substance, but the oceans have much mineral in their waters.
Within any of the three great hydroterræ (ocean, freshwater,
or land) the chief regions (*contigua*) are determined largely by
proximity to other great areas. In the ocean, for example, there
is a characteristic and widely distributed set of conditions where
the salt water meets the atmosphere, shore, or bottom. An
isoterra exists where part of a contiguum shows uniformity of
conditions over a considerable area. The shore of the ocean,
for example, may be rocky, sandy, or muddy; the bottom may
consist largely of siliceous or calcareous deposits. A *heterohabitum* is a subdivision of an isoterra in which certain factors
show constant differences from other subdivisions. On a rock
beach along the ocean there is a characteristic zonation from low-
to high-tide mark. Each zone will constitute a heterohabitum.
A *mesohabitum* is a subdivision of a heterohabitum in which
most factors are the same, but one or more factors vary so that
the mesohabitum differs from others. On a rock beach the zone
dominated by brown algæ may contain many crevices in the rocks
at one place and consist of a smooth wall at another. An
isohabitum is a continuous area where there is no important
variation in any environmental factor. A smooth rock surface
which has a uniform angle of inclination to the earth's surface
and a uniform exposure to the actions of ocean water is an
isohabitum.

TABLE I.—TERMINOLOGY USED FOR SYSTEMATIC, ECOLOGIC, AND HABITATIC
CLASSIFICATION OF ANIMALS

Systematic	Ecologic	Habitatic
Species	Mores	Isohabitum
Genus	Consocium	Mesohabitum
Family	Stratum	Heterohabitum
Order	Association (or society)	Isoterra
Class	Formation	Contiguum
Phylum	Province	Hydrosal
Kingdom	Realm	Biosphere
Natural phenomena		(Universe)

CHAPTER II

PHYSICAL AND CHEMICAL ECOLOGICAL FACTORS

In attempting to discover why animals are so closely associated with particular habitats, ecologists are continually led to look for causal factors in the environment. When an ecologist says a certain factor is a cause, he, of course, understands that the word "cause" is used in a very general sense. A bass must live in water and it is perhaps proper to say that water is the primary and most essential factor of the environment in which a bass lives. In one sense water is the primary cause of the existence of the bass system of activities and the absence of water might be the cause of its extermination. But water is not the only "cause" to be found in bass environment and it is no more essential than many other less apparent "causes." The environment must be complete, and one "factor" cannot make it so. When it is said that a particular factor is a cause, it is understood that this is merely a way of saying that the particular factor is the important, apparent, or immediate cause of any particular relation between an animal and its environment.

In their relations with animals, environmental factors may be divided into two groups: (1) physical and chemical, and (2) biological. The first group is largely concerned with energy and chemical combinations in the inorganic environment, the second with influences due to living organisms in the environment. In this chapter the chief physical and chemical factors are considered under the convenient headings: water, temperature, specific chemical and physical agencies, light, gravity, molar agents, soil and bottom. The biological factors will be discussed in the next chapter.

Geographical and ecological, or climatic and local, factors affect animals in essentially similar ways. The "causes" of local habitat relations usually furnish the keys to the geographic distribution of the same species. Much information has been collected, but there is still pressing need of more knowledge concerning the actual distribution of animals in relation to

24

factors in environment. It is the chief purpose of ecology to explain such distribution and discover its causes.

In the given earth environment, factors seldom, if ever, act singly when they affect animals. A bass must live in water, and water itself has certain inherent properties that make it different as a habitat from air—such as peculiar powers of solution, which vary strikingly with different temperatures, property of changing temperature slowly, etc. Water, or any other "factor," probably cannot have a single effect upon an organism. Each factor has a certain optimum condition for each organism and has a certain range of variation, from maximum to minimum limit of toleration, throughout which a particular animal may be able to exist, but from the point of view of an animal the environment consists of more or less clearly defined units that are combinations of factors (Eigenmann, 1909).

If a single group of factors dominates a region, there are usually few species; but if there are many environmental units or habitats there is usually a considerable variety of species. Where one group of dominants merges into another, there may be zones of different types of animals through the transition areas.

In the following discussions, where factors are considered separately, it must be constantly remembered that factors seldom act so, but influence animals as parts of complexes.

WATER

Water is the substance whose movement in the inorganic and in the organic world constitutes the first, the most fundamentally important activity in the world that we live in (Henderson, 1922).

Though water constitutes only $\frac{1}{4540}$ of the earth's mass, it covers about 72 per cent of its area and would, if uniformly distributed over the surface, make an ocean about 2 miles deep. From the surface of the ocean there is continual evaporation. At the equator, water equal to a depth of about 7 feet is vaporized annually in this way. The evaporation of water requires heat and thus cools surrounding bodies. As vapor, water carries latent heat, which is released when it condenses. Water vapor is transported to all parts of the earth and is precipitated as dew, fog, rain, snow, and hail, thus supplying regions far distant from oceans. Considerable water is vaporized from land surfaces, but about 6500 cubic miles run off the land annually, carrying

some five trillion tons of dissolved matter with it. All chemical
elements are thus transported into the ocean, though some, of
course, occur there in very minute quantities. The continual
circulation of water from ocean to atmosphere, from atmosphere
to land and back to ocean again has vast importance for the life
on the earth.

Water in Organisms.—Water, according to Henderson, has
another important circulation through living things—where it
serves as food, solvent, circulating medium, temperature regula-
tor, and as catalytic, hydrolytic, and ionizing agent. Water is a
necessary constituent of all protoplasm and constitutes from 40
to over 90 per cent of the substance of living organisms. The
amount present in an animal often has a marked influence on
the animal's adaptability to other environmental factors. For
example, many animals are able to endure wider ranges of temperature variation when they have a minimum of water in their
bodies. With carbon dioxide water is built by plants into
sugars and then into organic compounds that form the food basis
for all animals. Water is essential for all "vital" phenomena,
and if a supply is not readily available animals may satisfy their
needs by breaking up chemical compounds in their food to get it
(Babcock, 1912). It is necessary for circulation, nutrition,
respiration, excretion, and the regulation of temperature.

Water in Relation to Temperature.—Having great specific heat,
water exerts an important influence on earth temperatures. It
is capable of absorbing enormous quantities of radiant energy,
which are given up again, especially when the sun is obscured or
below the horizon. Land areas near large bodies of water have
an equable climate because the water does not permit rapid thermal variations. Water vapor in the atmosphere also operates
against sudden variations in temperature, for the saturation point
varies remarkably, and when cooled the air gives up heat through
condensation and when warmed requires heat for vaporization.
The control of evaporation from the surfaces of the bodies of
animals helps in the conservation or dissipation of heat.

Water as a Solvent.—No other liquid is capable of dissolving
so many substances as is water. Except for its hydrolytic and
electrolytic effects, water usually acts upon its solutes very
little, and is, therefore, an excellent carrier for a great variety of
substances. The remarkable solvent capacity of water gives it
certain inherent advantages and disadvantages as a medium in

which animals may live. There is a relation between temperature and the solvent capacity of water. In general, larger quantities of solids can be dissolved at higher temperatures and larger quantities of gases at lower temperatures. When water nears the freezing point, salts tend to precipitate out, and when it nears the boiling point, gases pass out of solution. There is often relatively more oxygen and more carbon dioxide in water than in air, and the latter gas when combined with water has the properties of an acid. Many substances that are readily soluble in water are poisonous and may cause the death of animals that are restricted to aquatic habitats; other substances are nutritious and hence of value to animals. Water has an intimate relation with living matter which is so largely made up of it. Protoplasm readily combines with water and may take in water without changing its essential character. A part of the peculiar properties of life lie in the ability of these two substances to mix with and form various more or less stable compounds with each other.

Density of Water.—The density of water is influenced by changes in temperature and by the presence of dissolved substances. Living protoplasm is covered by semipermeable membranes through which diffusion may take place. Animals placed in solutions that are denser than their own body fluids usually tend to shrivel and those put in weak solutions usually tend to become turgid. Some animals (cladocerans, brine shrimps, rotifers, etc.) take on various forms that are associated with differences in the density and viscosity of the water in which they live. The internal liquids of animals may vary in density to correspond with the surrounding water. The quantity of salts in the blood of the rock crab ranges from 1.5 to 3.1 per cent. Animals have various special means of adjusting their own density in relation to that of the surrounding water (*e.g.*, the variation in the amount of gas in the swim-bladders of fishes; the formation of light, oily substances in many animals, etc.). Some animals are extremely sensitive to changes in the density of water. Nelson (1921) found that oysters that were acclimated to a salinity of 1.014 to 1.018 closed their valves and did not feed when the density was reduced to 1.008, but became active again when it rose to 1.010.

Water in Soil.—In soil, water is important, not only as a solvent and transporting agent, but in various ways makes soil habitats livable for plants and animals. Bouyoucos (1921) has recently classified the waters in soil as: (1) *gravitational,* which, of course, stands at the lowest level possible; (2) *free,* which is between the soil particles and freezes at $-1.5°C.$; (3) *capillary-adsorbed,* which freezes at $-4°C.$; and (4) *combined* water of solid solution or hydration, which does not freeze. The "wilting coefficient" of plants, which has been used by botanists as a measure of available soil moisture, appears to be "at the point where free moisture ends and capillary-absorbed moisture begins." The availability of water in soil, therefore, depends not only on the amount present but upon the physical character of the soil itself. Many instances might be cited to demonstrate the importance of soil moisture for the activities of various animals. Earthworms come out on the surface of the ground when the soil is full of water, and when the soil dries they burrow, seek deeper levels, and finally roll up into balls. Certain species of tiger beetles will not lay their eggs except where the moisture content of the soil is within certain limits and the larvæ of these insects burrow deeper during dry seasons. Porous soil is favorable for insects because there is less likelihood of drowning during rains. The reaction of soil water is important, and poor drainage through the soil usually brings about stagnation and acidity. An unusual quantity of mineral salts in soil may make it "physiologically dry" because, though water may be abundant, organisms are not able to use it.

Water in the Atmosphere.—From the atmosphere, water is precipitated in various ways and thus directly or indirectly affects animals. Dew is a most important water supply for some animals. Rain usually falls with little force, but clears dust from the air, modifies temperatures, and washes away soil. Hail may do actual injury to animals. Water vapor as clouds prevents radiant energy from reaching the earth. Enough water falls each year to make a uniform layer about 3 feet in depth over the entire earth. The seasonal and geographical distribution of water of precipitation exerts an important influence on climate and exercises more or less control over the types of vegetation that may exist. Where a hot and dry season coincide, there is usually a steppe or desert formation; where moisture and heat come together there is forest. When precipitation is erratic, many plants and animals cannot become established where an evenly distributed water supply would otherwise permit them to live. Harper (1918) has pointed out that the productive agricultural districts in the United States are those where rainfall comes largely in early summer. Many seasonal, cyclic activities of animals are initiated by seasonal rains—*e.g.*, the migration and spawning of many fishes and amphibians.

Variations in Humidity.—The most important relation between air and water that affects land animals is probably that exerted through evaporation. For an animal, the absolute humidity of air is usually not so important as the moisture saturation deficit. The evaporation power of dry air tends to withdraw the water from animals and thus leads to diverse and important regulatory responses. The atmosphere is never absolutely dry, but whenever it is not saturated with moisture, it can carry away water and thus exert a drying effect through movement. If the temperature rises, the drying effect of air is, of course, increased, because more moisture can be carried, and if the temperature falls the air must give up some of its moisture if saturated. In the presence of water high temperatures are associated with great humidity, but low temperatures are usually associated with dry air whether water is present or not. Usually the air is cooler and more nearly saturated with moisture at night and carries less water in proportion to its capacity during the day.

Probably no animal can live if it is completely desiccated, but many can exist for long periods of time in dry air. Even many marine animals when left exposed on beaches by low tides can stand the desiccating effects of air. Sea anemones have been kept for eight days in a laboratory without water. Though they came to look like dried raisins, there was apparently no particular injury, and the animals soon became active again when placed in sea water. Dragon-fly nymphs have been kept in dry sand for ten weeks and became active when water was added to the sand. Nematodes can be kept in a dry state for a quarter of a century without dying. The eggs of some aquatic animals (many crustaceans, rotifers, etc.) can stand long periods of desiccation and some apparently will not hatch unless they have been dried for a time—which may extend to as much as ten years.

Hall (1922) tried the effects of keeping various animals in a dry chamber. He found that different types survived the loss of water as follows, the figures representing percentages of body weight: earthworm, 69.6; leech, 70.3; mealworm, 52.6; salamander, 47; frog, 41; turtle, 33.1; lizards, 33.8 to 47.8; mice, 24.2 to 32.1.

The length of time that animals can endure atmospheres of low relative humidity in general depends primarily upon the kind of integument and secondarily upon the proportion of the body surface to the body mass.

Hall kept horned toads (*Phrynosoma cornutum* Harlan) alive without food for nearly four months in a desiccator. Babcock (1912) kept larvæ of the bee moth in a desiccator for 150 days.

Animals respond to the drying effects of the atmosphere in various ways. Usually the rate of metabolism becomes slower as an animal is dried. In many simpler animals secretions that aid in encystment are stimulated by drying. Encystment, æstivation, or some other resting state is often induced by desiccation. Shelford (1914) studied the effects of the evaporating power of air on a variety of animals and found that the responses occurred whether evaporation was "produced by movement, dryness, or heat," that "the sign and degree of reaction" were correlated with the rate of evaporation in habitats from which the animals were collected, and that there was a general agreement between survival time and the character of the integument.

Many animals are very sensitive to changes in humidity and numerous notes have been published concerning "weather prophets" among them. Shelford has suggested that such responses are induced by a disturbance of "neutrality" (in relation to acids and alkalies) in the body fluids by changed rates of evaporation. In the human body there is a high degree of cooperation between the skin, lungs, and kidneys, so that the amount and channels for water losses best suit the needs at any particular time. Loss of water through the skin cools the body most. That channel is usually used most during warm, and least during cold, weather.

A water-saturated atmosphere permits many animals that ordinarily frequent aquatic habitats to invade the land. In the humid regions of the tropics planarians, leeches, snails, and crustaceans have attained to terrestrial life and get oxygen from the atmosphere for respiration. Some animals, like crabs and snails, have been able to accomplish the same end by carrying water with them and through the aid of an exoskeleton that prevents the ready loss of water.

Stagnation.—Semper (1881) stressed the importance of movement or stagnation in water. So important is this difference that some modern ecologists are disposed to separate the aquatic realms into turbulent-water and quiet-water provinces. With moving waters are usually associated good aeration, great food-carrying capacity, and the molar forces associated with movement. In stagnant water there is usually poor aeration, low transportive capacity, and little influence by molar factors.

TEMPERATURE

Heat may be received by animals as molecular vibration, transmitted from objects in the environment, or as radiant energy, which, of course, comes largely from the sun. Radiant energy penetrates the soil very little. It may go hundreds of feet through water, but most of its longer vibrations (which have the greatest heating effect) are absorbed by the first few centimeters. Through the atmosphere, it travels with great facility. Part of the radiant energy from the sun is received on the earth as light, and in some respects light and heat have similar effects on animals. The migration of the pigment in melano-phore cells and arthropod eyes may be brought about by changes in either temperature or light. Merriam (1890) says:

Authors differ as to the period during which temperature exerts the greatest influence, some maintaining that it is the temperature of the whole year, and others that it is the temperature of a very brief period which determines the range of species. In the case of birds, it has been shown by Verrill and Allen that it is the temperature of the *breeding season*.

Thermal Stability.—Most animals continually seek for stability in the environment. In the past many types have left the water, which has a considerable degree of thermal stability, for the land, which offers gaseous stability. Absolutely stable temperatures are seldom attained in earth environments, but where they are approached, or actually obtain, animals usually flourish; where there are sudden, irregular variations, animals are often not able to live. Temperatures near the limits of toleration for animals may be withstood if they come about gradually. Survival of extremes is usually less dependent on the degree than the rate of change. On the other hand, the more rapid a thermal change is the more effective it usually is in stimulating animals. In the North Sea (Hesse, 1913) there is an abundant fauna in regions where there is uniform, though extremely low, temperature and a scanty fauna where the temperature varies. Huntington (1922) has shown that the human race is most productive where temperatures vary and accomplishes least in localities where there is a monotonous climate.

Temperature and Seasonal Succession.—Temperature is the most important causal factor for seasonal succession. In parts of the tropics where there is little seasonal variation in temperature, there is often a lack of periodicity in the reproductive activities of animals. The seasonal successions on the earth are largely due to periodic variations and are accompanied by corresponding fluctuations in humidity, precipitation, dissolved gases (in water), and salinity (in the ocean).

Thermal Stratification.—The two common environmental media, water and air, when undisturbed tend to become thermally stratified and such stratification is, of course, most pronounced in water—where it often leads to the establishing of seasonal or perennial zones of animal life. The deep-water fauna is a cold-water fauna and many of its members do not range into regions where there are higher temperatures. Cases have been reported where organisms were found in a particular stratum of inter-mediate water and were few or absent in regions above and below, where temperatures were respectively higher and lower. In the Rocky Mountains Dodds (1917) found that the microcrus-taceans that had a limited range of toleration to temperature changes had a restricted vertical range. Michael (1918) says of the salpas:

Solitary forms show an increasing preference, so to speak, for the surface, as the temperature of the surface water increases from 16 to 20°C., while aggregate forms show a similar preference as temperature decreases.

The animals that live in the region between the tide marks on ocean beaches show a zonation that is in part due to the limitations set by temperature. On land there are also stratification effects that are due to temperature. It has been noted by many observers that the alpine faunas are related to those in the arctic and antarctic, and that they do not invade the lowlands to any extent.

Temperature and Metabolism.—Temperature changes have a more or less direct effect on metabolism. Of course, an animal cannot survive supramaximal or subminimal temperatures, but the optimum rate of metabolism is usually much closer to the maximum than the minimum. This fact, together with observations on the metabolism of animals, justifies the assertion that, within certain limits, the higher the temperature the more rapid will be the rate of metabolism. Most animals live faster at higher and slower at lower temperatures. Stylonichia divides once a day at 7 to 10°C. and five times a day at 24 to 27°C. Esquimo girls that live in warm houses and have plenty of clothing reach maturity as early as girls in the tropics, but those that live an exposed life out doors mature much later. Many animals, though not wholly inactive, cease to feed at low temperatures; others pass through periods of cold in a hibernating state during which the rate of metabolism is extremely low. Development may be prolonged on account of cold; annuals may be transformed, for a time, into biennials. The number of animals growing to maturity and their individual sizes may depend on temperature. Weymouth (1918) has cited instances where crabs, oysters, and salmon on the Pacific coast were larger after seasonal temperatures were high, early, and long, thus giving opportunity for early spawing and a longer growth period. Cyclic metabolic activities, like reproduction, are often influenced by temperature changes. The breeding periods of marine animals usually continue throughout favorable temperatures and generally begin (1) at the close of periods of minimum temperatures, and (2) at the close of the maximum temperatures (Orton, 1920). Cladocerans, rotifers, and aphids have different types of reproductive activity associated with various temperatures, sex and sexual reproduction being controlled more or less by temperature variations. But the metabolism of some animals, on the other hand, is not essentially changed by temperature. Artemia eggs, for example, do not hatch sooner at higher temperatures.

Temperature Regulation in Animals.—Animals that do not have some internal mechanism for maintaining constant temperatures do not differ much from the surrounding medium. Animals may be divided into two groups: (1) variable-temperature (poikilothermal) and constant-temperature (homoiothermal) animals. The former have more rapid metabolism at higher temperatures and slower rates at lower temperatures. Behre (1918) has shown that certain poikilothermal animals, although they show striking changes in the rate of metabolism, when subjected to a new and different temperature will, if kept for a time at the different temperature, gradually assume the same rate as that before the change.   This metabolism-regulating mechanism operates slowly, but is, Behre believes, the basis from which have developed the more or less automatic internal changes that in homoiothermal animals keep the body temperature constant.   Pike and Scott (1915) have pointed out that, while poikilothermal animals have their rate of metabolism limited more or less directly by temperature, homoiothermal animals are more or less independent of environment because internal changes keep the body at optimum temperatures for metabolism, regardless of fluctuations outside.   The latter, therefore, have unusual ability to invade variable-temperature habitats.   Poikilothermal animals must live as the surrounding temperature dictates and perhaps on this account many have often become adjusted to cold and stability, rather than to a higher average temperature that fluctuates.

Stenothermic and Eurythermic Animals.—Animals are often classified into two groups: stenothermic and eurythermic, the former being restricted to a narrow range of temperature changes and the latter having ability to live through a wide range.   The optima for different species of animals vary widely and representatives of a widely distributed species may show different optima in various parts of the territory in which they are found.   The eggs of many fishes develop best at temperatures that are little above the freezing point of water; the optimum for birds' eggs is close to 40°C.   Amphipods swarm in the polar oceans and dragon-fly nymphs live in water that is considerably warmer than the human body.   The medusa, *Aurellia aurita*, at Tortugas is killed if subjected to freezing temperatures, but individuals at Nova Scotia readily survive such treatment (Mayer, 1912). The optima of comparable animals living in the frigid and torrid regions, of course, differ widely.   Many animals have special means for enduring unusual and extreme temperatures.   The reduction of the amount of water in an animal's body enables it to tolerate wider ranges of variation; the evaporation of water from surfaces may cool the interior; the presence of coverings, such as lime and silica, apparently enables animals to endure greater extremes.   There are instances where animals have gradually become acclimated to new ranges of temperature toleration when the temperature of their surroundings gradually changed. Dallinger (Davenport, 1903) performed a classical series of experiments on protozoans.   Starting with flagellates that were living at 15.6°C., and that died when the temperature reached 23°C., he gradually raised the temperature until the animals were living at 70°C. Such power of acclimation to new conditions makes it apparent how animals have become adapted to earth habitats. Welch and Loomis (1924) studied an enormous population of hydras in Douglas Lake, Michigan. When the surface stratum reached temperatures of 20 to 21°C. the hydras disappeared, but remained in deep water at temperatures near freezing when the oxygen content was as low as 0.3 cubic centimeter per liter.

Toleration of Low and High Temperatures.—When the temperature of an animal is raised beyond its maximum limit of toleration, a temporary heat rigor is induced, and if the temperature continues to rise there is *rigor mortis* caused by the coagulation of proteins. Heat rigor appears in different animals at from 26 to 60°C., usually below 45°C. When the temperature is reduced, metabolism grows slower and most animals cease to be active at about the freezing point of water. Many animals, however, readily recover after being frozen into ice and some remain active below 0°C. Though animals often stiffen at low temperatures, there is no radical change in the protoplasm, as there is at high temperatures. An animal that has been subjected to freezing temperatures will usually not recover its activity if suddenly brought to a higher temperature, but may survive if warmed slowly. Davenport (1903) says:

The effect of high temperatures is principally chemical, involving the living plasma; that of low temperatures is principally mechanical, involving the water of the body. Both raising and lowering the temperature act as irritants.

The stimulating effects of temperature differences may be important in inducing responses in animals. Marine fishes are sensitive to differences of 0.2°C. Ward (1921) asserts that the course of the migration of the Alaska salmon is primarily controlled by temperature, the fishes moving upstream always choosing the cooler water at every place where the river branches.

Climate and Temperature.—Climate depends largely on temperature. The plants and animals on the earth are arranged in zones which correspond in a general way with the isotherms. Allen (1907) was able to arrange many groups of vertebrates in regularly varying series from the tropics toward the poles. Gornitz (1923) asserts that in birds melanin pigment increases at high and decreases at low temperatures. It is well known that the animals on the slopes of mountains are arranged more or less in zones that correspond with prevailing ranges of temperature. Species of animals that are distributed through various climates may show differences in behavior—the sphinx moth larvæ burrow deeper in Canada than in Missouri. Cold air is usually dry air and the rays of the sun generally tend to turn water into vapor. When a tropical sun, a mountain range, and a cold ocean meet (as along the borders of Chile and Peru) the result is an extremely arid climate. When moisture-laden winds are free to blow over a flat valley, there is usually a heavy rainfall (as in the Amazon basin). Climate, as determined by temperature and moisture, is of prime importance in determining the availability of the terrestrial habitats on the earth. Even the most progressive cultural areas of man's civilization appear to coincide rather closely with the regions of optimum climate. When animals are transferred from one climate to another, the effect is more striking when they go from warm to cold than in the opposite direction (Gadow, 1913). Tropical animals may live in cold climates, but usually do not propagate. Insects that are introduced into cold climates tend to produce extra broods, and hence may appear to have longer seasons of activity. They often die off when there is rapid alternation of cold and warm periods.

On parts of the earth where there are marked seasonal cycles, temperature is one of the dominant factors in limiting the activities of many animals. The appearance and disappearance of migratory birds; the continuance or cessation of sexual or asexual methods of reproduction in insects, crustaceans, rotifers, etc.; the spawning of many fishes; the rapid multiplication of plankton organisms; and many other activities are more or less dependent on appropriate temperatures. Certain relict faunas show their dependence on the past by breeding during the coldest seasons, which bring conditions closest to those in the ocean (Ekman, 1920).

CERTAIN CHEMICAL AND PHYSICAL AGENCIES

The chemical substances on the earth supply the matter from which all living things are constituted, and all energy exchanges are apparently confined to matter. Long ago Heilprin (1887) stated his belief that climate was not so important a factor in the distribution of animals as the "physical character of immediate environment and the nature of the food supply." Jewell (1922) in a recent paper says:

Although the extent to which an environmental factor may affect a given life process may vary with size, age, etc., and although different processes in the same individual may be affected to a different extent by the same environmental factor, it is suggested that unsuitable hydrogen-ion concentrations, insufficient oxygen, low temperatures, and toxic substances affect development, regeneration, oxygen metabolism, and duration of life in the same way and according to the same laws.

These two quotations indicate the progress that has been made in analysis of environmental factors. Such analysis is as yet far from complete, but it is now apparent that the future will carry ecology more and more into studies of the effects of physical and chemical influences.

There is wide diversity in the chemical constitution of the media in which animals live. Fly larvæ, belonging to the genus Pelopia, remain active in 5.5 per cent salt solution; the vinegar "eel," *Anguillula aceti*, lives in 4 per cent acetic acid. Fly larvæ have been placed in a dish of absolute alcohol and remained alive, and apparently in good condition, until the liquid evaporated (Cameron, 1913).

Chemical agents in the environment may cause changes in the chemical constitution of animals or cause their death. If an animal responds to such agents it may become acclimated to new conditions or respond by motor activities which are usually adapted to bring it toward optimum conditions for existence. In some cases changes must be very gradual if an animal is to survive, but some animals can stand very rapid changes. The brine shrimp, *Artemia salina*, may live in concentrated or rather dilute salt solutions, but dies if suddenly transferred from one to the other; certain fly larvæ (Rhode, 1912) readily withstand such changes.

Effects of Chemical Changes on Animals.—The chief chemical changes on the earth are oxidation and carbonation. Chemicals, of course, exert general and specific effects on animals and the exact means by which a certain so-called chemical effect is brought about is often obscure. Beneficial substances may be of value for nutrition or as stimulants. Sodium chloride, for example, serves many purposes in the animal mechanism.

Carbon, oxygen, hydrogen, nitrogen, potassium, calcium, phosphorus, sulphur, iron, magnesium, iodine, and sodium are generally necessary building materials for protoplasm. Free oxygen is usually essential for heat production and the utilization of energy for physiological work. Certain substances are poisons because they break up and destroy protoplasm; others are poisons because they form insoluble compounds with body constituents and thus prevent the incessant changes necessary for metabolism. Other chemicals affect animals through ions or osmotic phenomena, or by initiating synthesis or analysis.

Salts in Blood.—It has long been believed by a majority of scientists that life originated in the ocean and physiologists have often suggested that animal blood is derived from sea water. It is true that the blood of certain marine animals, like that of the starfish, has a salt content that is practically identical with that of the surrounding ocean, and it is also true that certain marine animals, like the rock crab, not only have blood that resembles sea water, but this varies to correspond more or less closely with the surrounding medium when the animals migrate into beach pools or the estuaries where the ocean is diluted with freshwater. Most vertebrates, however, though their blood contains the same salts that are found in the ocean, have such salts occurring in different proportions and the total salt content is less. Even the strictly marine sharks and teleosts have blood that differs markedly from the medium in which they live. Johnstone (1921) has suggested that such animals have blood that resembles the primitive ocean, when there was less of salt and a relatively larger percentage of calcium—on this account. Modern animals that have left the ocean are believed to have the "calcium habit," *i.e.*, while sodium is the chief buffer base in the blood, calcium is essential for the proper functioning of nerve and muscle and is important for other metabolic processes.

Salts in the Environment.—Salts are of immense importance in animal environments. The difference between the ocean and freshwater is due primarily to salinity. A few animals may be changed with more or less impunity from the ocean to freshwater, but many types of animals apparently always have been confined to the ocean and are today. Some orchestiids migrate out on land but are unable to live in freshwater. The sockeye salmon, however, swims directly from the ocean into the Frazier River and apparently suffers no injury (O'Malley and Rich, 1919). The

ocean is supersaturated with calcium carbonate, especially near
the surface, and changes in the salinity are mostly brought about
by living plants and animals. In the shallow water near Tortugas, for example, *Pseudomonas calcis* and other organisms
greatly reduce the amount of lime by precipitating it out. The
alkalinity of the ocean is regulated to a considerable extent by
carbon dioxide through its unique solving and ionizing powers.
The salt content of natural waters fluctuates greatly with variation in temperature reaction, and ionization. Essenberg (1918)
believes that peculiarities in the vertical distribution of Pacific
Polynoidæ depend primarily on the chemical composition of
the sea.

Antagonistic Salts.—Many salts show a certain antagonism in
in their behavior toward protoplasm. The salts in sea water
have together an antagonistic action that serves to protect
protoplasm from injury that each might do if it acted alone. If
certain medusæ are placed in artificial sea water that has the
same total amount of salt as natural sea water but which lacks
one of the salts normally present, there is a striking influence on
the rate of pulsation. If magnesium salts are increased, pulsation
is slower; if sodium salts are increased, the rate is more rapid
(Mayer, 1906).

Salts in Aquatic Habitats.—The fluids that bathe the body cells
of animals have mechanisms for maintaining them near neutrality, and salts play an important rôle in this. Animals show an
almost infinite number of adjustments to various concentrations
of salts. Some species are able to leave the ocean for freshwater
and other nearly related species appear to be wholly unable to do
so. *Gammarus marinus* is confined to the ocean and *G. locusta*
lives in both ocean and freshwater. The copepod crustacean,
Limnocalanus macrurus Sars, and the minnow, *Fundulus heteroclitus* (Linnaeus), live in the ocean or in freshwater and the latter
may be transferred directly from one medium to the other without
injury. Corals live in water that has only 80 per cent of the salt
content of sea water. Vaughan (1919) believes that this fact
indicates that the ocean is growing more salty, and that its
salinity is now supraoptimum for marine animals. Devil's Lake,
North Dakota, is growing more salty and there is a dearth of
shelled rhizopods and certain other animals in its water. The
brine shrimps, *Artemia salina*, in Great Salt Lake will not live in
water having a density less than 1.027. Their optimum lies

between 1.027 and 1.044, but they are able to live in water that has a much higher salt content. Insects and amphibians are largely confined to land and freshwater habitats, but some insects live in the ocean and certain Philippine frog tadpoles develop in brackishwater having a salinity as high as 2.5 per cent. In the streams leading into the salt lakes in Lorraine, Florentin (1899) had an excellent opportunity to study the resistance of animals to salt solutions. He found that protozoans lived in 6 to 15 per cent salt solutions; *Cyclops bicuspidatus*, 3; Nais and other worms, 1; toads, 0.5; frogs, 0.3. It has recently been discovered that the larvæ of Anopheline mosquitoes live in sea water in Panama; other mosquitoes have been reported to breed only in water that is acid enough to show pH 4 to 5. Shelford (1916) showed that marine crustaceans from greater depths had greater resistance to alkaline solutions than those from near the surface. Adolph (1925) has discussed the distinctions between marine and freshwater animals and points out that:

For freshwater organisms the osmotic pressure of the medium usually limits survival, while for marine organisms a great range of concentrations can be resisted.

Adolph maintains that freshwater animals in gaining ability to retain salts in their body fluids have lost power of adjustment to variations.

Toxic Salts.—Many salts and other chemicals are toxic when they are present in the environment. Copper and arsenic compounds are often added by man to certain habitats in order to exterminate pests. Inadvertently or carelessly, and sometimes even maliciously, man also causes the deaths of countless animals by the products of his activities. The wastes of factories, sewage systems, and "purification" plants are often extremely harmful to the natural inhabitants of the habitats that they are permitted to contaminate.

Effects of Salts in Environment.—Salts not only affect animals by their ability to combine with or prevent combinations in protoplasm, but they also act as stimuli that control the activities of animals, often to a considerable degree. In certain animals particular morphological changes are brought about by variations in the salinity of the water in which they live. Artemia grows more and longer setæ on its appendages as water grows saltier. When sodium salyicilate is added to water it may produce various effects on animals—Arcella has been shown to lose its spines and take on a different fission rate; a certain rotifer was found to grow spines and thus change to another "species." Such changes are probably due to differences in the chemical constitution of the animals subjected to the so-called stimuli, but there are many valid cases where the behavior of animals is quickly and radically changed by the presence of salts in the water surrounding them. Some fishes are quick to sense slight changes in the water. MacBride (1914) tells of a Danish agriculturist who reared eels in a pond on his estate and, when the slippery creatures were ready to return to the ocean, caught them easily by taking advantage of their responses to salty water. The astute fellow poured a little sea water into a small bay at one side of the pond and, as the eels rushed about there in a writhing mass, he stood on the bank and dipped them out with a net. The recent work on artificial parthenogenesis shows that eggs may be stimulated to develop by salts and by other means than the entrance of sperm cells into them. Such stimulating effects are doubtless due more or less to changes in ionization, but there is no doubt that they may be concerned, in a general way, with the degree of concentration of the salts present.

Soil Salts.—In soil, salts have important relations to living organisms. The growth forms of plants are influenced by nutritive substances, among which sodium and calcium salts are important. Acidity generally hinders and alkalinity helps in the decay of organic materials in the soil. Snails that bear hard shells are limited more or less to regions where considerable calcium is present. Many burrowing animals, like the earthworms, are rather closely adapted to the presence of certain amounts of salts in the ground around them.

Acids.—Acids, like salts, are most potent as environmental factors in aquatic and soil habitats where they are associated with water. Jewell (1922) made an interesting study of an acid stream—finding certain clams, fishes, and shrimps abundant, though branchiate snails and may-fly nymphs were absent. Some soft-water lakes give an acid reaction at all depths. In freshwater habitats the most important acidifier is carbon dioxide. Aquatic plants may make the water about them alkaline by using up all the carbon dioxide. In soils, acidity is necessary for some plants and animals, while it excludes others. Organisms are adjusted to various degrees of acidity in the environment, and in some cases a slight change in acidity is an important stimulating agent.

Ionization.—It has recently come to be realized that electrolytes may be important factors in environment. Many species of plants and animals appear to have a rather definite pH optimum, and many give characteristic responses to changes. Libellulid nymphs have been found in water showing pH 1 and certain cell earthworms live only where the pH is 6 to 7. Fishes and earthworms are able to respond to some solutions in a way that shows that they are able to discriminate between different degrees of ionization. The most favorable medium for the regeneration of lost parts by mutilated tadpoles is a neutral one; the human body maintains the neutrality of the fluids that bathe the living cells by the use of carbonates and phosphates as buffers. Anæsthetics apparently retard all processes that depend on the transportation of ions through living tissues. The study of ionization in nature is still a new subject of investigation and interesting facts are being daily brought to light. In one creek that was studied the pH was found to be correlated with the carbon dioxide content of the water. Jewell (1924) made a comparative study of twelve Michigan bog lakes. She says:

The dissolved oxygen content of the surface waters of these lakes varied from 2.66 to 5.88 per liter, the oxygen-consuming capacity from 12.4 to 47.66 ppm., the hydrogen-ion concentration from pH 4.2 to pH 9.0. No correlation was apparent between these various factors nor between the pH and depth, marginal vegetation, or probable age of the lakes. Fishes were found in waters from pH 4.4 to pH 9.0, snails from pH 6.2 to pH 9.0, and sponges from pH 5.0 to pH 9.0. Preliminary experiments in transportation of fish from basic to acid waters and conversely seemed to show a high degree of resistance in the fishes studied to great changes in hydrogen-ion concentration.

Coker (1925) has studied the distribution of certain fishes in North Carolina and Massachusetts. He says:

The brook trout, *Salvelinus fontinalis*, is commonly associated with a very limited number of species of fish; the centrarchids (sunfish and bass) and percids (perches and darters) seem to be especially excluded from such association . . . The particular waters examined and known to be inhabited by brook trout were acid or neutral, while those inhabited by centrarchids were measurably alkaline. It is not concluded that such a distinction is of universal application, but the observations point distinctly to the desirability of broader investigations of the hydrogen-ion concentration of trout waters.

Juday, Fred, and Wilson (1924) found seasonal changes in hydrogen-ion concentration in Lake Mendota. During the spring and autumn periods of circulation it was substantially uniform at all depths. During winter and summer periods of stratification the upper water was more alkaline than the lower. Photosynthetic activity of algæ caused an increase in the alkalinity of the upper water. In Chesapeake Bay pH showed a gradation from surface to bottom and conditions were found to vary during daylight and darkness. Two beach pools on the eastern Canadian coast had pH values of 6.2 to 6.8 and 7.6 to 9.2 respectively, the differences being correlated with the fact that the first was in granite and the second in limestone.

In the ocean, carbon dioxide is driven out as the temperature rises and the alkalinity of the water increases; the opposite is true when the temperature falls. In pools on Tortugas, differences were found between conditions during day and night, changes in temperature and in the photosynthetic activities of plants being important in modifying the ionization of the water. Fishes placed in a graded series of ionizations have been found to rest slightly on the alkaline side of neutrality. Bottom fishes and those associated with vegetation have been observed to display little reference to ionization in their behavior, but those of the open water reacted very quickly to changes. It has been suggested that the migrations of salmon into particular streams and to particular spawning grounds may be accomplished through the selection of certain ionizations, where opportunity is given for such selection at the branchings of streams. Ionization is important in soil. Drying acid soils affects the hydrogen-ion concentration very little, but drying alkaline soils makes them less alkaline by changing the hydrogen-ion concentration of salts (Burgess, 1922).

In the physiology of animals, electrolytes play an important rôle through the control of enzymatic actions and the permeability of protoplasm to various substances. The permeability of cell membranes is largely influenced by the changes of the electrolytes that surround them. Antagonism between two salts occurs when they have dissimilar electrical effects upon protoplasm. As all vital phenomena are concerned largely with water and its solutes, osmosis exercises a controlling influence in the relations of living things to environment. Life is perhaps concerned as much with the passage of liquids through membranes as with anything. Loeb has suggested that the chief rôle of salts in the preservation of life is in the tanning effects that they have on membranes. The membranes that bind the exterior surfaces of animals and those that separate internal parts from each other are very important. Some marine animals lose their internal salts and die when placed in freshwater; others retain them and suffer no injury. Osmotic action may under appropriate conditions exert great pressure, and thus produce turgor. Some animals, like certain nematodes and fly larvæ, can survive immersion in all sorts of solutions with little or no injury because the membranes covering their bodies do not permit harmful substances to enter; other animals, like earthworms and certain marine larvæ, that are covered with readily permeable membranes, are easily killed by slight variations in their surroundings. In general, animals have made two types of responses to osmotic action: (1) the development of coverings to resist such action, and (2) the development of physiological mechanisms to control the rate and nature of osmotic action through semipermeable membranes so that an animal may be able to adjust its metabolic activities to the range of conditions that it would ordinarily encounter.

Surface Tension.—Surface tension and other adsorption phenomena are concerned with the passage of substances through the membranes of living animals. Surface tension is also important for animals in quite a different way—enabling them to run about on water and permitting those living under water to hang suspended from the surface film.

Organic Compounds.—As has been said, from an ecological point of view the most important chemical changes that take place on the earth are perhaps oxidation and carbonation. The latter gives rise to the endless variety of organic compounds that make up the substance of living organisms and permeate the physical environment wherever organisms are found. Organic compounds form a necessary part of earth environment as it relates to animals—forming the basis of food resources. On land the rooted vegetation furnishes the bulk of the food for animals, but in the ocean and in freshwater floating, microscopic plants are more important. As organisms die and disintegrate, various compounds are freed, usually to be dissolved in water for transportation or further simplification. When organic compounds are almost completely broken down, the chief end products are carbon dioxide, water, and nitrogen compounds. All these are used again by plants and animals: carbon dioxide and water as the basis of photosynthesis; water in many ways as solvent, hydrolytic agent, medium for electrolytic dissociation, etc.; nitrogen compounds as a basis for protein synthesis, both as ammonia and in the form of nitrates and nitrites.

Gases.—Gases, as constituents of environment, affect animals in many ways.   Oxygen is a constant necessity for metabolism in protoplasm.   Yet some organisms are able to remain active in the absence of oxygen.   Many animals, including insect larvæ, molluscs, and oligochætes, live in the stagnant water on the bottoms of deep lakes where there is no oxygen for as much as three months during each year.   Juday (1919) has described an anaerobic ciliate that appears in great numbers during seasons and in regions where there is no oxygen, and disappears when there is again oxygen in the water.   In the ocean, sulphur bacteria, that contain free sulphur, live in the absence of oxygen. The atmosphere contains about 21 per cent of oxygen, and therefore furnishes an abundant supply to all air breathing animals, but aquatic habitats show considerable variation in the amount of oxygen present.   Great epidemics, due to lack of oxygen, are not infrequent among fishes.   Among aquatic animals there are various degrees of toleration to oxygen deficiency—some live without any supply of free oxygen; some, like the lake trout, can get along with very little; some need a continuous and abundant supply.   The beaver and the muskrat in winter breath a bubble out under the ice and wait for it to be aerated from the surrounding water before inspiring it again. Many air-breathing aquatic animals, and even some that secure their oxygen supply from the water itself, have special means for storing oxygen, so they are able to remain submerged for considerable periods without a fresh supply and thus may invade stagnated regions.   Though a continual supply of oxygen is essential for the life of most animals, oxidation may at times be highly injurious.   Some of the most deadly poisons are substances that bring about rapid oxidation.   In aquatic habitats of limited size the type of bottom usually indicates, in a general way, what the amount of oxygen above it may be, because currents are so important as aerators in water.   Mud can be deposited only where there is more or less stagnation; sand indicates an intermediate amount of water movement;

and rock is usually associated with much movement and good aeration.

Carbon Dioxide.—Carbon dioxide, like oxygen, has a reasonably uniform distribution in the atmosphere throughout the earth, but varies greatly in the water. It is important as an essential compound for photosynthesis and also serves important functions as an acid, electrolytic agent, and stimulant. It is produced by the disintegration of organic compounds, combustion, respiration, and through the freeing of carbon dioxide from bicarbonates. Algæ may, under certain conditions, take carbon dioxide from dissolved compounds. The amount of free or half-bound carbon dioxide in water limits the total productive capacity of an area, because plants cannot carry on photosynthesis without it. Sometimes plants when very active use all of the carbon dioxide in an area and oxygen may rise above the saturation point. Fishes and other aquatic animals are in some instances more sensitive to variations in the carbon dioxide content of water than to those of oxygen. Carbon dioxide, if present in quantity, may suffocate animals. Gaseous conditions in the environment may stimulate particular activities. For example, the axolotl is said to be more likely to undergo its metamorphosis into the adult form if kept in poorly aerated water; whereas, if kept in water containing an abundance of oxygen, it may retain its larval form for years. The gases in soil are important for animals that live there. Aeration is necessary, and burrowing animals therefore prefer loose soils. Some insects that are free to fly about and choose avoid firm soils.

Ammonia, Hydrogen Sulphide, Methane.—Free ammonia is one product of the final stage in the breaking down of proteins. It seldom occurs in large amounts, but is continually utilized by plants and animals, usually not as ammonia, but in combinations as salts. In certain habitats various gases of limited distribution may at times be important ecologically. Some marine fishes are very sensitive to hydrogen sulphide and avoid water that contains it. Beerman (1924) tested the effects of this gas on protozoans and found that it acted somewhat like carbon dioxide. He says:

Hydrogen sulphide like carbon dioxide in acid, neutral or slightly alkaline media will produce intracellular acidity because of the penetration of hydrogen sulphide molecules into the cell.

Methane and other gases occasionally do injury to animals or cause them to migrate from particular habits.

The Atmosphere.—The atmosphere is a mixture of all the gases on the earth, the bulk of it being, of course, composed of nitrogen (79 per cent) and oxygen (21 per cent). It constitutes $\frac{1}{1,200,000}$ of the earth's mass, and serves as a transporting medium for aqueous vapor, dust, volcanic emanations, etc. There may be as many as 400,000 dust particles per cubic centimeter, and these serve as nuclei for particles of fog, rain, mist, snow, and hail. The atmosphere through its gaseous properties serves as a sustaining yet readily traversed highway through which organisms may be distributed. Its mobility makes it an important factor in many habitats—causing waves and currents; carrying and depositing dust; shifting great dunes of sand; disseminating the reproductive phases of organisms. It acts as a thermal blanket for the earth and equalizes temperatures through convection currents.

LIGHT

Light, though still somewhat of a mystery to scientific men, is generally described as a succession of wave pulses in ether, initiated by vibrating electrons. Radiant energy is given off by every body that has a temperature above absolute zero and a considerable range of the shorter wave lengths, produced by the more rapid rates of vibration, are known to man as light. Different wave lengths have different effects on various living things. For chemical actions, such as the changes produced in silver salts and the injury that is generally done to protoplasm by exposure to light, the short vibrations are generally most effective. The photosynthetic activities of plants usually depend on both long and short vibrations, while those of intermediate lengths usually are less potent. The human eye is most readily stimulated by fairly long vibrations, which fall in the yellow region of the solar spectrum. From a behavioristic point of view, animals show various relations to light vibrations. Some responses are apparently related more or less directly to beneficial or injurious changes produced in protoplasm by the light; others, though they may be of benefit to an animal, show no such direct relation. An amœba avoids light and is apparently injured by it; a flounder receives photic stimuli through its eyes that give rise to movement of pigment in cells in the skin, and the pattern and coloration of the fish thus come to match the background that surrounds it with remarkable accuracy.

Effects of Light on Organisms.—Light, given direct access to protoplasm, generally causes injury—producing syntheses, analyses, substitutions, polymerizations, etc. It inhibits the growth of plants and animals and they are adapted so as to be protected from it by the shielding of growing regions, the formation of pigment, etc. Light kills many plants and animals if they are exposed to it continuously, and those that live in strong light often have protective adaptations that enable them to survive. On the other hand, light is essential in most animal habitats because photosynthesis depends upon it, and without photosynthesis food resources fail. It has been well said that the cow is assimilated grass, and grass is sunlight, carbon dioxide, water, ammonia, and salt. Fish are assimilated algæ, and algæ are sunlight, water, carbon dioxide, ammonia, and salt. British scientists have been able roughly to predict the catch of mackerel for a season by computing from the days of sunshine preceding. Light in limited quantity may at times benefit protoplasm by virtue of the chemical changes it causes—producing sterilizing effects or stimulating greater metabolic activity. Animals that live on the earth are always between two horns of a dilemma— shun light because it is injurious, or seek light because it furnishes the energy for the production of organic food and certain beneficial chemical changes. Habitats have advantages and disadvantages as they afford too much or too little light, but light is not always beneficial or always injurious.

Light Variations in Environment.—Radiant energy varies with latitude, season, humidity, and altitude. The transparency of air and water is important in regulating the amount of light that may be available in particular habitats. In water, there is selective absorption of light at various depths, the longer vibrations (red) are absorbed near the surface and the shortest vibrations (violet) penetrate deepest. In the ocean the algæ are distributed according to the length of light vibrations that their colors are best suited to absorb and utilize—green algæ live along the shoreline, brown algæ descend somewhat deeper, and red algæ are generally characteristic of deep water. Ditlevsen (1911) experimented with marine plankton in an aquarium and found that it migrated from red to blue light. This, if light was used as a sign by the organisms, would be equivalent to movement from shallow to deep water in the ocean. In lakes, spermatophytes are confined to shallow water, but some algæ are able to grow at greater depths—depending on the transparency of the water. Some animals carry algæ within their bodies and depend on them more or less for food. These are limited to shallow water because the enslaved algæ cannot manufacture food in the absence of sunlight.

Photic Stimulation.—The stimulating effects of light are apparent in the physiology and behavior of animals. Pigment formation is due to light in many cases—the flounder has under experimental conditions been made to form pigment on the upper, lower, or both sides, according to the illumination to which its body was subjected. Pigments are frequently arranged in such patterns that animals match the backgrounds on which they usually rest. Such protective resemblance would not be possible without light. Animals that live in caves lack pigment, and those that dwell in the depths of the ocean, where the environment is monotone, though pigmented, do not show patterns in their coloration.

Light influences the behavior of animals in many ways. There are certain species, attuned to low intensities, that are well known as nocturnal or crepuscular animals; others that are as characteristically diurnal. Some animals, like leeches, chase shadows; others, like hermit crabs, avoid them. Sunlight is said to be the most potent factor that induces bees to go afield in search of honey. The stimulating effects of light may be due to various wave lengths, and it is probable that light produces chemical changes when it stimulates, but there is apparently no direct relation between chemical effect and the degree of stimulation. Ultra-violet light is potent chemically, but is invisible to the human eye.

Light and Animal Activity.—The rotation of the earth on its axis has led to many adaptations in animals. Perhaps the most striking examples are in animals that are strongly diurnal or nocturnal, and in the migrations of plankton. That light has a direct photokinetic effect on some animals is shown by the fact that many animals assume sleeping positions during an eclipse, instead of remaining active as they would if light continued as usual. The migratory locust is said to stop its flight at once if the sun goes behind a cloud. Young eels, migrating up streams, stop and hide at night. There are some organisms, however, that appear to have an established physiological rhythm that continues for a time even when the alternating conditions of

illumination that go with day and night are not present.   Acacia
leaves continue to assume "sleeping" positions at regular intervals in the absence of light.   The shrimp, *Hippolyte varians*,
continued to turn green, which is its usual night color, at rather
regular intervals when it was kept continuously in light or dark
(Keeble and Gamble, 1900).   Everyone knows that certain
animals are adapted to activity during light and that others
are adapted to activity during comparative dark.   Many birds
go to roost when night falls.   Some fishes, like the perch, take
food only during the day; others, like the bullhead, seek food
at night.   Cave animals commonly have degenerate eyes or
are actually blind, but nocturnal animals usually have highly
developed eyes—vertebrates frequently showing vertically elongated pupils and insects having eyes with very large facets.
Graenicher (1911) describes a species of nocturnal bee in which
the female is flightless, creeping over the ground, and has normal
eyes, but the male, which flies, has eyes with enormous facets.
Some animals that become active at night do not do so on
account of the reduced amount of light, but on account of other
conditions prevailing at that time.   Nighthawks fly when they
can catch insects, and, although they are usually seen at dusk,
may fly during the day if food is abundant.   Land snails become
active when there is plenty of moisture, which is usually, but
not always, at night.

Plankton Migrations.—Many species of plankton animals in
the ocean and in lakes make periodic migrations, coming to the
surface at night and descending into deep water during the day.
Light is doubtless the controlling factor in such migrations, but
is not the sole factor that operates to produce them, and does
not by its presence or absence cause planktons to move immediately toward or away from the surface.   One species of crustacean comes up at sundown and leaves before midnight; another
comes up at midnight and goes down at two o'clock in
the morning, before the faintest dawn has appeared.   Each
species is adjusted in its own particular way to the daily rhythm.
Ewald (1912) found that cladocerans became adapted to new
light intensities rapidly; that increases in intensity made them
positively, and decreases negatively, phototropic.   He believes
that plankton migrations are wholly explained by the responses
of the animals concerned to light.

Seasonal Variations in Light.—The seasonal variations in light have a marked influence on the animals in frigid and temperate regions. Such variations are, of course, always associated with corresponding differences in temperatures. Summer is a season of comparative warmth, intense illumination, and great photosynthetic activity; winter brings cold, scanty illumination, and lowered metabolic activity. British scientists have shown that light has an effect that may be independent of temperature. Sunshine in May brings an abundance of marine copepods and a good catch of mackerel, regardless of whether the seasonal temperatures are low or high.

Luminescent Animals.—Throughout the animal kingdom there are animals that produce light.

The best-known forms are the dinoflagellates; Noctiluca; hydroids; jellyfish; ctenophores; sea pens; Chaetopterus and other marine worms; earthworms; brittle stars; various crustaceans; myriapods; fireflies and glow worms; *Pholas dactylus* and *Phyllirrhoe bucephala*, both molluscs; squid; Pyrosoma, a colonial ascidian; and fishes (Harvey, 1920).

All these animals are marine or terrestrial, no luminescent animals being known to inhabit freshwater. The eggs and larvæ of some animals (firefly) are luminous. In some animals bacteria serve as a source of light; a fish has been reported which bears cultural pores for bacteria.

All luminescence emanating from animals is associated with oxidation. Most luminescent organs flash only when stimulated. Harvey divides such organs into two classes: (1) those in which oxidizable material is included within cells, and (2) those in which it is burned outside the cell substance. Some organs are constructed somewhat like eyes, with lenses, screens, etc. Luminescence is often under nervous control; even colonial animals, like Renilla, may show flashes over a whole group of animals at the same time. In some animals luminescence is a periodic phenomenon, and in such instances light is usually given off at night. Some animals are luminescent only during the breeding season.

Harvey believes that luminescence is brought about by the action of luciferase, an enzyme, on luciferin, a protein substance which has various forms, in the presence of oxygen. The light from luminescent animals is usually of low intensity, that of the firefly having a strength of 0.02 to 0.0025 candle power. The light from animals is peculiar in having a spectrum similar to luminescent chemicals. It appears only at certain temperatures which vary in different species of animals. That from the firefly will, like X-rays, pass through wood, paper, leather, and flesh in sufficient quantity to affect a photographic plate, but such "invisible" rays, like ultra-violet light, will not penetrate glass.

Various functions have been assigned to luminescence in animals. Such light undoubtedly serves as a signal for sex recognition, and perhaps also in keeping schools of marine animals together. It is used as a lure for attracting prey by certain angler fishes and cœlenterates. It may serve as a lantern and as a warning to predaceous enemies, though no valid examples of this kind are known. In many organisms luminescence apparently serves no useful function—as in certain bacteria, fungi, protozoans, cœlenterates, firefly eggs, and larvæ. Some luminescent animals are blind; and others have photogenic organs in peculiar situations where use seems doubtful, as in the case of a deep-sea crustacean that has luminescent organs inside its branchial chamber.

GRAVITY

Among the forces on the earth, gravitation is peculiar in that it acts continuously, uniformly, and, in its relation to animals, in one direction. Probably its most important ecological aspect is the differences in pressure that it causes in fluid media. The pressure of the atmosphere at sea level is 760 millimeters at 0°C. The differences between mountain tops and sea level, littoral water and deep sea, are chiefly due to gravity. If an animal moves from the sea level upward through the atmosphere, the pressure decreases about 11 per cent during the first 1000 meters, and progressively more through strata farther from the earth; in passing through water toward the center of the earth, an animal would encounter an increase of about 1 atmosphere every 10 meters. Animals that are adjusted to particular pressures usually cannot change suddenly from one stratum to another. An aeronaut or a deep-sea diver may bleed through the delicate membranes on the surface of his body when external pressure becomes different from that within. A deep-sea fish cannot come quickly to the surface, and those brought up in trawls often explode on account of decreased pressure in the surrounding medium. Some fishes, however, have considerable ability to endure changes in pressure and make rather extensive vertical migrations. Though the range of variation is less in the atmosphere than in water, flying birds that ascend to high altitudes have similar ability. Dewar (1924) has made an extensive study of diving birds and finds considerable convergence in habits among various species. He states that divers do not compete with wading birds for food and discusses six families that obtain food by diving: ducks, cormorants, grebes, loons, auks, and rails. He did not study penguins, petrels, finfoots, jacanas, or dippers. Dewar observed 5991 dives and the longest ranged in different species from thirty seconds to three minutes. The greatest depth attained was about 10 fathoms and the average speed under water was 1 to 2 feet per second. Dewar found that each species had a favorite diving depth. Most dives were primarily for feeding from the bottom. He believes that diving habits in birds arose from habits of shore feeding. According to their diving ability, the birds studied by Dewar came in the following order: auks, cormorants, grebes, ducks, and coots.

Adaptations to Gravity.—Gravity attracts animals toward the center of the earth, and there are many adaptations in animals living in air or water that enable them to overcome this pull to a greater or less extent. Buoyancy is usually brought about in aquatic animals by the secretion of oily or gaseous substances; sinking is impeded by long spines, helmet or bell shapes, and swimming is made easy by the presence of many setæ. Aerial animals have air spaces, pneumatic bones, and other adaptations which increase bulk without a proportionate gain in weight. Gravity in a rough way fixes the size that an animal may attain. Certain mechanical schemes for securing locomotion have inherent limitations in the media on the surface of the earth. For example, the scheme commonly employed by insects appears to be most successful in animals of small size, and that in use by vertebrates permits a reasonable degree of agility in animals of larger size. Some of the largest vertebrates, like dinosaurs and elephants, though not flying in air or swimming in water, possessed adaptations, such as hollow bones, for making the body lighter in proportion to its bulk.

Geotropic Responses.—Gravity is a potent factor in relation to the growth and orientation of plants. The same relations hold to a less extent in connection with sessile animals, like hydroids and sponges, but the forms of freely moving animals are adapted to particular types of locomotion. Gravity serves as a stimulus to orientation in many animals, however. Such orientations may be passive, induced by structural or other peculiarities which limit orientation to certain relations with gravity, or they may be active and animals then respond to stimuli which result in loco-motor responses that bring the body into particular relations with gravity.

MOLAR AGENTS

In speaking of molar agents Davenport (1908) said:

The subject is so ill-defined that it is impossible to draw any line of distinction between contact on the one hand and a crushing pressure, or wounding, on the other. The molar agents may be solid or fluid. The methods of application may vary from a blunt contact or a sharp cut or puncture to the impact of a flowing liquid. All these agents have this in common, however, that they act in a gross, mechanical way.

Molar agents are important as makers of habitats. Running water carries earth and even wears rock away. Rain and river erosion are familiar aspects of physiography. Ice also pushes up ridges, scours out valleys, cracks up rocks, and works in other ways. Wind moves sand dunes, dries soil, transports floating objects and leaves them along drift lines, and may break down vegetation. The wind also brings about the ceaseless pounding of water waves, which are so important in many habitats. Tides and other movements in water cause currents that pick up, carry, and deposit sediment, and in other ways markedly affect the activ-ities of animals. Currents and waves in water move material by rolling and carrying it. Minor upward currents keep material in suspension, the amount of sediment depending on the volume of particles and other factors.

Winds.—The ecological effects of winds are apparent in many habitats. The most important physiological influences of mov-ing air are perhaps due to its drying and temperature-changing qualities, but air movements in themselves are important. Migrations are helped and hindered by winds; floating objects bearing animals are blown across oceans, and animals are carried across deserts. Scale insects and the gypsy moths are known to spread down the wind. The cotton boll-weevil traveled north through the United States most rapidly during windy years. Aphids have been seen to tumble off the tops of plants into strong winds. Mosquitoes and flies, which usually do not travel more than a mile or two, may be blown many miles by hurricanes. Honey bees are often lost during storms. Winds blow many land animals into the water, where they are drowned. Certain insects and birds on oceanic islands largely escape such danger because they are wingless. Winds help many animals find food or mates, and may give notice of the presence of enemies by carrying odorous substances. Most flying animals depend on air currents to a considerable degree as a means of locomotion—not that flyers are necessarily carried with the wind, but air in motion enables animals moving through it to overcome gravity more readily. Wind often limits the local distribution of animals, particularly in exposed situations where they may be confined to hollows or other sheltered places. Wind benefits certain habitats by removing injurious gases, and by disseminating the minerals, carbon dioxide, pollen, and seeds that are so necessary for the maintenance of plants, which, in turn, always furnish the ultimate food resources for animals.

Currents.—Currents in water are largely due to winds, and differences in pressure due to variations in level. Their direction is often influenced by the contours of containing basins and the positions of outlets. Currents in the ocean are not sharply defined and rarely run along as "rivers," but appear at the margins of great eddies. They serve to distribute, select, and annihilate myriads of animals. The abundance of animals on certain parts of the ocean bottom is due to currents, for where two different types of water meet, many organisms are continually dying, and these furnish abundant food as they sink. The growth form of individual animals and of great aggregations, like oyster beds and coral reefs, is often dependent on currents. In freshwater, currents not only distribute food but are important in the oxygen supply of many animals. In streams and lakes the amount of dissolved oxygen is frequently correlated with the rate of flow. Stream and pond isopods react to currents according to the amount of oxygen present in the water that surrounds them (Allee, 1912). Shallow lakes in which there is vertical circulation at all times are quite different habitats from deep lakes in which the deeper water stagnates through all or part of the year. In rivers the most abundant bottom fauna is usually found where the current is most sluggish (*i.e.*, on mud), and currents above a moderate speed appear to limit the quantity of plankton that may develop. The species of fishes in streams are arranged roughly in a graded series from headwaters to mouth according to the swiftness of the current. The larvæ of caddis-flies are also arranged according to the swiftness of the water, different types of cases being apparently adapted to different strengths of current. The areas of the gills of may-fly nymphs are correlated with the swiftness and oxygen content of streams.

Waves.—Waves in water are due to currents, winds, or the combined effects of both. There may also be waves in loose sand or snow when moving air can pick up, carry, and drop particles. Surface waves in water generate a series of trichoidal circles which grow smaller with increasing depth. In great storms the effects of surface waves may extend down as much as 600 feet, which is about the depth of continental land shelves. Waves on beaches tend to move stones and other large objects up toward high-water mark, and to move sand back and forth according to their direction. Sand settles about 2 inches per second and it cannot be carried by water that has an upward movement of less than 2 inches per second (Cornish, 1910). In lakes, exposed shores usually have a scantier population than protected bays, and, to a less degree, the same is true in the ocean. There are some marine animals, however, like acorn-barnacles, that flourish on rocks that extend into the open ocean, where they receive the full force of the waves, and, of course, have opportunity to capture much food from the water.

Tides.—The ocean tides cause a rhythmical succession of currents in littoral habitats. Many animals are adjusted to this rhythm. Podurans migrate up the beach and burrow to a depth of 6 to 8 inches when the tide comes in and emerge in great numbers when the tide ebbs. In clams there is a rhythmical formation and destruction of the crystalline style that is correlated with the ebb and flow of the tides. Nelson (1921) found that oysters fed over twenty hours each day and that 73 per cent of the shell closures were at ebb or very low tide. It has been stated that the periwinkle, *Littorina litorea*, shows a vertical migration that is synchronous with ocean tides and that such migrations take place regularly when the snail is placed in an aquarium where there is no tidal action. Haseman (1911) has shown, however, that this snail is stimulated to move up and down by the surface film as the water rises and falls, and that in the absence of tides no rhythmical migrations occur.

Adjustments of Animals to Molar Agents.—The adaptations of animals to waves and to strong currents are similar. Many animals that live in moving water are sedentary or fixed. Onchidium, a pulmonate snail in Bermuda, lives in crevices in rocks and comes out for a little time each day when the tide is out. Some animals have flattened bodies and have developed organs for adhesion, such as suckers, clinging hooks, and mucous or cement glands. Others have strong shells that cover the body (clams, snails, barnacles). The horny layer on the outside of many mollusc shells protects them from abrasives. Animals that live on shifting sand bottoms are usually burrowers or good swimmers. Many of the animals in moving water depend for food on adhering algæ or the floating life in the water itself. In rapids, caddis-fly larvæ spread delicate nets that they scrape off at intervals for food. Slender-legged spiders run over the surface and catch struggling insects, if trout do not pick them off from below before they arrive. On the ocean beaches, snails continually rasp algæ off the rocks; clams siphon water through themselves and strain food from it; bryozoans and barnacles spread their nets and catch what they can. Along lake beaches crayfishes lurk among the rocks; waterpennies, may-fly nymphs, and leeches hide beneath stones. Some net-fishing crustaceans have taken up their abodes inside the shells of molluscs and in worm tubes, where strong currents bring them food.

Stagnation.—Semper (1881), in his classical chapters on "the influence of stagnant water" and "the influence of a still atmosphere," has carefully considered the adaptations of animals that live in the absence of molar agents. Stagnation is associated with adaptations in organs of respiration and many aquatic animals that live in quiet water have means for acquiring oxygen from the atmosphere. Some animals when they grow in quiet water show different forms from those that they assume on wave-beaten rocks. Certain sponges and corals growing in lagoons or deep water may assume a branched or spreading form, and the same species on exposed beaches are flat or encrusting. Some animals die very quickly if water becomes stagnant, others can stand prolonged submergence in it. Fulton (1921) kept a Bermuda anemone sealed up in 100 cubic centimeters of water for six days without apparent injury.

SOIL AND BOTTOM

The solid surface mantle of the earth is made up of sand, clay, gravel, rock, and soil, which is a mixture of mineral and organic materials. Loose soil contains water and air in the spaces between the solid constituents. These spaces constitute the "pore volume," which is important ecologically. The soil environment is a complex of many factors which have not been completely analyzed. The physical factors are perhaps more important for most animals than the chemical. The physical structure, water capacity and content, temperature, and permeability of topsoil and subsoil play leading rôles in soil habitats. Soil colloids, particularly those of silica and alumina, are rather inert chemically, but help absorption and the cohesion of solid particles.

Types of Soil.—Clay is cold, dense, poorly aerated, and, though it holds much water, does not give up water readily to plants or animals. Sand is dry, loose (caves in readily), and has a variable temperature. Rock heats and cools quickly, has little available water, practically no air, and is usually too resistant to allow penetration by burrowing animals. Alkaline soils are "physiologically dry" because the salts present hold the water so that it is not readily available to organisms. Humus has a great water capacity and gives up water readily, is usually well aerated, and furnishes nitrogen, as well as mineral salts and water. Peaty soils and raw humus are uninhabitable for most animals because they are poorly aerated and have an acid reaction.

Soil Drainage.—If a porous soil rests on an impervious substratum, the slope is important. If there is a depression, water does not run off and collects—thus forming a swamp or wet meadow. If both topsoil and subsoil are readily penetrated by water, conditions may be too dry for animals. In general, the character of the vegetation cover serves as a good index of the habitability of soil for animals; conditions that make plants flourish are usually favorable for animals.

Soil Water.—Water in soil affects animals in various ways. A wet soil usually contains very little oxygen and may be "sour" on account of putrefaction. Winter and spring are bad seasons for subterranean insects because water forces the air out of the soil. In dry soils the height of the water table controls the available moisture to a considerable extent. Above the standing water, animals depend on percolation and the ability of the soil itself to "raise" water. The total amount of water present is not as significant as the amount that is available for the use of animals. A soil is physiologically dry if an organism cannot extract water from it.

Soil dries through the evaporation of its water and on account of the consumption of water by organisms in it. The rate of loss by evaporation depends on the saturation deficit of the atmosphere, slope, and exposure. Other factors being equal, dark-colored soils dry most rapidly. The seasonal distribution of soil moisture is important. The most productive agricultural regions in the United States are in areas where rains occur in spring and early summer; and in regions where rains come in late summer, land is not so valuable.

Soil Aeration.—The air in soil usually contains a larger proportion of carbon dioxide than that of the atmosphere. For animals it is important that there be good aeration. The pore capacity, due to the physical character of the soil itself, is therefore important. Earthworms, moles, and other burrowers also help aeration.

Soil Temperatures.—Soil is warmed by the sun and by the decomposition of organisms in it. Most soil animals are adapted so that dry cold does them no particular harm. Some burrowing animals, like the earthworm, have a very wide range of toleration for temperatures; others, like the mole, are stenothermic. In the temperate regions of the earth there is a vernal and autumnal "overturn"—when the thermal relations between shallow and deep soils change. Where there is no snow, the average temperature of soil is higher than that of the atmosphere above it; where snow falls, soil temperatures vary. Daily fluctuations in temperature extend to a depth of about 1 meter. Annual fluctuations may reach down to 25 meters. In England the differences between depths of 8 and 67 centimeters vary from 2 to 4.5°C. at different seasons. In Michigan the average annual range for two years has recently been determined as follows: at 1 foot, 27.8°C.; 2 feet, 21.4°C.; 3 feet, 15.7°C.

Soil Cover and Its Effects.—The living and non-living covers for soil have a marked influence on its characteristics as a habitat. Snow, dead leaves, and grass conserve moisture and serve as a blanket to prevent rapid thermal changes. Each species of plant does best in certain degrees of alkalinity and of electrolytic dissociation. Many plants are able to change the soil to some extent, so that it better fulfils their requirements—*i.e.*, they change the substrate into that in which they flourish best. Calcium is apparently necessary for plants, not only for its own peculiar qualities, but as a catalytic agent in the assimilation of other mineral substances. It is also a necessary constituent of soil for certain animals—*e.g.*, land snails do best in limestone regions. In bogs, soil acidity increases at greater depths, but in drier soils it usually decreases.

Activities in Soil.—The soil is a great digestive system that breaks down organic materials. In this it is assisted by living bacteria and other fungi, and by certain animals. Earthworms and millipeds often initiate leaf decay; fungi finish it. Soil contains nourishment for organisms as solid minerals, dissolved salts, and organic compounds. It is continually impoverished by the loss of true and colloidal solutions, and may thus be "fatigued," or show decreased fertility. The soil is used by various animals as refuge for protection from enemies, evaporation, and extremes of temperature; as material for abodes; and as a highway.

Number of Organisms in Soil.—In one locality the bacteria in raw humus have been estimated to number 22,000 per cubic centimeter; and in rich soil over 2,500,000. Lohnis and Fred (1923) say:

Not infrequently a hundred million are found in 1 gram of soil, where they nearly always exert the greatest activity . . . One acre contains, therefore, about 350 pounds of living bacteria besides 175 to 350 pounds of fungi, protozoa, and algæ, altogether 525 to 700 pounds per acre.

Waksman (1924) has shown that the hyphæ of fungi are usually abundant when soil is acid and decrease when fertilizers that make the soil less acid are added. Protozoa in soils appear to feed largely on bacteria and are an important factor in decreasing them. There may be thousands of nematodes in the upper foot of an acre of fertile soil. Insects are most abundant in a stratum from the surface to about 10 centimeters below, but often burrow deeper to pupate or hibernate. The distribution and the activity of earthworms are largely influenced by moisture. Burrowing animals help to form, renovate, and maintain soils. Branner (1912) studied ants and termites in Brazil. He found that their excavations aggregated several miles per acre. They affected the soil by admitting air and rain through their burrows, bringing dirt to the surface, carrying down organic matter, and producing substances that attacked the soil and broke it up. In an area near small ponds in the Indiana sand dunes Sanders and Shelford (1922) found about 100,000 burrowing and surface animals per acre (250,000 per hectare). Important among these were tiger beetles and their larvæ, digger wasps, with smaller numbers of ground beetles and white grubs. A considerable part of the surface fauna consisted of adult insects that came from neighboring aquatic habitats.

Types of Bottoms.—In marine and lacustrine habitats the character of the bottom is determined largely by the movement of water. Rocks are characteristic of exposed, wave-beaten shores; sand is found in turbulent bays; mud and ooze typify quiet water. While the same is true to some extent in streams, the bottom also reflects the nature of the soil traversed in each drainage system. Rock and sand are generally not so productive of animal life as mud, but some rocky sea beaches have a very abundant fauna. Mud bottoms usually have the advantage of an abundance of food, both from mineral sediments and from the organic remains of plants and animals, but have poor aeration. Plants often flourish and alleviate stagnation in such places by using up carbon dioxide and producing oxygen. Mud dwellers often have special means for respiration. They come to the surface for air, possess hæmoglobin for carrying oxygen, or have other peculiarities.

Animals Associated with Various Bottoms.—It is well known that certain species of fishes, worms, molluscs, and other animals are associated with particular bottoms. Pond (1905) maintains that aquatic plants draw nourishment in through their root hairs and require certain compounds for growth. There is selection of habitat by animals on the basis of bottom material. In his study of the molluscs of Oneida Lake, Baker (1918) found the number of species indicated on each type of bottom: mud, 50; sand, 42; clay, 35; gravel, 33; boulder, 27; sandy clay, 25. The living organisms on or in a bottom may change its character by causing sedimentary deposits, precipitating substances from the water, and in other ways. Calcium carbonate is often deposited by green plants. Mangroves, eel grass, and the biota associated with such plants cause characteristic accumulations. Quicksands often engulf and smother animals. They occur only where water flows upward through finely divided material.

ALTITUDE

Gadow (1913) says:

Broadly speaking, the annual mean temperature decreases toward the poles at an average of 1°F. for each degree of latitude. With increasing height the temperature falls nearly a thousand times as rapidly, namely, 0.5°C. for every hundred meters; this is equal to 1°F. for every 365 feet, an easy number to remember. On mountains the rate is somewhat greater, 1°F. = 300 feet . . . Atmospheric pressure also decreases, roughly by 1 inch with every thousand feet of elevation.

High mountains usually have a more or less permanent belt of clouds and may possess a perennial snow cap.

Life Zones.—On most mountains the flora and the fauna are arranged in zones. In the tropics there may be five such zones on a single mountain: (1) tropical; (2) warm temperate, with clearly defined summer and winter seasons; (3) cool temperate, where trees lose their leaves in winter and at the top of the zone cease to grow altogether; (4) cold, where trees are absent but grasses, annuals, mosses, and lichens persist; (5) arctic, which has its lower limit at snow line. Some types of animals that are active throughout the year in the lowlands of the tropics hibernate during the winter at higher levels. In limiting animals to definite zones, temperature and available moisture are probably more important than variations in air pressure. However, barometric pressure at 10,000 feet is only about two-thirds that at sea level, and at high altitudes the amount of oxygen is also less. Some animals are very sensitive to pressure changes in the atmosphere, and future studies may show that these are of more importance than is now recognized. In speaking of the effects of high altitudes on the human body Schneider (1921) says:

It is today recognized that the controlling element in the physiological reactions is the diminished partial pressure of oxygen and the consequent imperfect aeration of the arterial blood.

To this the body responds by (1) increased respiration, (2) chemical alterations in the blood, and (3) increased hæmoglobin.

CONCLUSION

In this chapter the ecological importance of various environmental factors has been discussed and an attempt has been made to show that, though one factor or another may at times play a leading rôle in the relations of an animal to the world in which it lives, the completeness of the environment and the interaction of factors within it in such a manner as to make it suitable for animals are at all times most important.

Animals must live where substances are present that can furnish food and in other ways make the continuance of life possible. In this connection water, oxygen, and other substances continually function as essential constituents of the environment. The effects of energy, as gravity, and as varying degrees of temperature, light, and molar agents, are also important.

CHAPTER III

BIOLOGICAL FACTORS

In the last chapter the qualities of environment were considered that are more or less characteristic of the surface of the earth, regardless of the presence or absence of living things. In this chapter those relations of animals are to be considered that are more or less dependent on the inherent qualities of living things or that are due to the presence of organisms as constituents of the environment. The discussion will deal with such relations as are necessary on account of reproduction; the procuring and assimilating of food; escape from living enemies and other dangers; the types of activities associated with particular morphological or physiological patterns; the reactions, instincts, and other types of behavior through which adjustments are brought about; and competition.

REPRODUCTION

Reproduction in animals serves two functions: (1) to increase the number of individuals, and (2) to produce individuals that have combinations of characteristics that differ from those of their parents and that may enable them better to survive in the particular environment in which they are produced. Multiplication by fission, budding, and other similar methods may depend to some extent on environment, but usually has no very complicated relations with it. Child (1915) has shown that asexual reproduction is in many cases due to the physiological isolation of parts by the growth of an animal's body to such an extent that portions of it are beyond the influence of the controlling region, and thus may readily become independent. Conjugational reproduction, however, has many complications that are concerned with various phases of the fusion of gametes, cross-fertilization, courtship, the care of young, and other activities.

Breeding Instincts.—During the breeding season many animals have instincts that make reproductive activities dominant. If feeding is antagonistic to breeding, the former is often neglected. Many species also become an easy prey for enemies during the excitement of the breeding period. Among some diœcious animals individuals of the two sexes may never see each other. The males of certain salamander, myriapods, and pseudoscorpions deposit spermatophores that are later picked up by females. Among species that mate, many expedients are employed to bring two individuals of opposite sex together. The male fiddler crab waves his bright claw before the female; spiders dance and posture; birds sing and display their visible charms; a male moth finds his mate by her odor, though she be a mile away. In some species eggs are fertilized after they leave the body of the parent, in others impregnation is internal and more than a year may elapse before young are born. Among some species of fishes and birds the males early invade the breeding grounds and await the coming of the females.

Seasons for Reproduction.—Reproductive activities are commonly cyclic in their nature and often show correlation with annual, lunar, or other rhythmical environmental changes. Many birds migrate north, court, select a nesting site and build a nest, lay eggs, incubate, rear young, migrate south, feed and rest—then repeat the cycle again. In such a cycle of activities the sexes may play slightly different rôles. For example, the male often arrives on the breeding ground first and selects a general area; the female follows, selects the actual site for the nest, and does most of the building. The reproductive cycles of birds are usually closely correlated with seasonal succession, but those of many other animals are not. The fish, Gambusia, brings forth its young without apparent relation to temperatures, and hydroids often pass through several reproductive cycles while environmental conditions remain reasonably uniform. On the other hand, Orton (1920) states that the oyster spawns at about the same temperature throughout its range. Some events in a reproductive cycle, though they may be correlated with definite seasonal periods, take place but once. When a female pocket gopher is mature, the bones on the ventral side of her pelvis are resorbed, so that she may bear young; a salmon spends a few years in the ocean, then migrates up some river to spawn and die.

Stimuli for Reproduction.—Changes in environment often release potential reproductive functions. It is well known that the presence of small quantities of certain substances help in the fertilization of the eggs of many animals. On the other hand, extracts from the larvæ of the sea-urchin, *Arbacia punctulata*, will inhibit the development of eggs of the same species.　If a squid spermatophore comes in contact with the sea water, it discharges its spermatozoa; a Crossobothrium proglottid, passing out of a sand shark and encountering the same stimulus, undergoes active contractions and sheds its eggs.　Polypterus goes out into the surrounding lowlands to spawn when the Nile overflows.　Certain marine annelids spawn when the proper season and sign of the moon arrive.　Some animals mature their reproductive products and, when there is a failure of food or other unfavorable circumstances, resorb them again without producing offspring.

Productivity of Animals.—The rate of development and increase through reproductive activities, of course, varies greatly. Krogh (1914) has shown that the rate of development of amphibians, fishes, insects, and echinoderms varies in relation to temperature according to Van t'Hoff's law.　Changes in moisture, temperature, and oxygen supply are important in causing variations in developmental rate.　Peterson (1918) during his studies off the coast of Denmark showed that there was not a great renewal of the stock of marine animals each year, but a large production in certain favorable years, which recurred at more or less regular intervals.　The annual production of some animals is enormous.　A blue crab has been estimated to carry 1,750,000 eggs at one time; an adult cod averages about 4,398,700 eggs per year; a female termite in her prime may lay sixty eggs per minute.　In general, the number of young produced is inversely proportional to the amount of care given to the eggs and young, but there are many exceptions.　The size of birds' eggs is roughly related to the length of time that they remain in the nest, those that remain for longer periods generally being larger.

Length of Breeding Periods.—Breeding may extend through long periods if conditions are favorable.　Certain species of freshwater amphipods produce young for from 152 to 299 days out of each year.　In deserts, on the contrary, where conditions for reproduction are rather unfavorable, animals tend to live longer and to produce a few offspring which are carefully reared. Orton (1920) found in the north Atlantic that breeding periods, in general, began at the close of periods of maximum and of minimum temperatures.

Breeding and Food.—Among birds there is a striking relation between the availability of food for the young and the size of the nesting area. Birds like plovers, that have difficulty in securing sufficient insect food for their young, defend large nesting areas; whereas certain sea birds, that have no difficulty in securing an abundance of fish from the neighboring ocean, crowd so close together that they have barely room to sit on their eggs.

Care of Offspring.—Most animals are not only able to produce offspring, but also have some means for insuring their survival. There is, however, every degree of variation in this respect. A cod produces millions of eggs and leaves them unprotected on the surface of the ocean, enough nourishment being present within each egg to provide food for the young fish until it is able to shift for itself. Some animals cease their reproductive cares when they have deposited their eggs in proximity to a food supply for the young. Pratt (1912) reared insects from cow manure and obtained thirty-one species of Diptera, seventeen of Coleoptera, and one of Lepidoptera. The tumble beetle rolls a ball of manure to a secluded spot and buries it with its eggs, thus giving its larva both protection and food. Girdling and leaf-rolling insects make similar provision for their larvæ. The female leaf-cutter ant while establishing a new colony feeds herself and young on her own eggs and also raises fungus on manure beds for food. Bees, wasps, and ants generally build nests which they store with food and in many cases feed their young. Many animals though not always attending to the food supply of their offspring furnish special means for protecting them. Some frogs build nests attached to leaves over water and the tadpoles drop into the proper habitat when they hatch; others lay eggs in masses of froth, far from water. Spiders and myriapods enclose their eggs in carefully constructed cocoons. McCook (1889–1893) says there is a definite relation between the protective value of spider cocoons and the amount of care given them by parents, the poorly constructed cocoons being watched or carried by the parents. Birds brood their eggs and young, thus providing protection from cold, heat, and rain; the young are also fed and excreta are removed from the vicinity of the nest.

There are many animals that guard their offspring or actually carry them about with them. The mound-building birds of Australia, though escaping the tiresome routine of keeping their eggs warm with their own bodies, attend their incubators with watchful care, opening up the mound to admit radiant energy from the sun and adding or removing rubbish as humidity varies. A skink remains with her clutch of eggs in a rotting log, and if one of her treasures is moved a little distance, she moves it back with the rest. The male hellbender guards his nest, eating eggs from it, but exercising a generally protective function by his presence. Pycnogonids, sea-horses, crayfishes, certain frogs, and other animals carry their eggs and often also their young about with them. The male gaff-top-s'l catfish carries his eggs in his mouth for nearly three months and probably takes no food during that time.

A great advantage accrues to those animals that pass a period of adolescence during which they are fed and gain experience under the tutelage of their parents. The male freshwater dogfish not only builds and guards a nest, but swims about with his young for a time after they hatch. Mammals give their young a prolonged period of nourishment and protection within their bodies, and attend them afterwards until they attain some degree of maturity. The young of birds fall into two classes: precocious, which are able to shift more or less for themselves soon after they hatch, and altricial, which pass a period of helpless development during which they are cared for by their parents.

Length of Life.—The length of life of animals varies within wide limits. Some Protozoa exist as separate individuals for only a few hours; an elephant may live for 200 years. There is no general correlation between size, activity, complexity of structure or "constitution," and longevity. Some animals that normally live short lives may have their usual span prolonged by adverse conditions. Tiger beetles are usually annuals, but in Canada, where the larvæ do not have time to acquire sufficient food to complete their growth in one season, these insects are often biennials. In general, animals that live for long periods produce fewer offspring and bear them at less frequent intervals than those that live for a briefer time. In many species of animals males live shorter lives than females and some live only long enough to exercise their fertilizing functions. Female insects are likely to live longer than usual if they do not lay eggs. Moths that mate early have been shown to live shorter lives than unmated individuals. Some animals die soon after reproducing. In many species large and small individuals are more apt to remain unmated than those of average size, though there are some instances, as in the case of the male walrus, where extremes of size are of advantage in securing mates. Where a species has reached a state of equilibrium in a particular locality the death rate about keeps pace with the production of new life. Cary (1918) found that reef gorgonians seldom died of old age; the corals required two to five years to reach medium size and about one-fifth of the population died from various causes each year.

Influence of Environment on Type of Reproduction.—The type of reproduction or the duration of a particular type may be controlled to a considerable extent by environment. There has lately been some controversy concerning the "necessity" for conjugation among protozoans and the ability of various protozoans to live in culture media of unvarying composition. It has been shown that some species thrive for great numbers of "fission generations" in unvarying media and that others apparently become weak and die out if the environment does not vary. Some species have been kept active for several thousands of generations without conjugation when the culture medium was varied, and in some instances when it was not (Woodruff and Moore, 1924; Spencer, 1924). Among rotifers, crustaceans, and insects there are many species in which a series of parthenogenetic generations alternates with sexual generations and it has been possible in some cases to determine somewhat of the causes that induce one or the other type of reproduction. By varying food and temperature investigators have been able to maintain cultures of such types without the appearance of sexual individuals or to cause them to appear at rather frequent intervals. By parthenogenetic reproduction alone rotifers have been propagated for over 500 generations and aphids for over four years. Other factors than temperature and food may be important in initiating new types of reproduction. For example, Mrázek (1913) described an oligochæte that propagated inside a cyst which was formed when the water in which it lived dried up. Notwithstanding the nice agreement that the reproductive phases of many species show with varying conditions of environment, there are some species even in groups where such agreements are common, in which the types of reproduction take place without particular relation to changes in environment. Green (1919) found that, although *Simocephalus vetulus* was apparently "indefinitely viable parthenogenetically," when sexual individuals appeared they did so in no definite order, even from the same mother, and in cultures parthenogenesis could never be wholly inhibited by varying conditions.

There has long been a superstition that the inbreeding of close relatives is invariably injurious to a race, but recent experiments have shown that some animals can be inbred for many generations without apparent loss of virility and in some experiments the stock appeared actually to improve. It has also been shown that cross-fertilization is not essential in some hermaphroditic animals. *Limnœa columella* has been reared by self-fertilization for forty-seven generations without apparent loss of vigor in the stock (Colton, 1918). Conjugation and cross-fertilization in many metazoans apparently serve somewhat the same purpose as encystment, hibernation, and similar phenomena. In times of stress mixings from different stocks produce more types of variants, some of which may be able to pass over an unfavorable period. In other words, changes in environment, at least in a number of instances, appear to induce changes in the modes of reproduction of animals and probably also initiate the temporary dominance of new types of variants because these better fit the changed environment.

There are stages in life histories that appear to develop at a certain rate, more or less without relation to the condition of the environment. Artemia eggs do not hatch sooner if kept at higher temperatures. The palolo worm gives off more carbon dioxide as the spawning season approaches. Treadwell (1915) believes that this indicates an increase in metabolism and believes that egg laying is due to internal, as well as external, stimuli. A serricorn beetle of the genus Micromalthus passes through a very complicated life history—including three types of larvæ and two or three generations—in a rather uniform environment in rotting wood (Barber, 1913). On the other hand, there are many stages in life histories that are more or less dependent on conditions in the environment. Swingle (1922) maintains that iodine and tyrosine are essential as constituents of the food of frog tadpoles if metamorphosis is to be completed. The length of the pupal life of insects is often dependent on the rate of evaporation of water and some pupæ are surrounded by a layer of gum that retards evaporation (Folsom, 1922). Baker (1918) found a relation between age and the depth at which certain species of molluscs were found in Oneida Lake. In termites and ants the attainment of certain stages in the life cycle appears to depend on the living environment. When royal termites are present in a nest, substitute forms do not lay eggs, but if the royal forms are removed the substitutes mature. Winged forms do not appear in nests of the carpenter ant until colonies are two years old and until about 2000 workers are present (Pricer, 1908).

Some events in life cycles come as the result of the attainment of a particular degree of development. Different species of salmon spend from two to five years in the ocean. They then migrate into streams, apparently in the full vigor of maturity, but after breeding become senile very rapidly and soon die of old age (Moore, 1919). The eel hatches 500 fathoms deep in the ocean, lives a pelagic life for a time, then invades freshwater for a period of years, and finally returns to the ocean to breed. Herrick (1909) describes three interesting stages in the development of the young cuckoo after hatching: (1) a period of more or less helpless infancy up to the sixth day, (2) the complete quill stage, and (3) the climbing stage, characterized by the desertion of the nest and the development of feathers, between the seventh and seventeenth days. The young do not show fear until the end of stage 2 and the last one to leave the nest may be deserted because the instincts of the parents are diverted by attention to those already in the bush. The development of a cuckoo is associated with the progressive development of cyclical instincts in both young and parents.

An animal starting in life inherits a capacity to develop in a particular way. In some cases development depends on the encountering of a series of very complicated environmental conditions in a definite order; in others it takes place in a very uniform environment where surrounding conditions change little or not at all and the progressive changes that take place originate from stimuli within the animal itself.

FOOD

Bayliss (1918) defines a food as any substance that is taken into an organism and used for any purpose. Foods furnish material for increase in size, for repair, and for energy. They must contain certain chemical elements that are essential for all protoplasm and these must occur as particular compounds. Though a number of amino-acids may furnish energy for metabolism, only a few types are of value as body builders. Plants are able to synthesize starches and sugars, but animals must have carbohydrates at least built up into glucose.   The ultimate organic food resources of animals are always derived from the plant kingdom. Chlorophyll is essential for the building up of simple organic compounds and various bacteria are necessary for important steps in the degradation and synthesis of nitrogen compounds that may be used as foods.   Johnstone (1921) has pointed out that the production of nitrogen-containing compounds that may be used as foods for animals takes place largely on land and in freshwater; the shorewaters of the ocean contain greater amounts of such compounds and of carbon dioxide than the pelagic and abyssal regions.

Vestal (1914) has summarized the characteristics that enable an animal to obtain food as: (1) structural, including such adaptations as the tongues of woodpeckers, and the variation of the length of the alimentary canal in relation to different types of food; (2) physiological, relating to the range of ability of particular animals to assimilate foods; (3) psychological, concerning the ability to select proper foods; (4) biographical, the timing of the life history to correspond with available food; and (5) numerical, the adjustment of the rate of reproduction to food supply.   Mottram (1918) gives a list of the factors that control the desirability of food for a preying animal: (1) general hunger, desire for fuel; (2) special hunger, desire for variety—an animal may be satiated with one food, but need another; (3) ease of access to food; (4) prevalence of food—one thing is usually hunted at a time; (5) palatability—an abundant food may be refused because it is distasteful.

Types of Food Habits.—It is difficult to classify animals according to foods eaten, because there are so many gradations and so many animals fall in more than one class or change their food habits.   Animals that have a narrow range of foods are called *stenophagous* and those that eat a wide variety are *euryphagous*.   Animals that are restricted to one food are *monophagous* in distinction from *polyphagous* species that eat many foods.   Johnstone (1908) includes modes of nutrition for all organisms in five groups: *holozoic*, animals that prey on other plants and animals; *holophytic*, plants that live on inorganic substances and carry on photosynthesis; *saprophytic*, organisms like yeasts and molds that ferment organic materials; *myxotrophic*, chlorophyll-bearing Protista and alga-containing animals that have two modes of nutrition in the same organism;

saprozoic, organisms like the tapeworm that absorbs organic liquids. Folsom (1922) gives a most elaborate classification of insects according to food habits: *microphaga,* feeders on sugars and salts, with yeasts and bacteria; *sarcophaga,* flesh eaters; *copraphaga,* eaters of molds and bacteria; *mycetophaga,* consumers of fungi; *necrophaga,* eaters of dead animals, etc.

Types of Foods.—The importance of particular types of foods, of course, varies in different habitats. Proteins are the chief builders of protoplasm, but carbohydrates and fats are also essential. The presence or absence of water exerts an important influence in the distribution of many animals, and some of them often make long journeys to obtain salt. Though the necessity for vitamines has not been investigated throughout the animal kingdom, they are probably essential.

The distribution of animals often has direct relation to the availability of food and particular foods are the leading factors in the lives of many animals. The oak is estimated to serve as food for 500 species of insects; apple, 400; clover, 200; corn, 200. In rivers the dead plankton that has settled down from the water above is a very important source of food for bottom animals. In Oneida Lake, Baker (1918) found that the plant- and detritus-feeding animals outnumbered the carnivorous species by a ratio of 337:1. According to Vaughn (1919) corals eat nothing but animal food and their distribution is accordingly limited. Megnin (1896) studied the succession of insects in cadavers. Sarcophagid flies began the feast, depositing eggs in natural openings. With butyric fermentation Dermestes and Aglossa were characteristic, but with ammoniacal fermentation the flies of the genera Pyophila, Ophira, Phora, Louchoea, Anthomyia, and the beetles Corynetes and Necrobia were present. When there were liquids in the cadaver the beetles Silpha, Hister, and Saprinus worked and when it was dry tyroglyphid mites occurred. Very often animals that are closely related systematically have quite different food habits. Leathers (1922) places chironomid larvæ in six classes according to food habits: (1) feeders on bacteria, protozoans, small crustaceans, and diatoms that are strained by means of delicate nets from currents passing through dwelling tubes; (2) those straining food from flowing water; (3) those living on accumulations of diatoms and plant débris; (4) feeders on floating aquatic leaves; (5) those eating filamentous algæ; and (6) those moving about and actively seeking living food. Coker (1918) suggests that it is of fundamental importance from an economic point of view to rear species together that will not compete with each other for food. If this principle is followed, the productivity of an area may be greatly increased.

Amount of Food Required.—The amount of food necessary to maintain an animal varies considerably, even among individuals of the same species. The size of many animals depends more or less on the amount of food they have been able to obtain and assimilate. If two starfishes hatch at the same time, one may be a hundred times as large as the other after three months. The largest jellyfishes are found in cold seas, where there is the most abundant supply of food. An oyster strains about 135 liters of water per day to obtain its food. A Didinium may swallow a Paramœcium that is ten times its own bulk. A caterpillar may eat twice its own weight daily, and a flesh-eating larva has been reported to eat 200 times its own weight in twenty-four hours. A humming bird has eaten twice its weight in sugar in a day; a goosefish may eat half, and a mole two-thirds of its weight in the same time. The black swallower is able to ingest other fishes that are larger than itself. It has been estimated that the larva of a moth before it pupated ate 86,000 times its own weight at the time of hatching. The renewal coefficient for the food in the alimentary canals of certain cladocerans has been found to be from 15 to 60 minutes. The rate of digestion in different animals varies greatly: A Didinium will digest a Paramœcium in two hours and eat another; a cockroach may take two months to absorb a large meal of fat through the wall of its intestine. The Danish naturalists estimate that a bottom fish eats about one-thirtieth of its own weight daily during 300 days of the year, thus consuming a total of about ten times its own weight of flesh. They believe that it takes about 18 kilograms of food to produce 1 kilogram of plaice; as against 3.4 kilograms of food for 1 kilogram of trout as estimated by British investigators. In Bermuda the amount of bottom material that passes through an adult Stichopus is 6 to 7 kilos, dry weight, per year.

Starvation.—Some animals require a continual supply of food for their maintenance, others can fast for days, months, or years. The length of time that certain animals have been kept without food is as follows: lobster, 7 months; dragon-fly nymphs, 3 to 8 months; puffin, 28 days; albatross, 35 days; bowfin, 20 months; sea elephant, 1 month; dog, 117 days. The form and the structure of some animals are dependent to a considerable degree on the amount of food received and many fasting animals not only decrease in size but change their form when without food. Planarians have been known to decrease in size to half their original length and one-hundredth of their original volume while fasting. Other invertebrates also undergo remarkable reductions in size under similar conditions and many are even able to regenerate lost parts of their bodies. The museum pest, *Trogoderma tarsale*, has been kept alive without food for over four years, continuing to molt at intervals, but decreasing in size after each molt. There are some animals that regularly fast for long periods—the bull seal goes without food for three months while guarding his rookery. Certain male ticks never eat, but go through their entire life cycle on the nourishment they receive from the egg.

Selecting and Procuring Food.—Animals, in general, select particular foods from their environment and many specialists on particular foods have elaborate adaptations for securing and handling them. The caddis-fly larva, Hydropsyche, that lives in rapids builds a net which it scrapes off at intervals. The movements of the water scorpion are not perceptible until it grasps its prey with one lightning-like movement. The archer-fish with drops of water shoots flies down from vegetation to the surface, where they may be secured. The anglers display luscious lures to attract their prey. Patient spiders keep their webs in repair and wait long hours for some blundering insect, which they secure by enswathing it in silken wrappings. A number of birds periodically shed and cast out the lining of the gizzard, the character of which changes more or less with variations in food. There are endless means for getting food.

Food and Reproduction.—As was stated in the last section, the reproductive activities and life cycles of many animals are markedly influenced by the character or amount of food available. Jackson (1923) asserts that budding and other types of asexual reproduction are generally inhibited by inanition and sexual reproduction is stimulated. Among aphids there is good evidence that parthenogenetic females are succeeded by those that produce fertilizable eggs and male-producing eggs when the food supply fails. Rotifers have been similarly influenced by variations in the supply of manure or of certain algæ. A caterpillar that is underfed lives an unusually long larval life and spends a relatively shorter time as a pupa. Jackson (1923) asserts that the gonads of animals are generally resistant to inanition. Starvation, however, is known to inhibit the development of the gonads in Drosophila. It is also an important influence in the development of castes among certain social insects.

Food as an Environmental Factor.—As a factor of the environment, food has various relations to animals. For most animals it is a necessity which serves as a continual spur to activity. The finding of food and its capture constitute the daily, year-round business of most animals. But there are also periods in the lives of most animals when food may take a secondary place and other factors become more important.

MORPHOLOGY

The forms of animals are adapted, often to a striking degree, to the habitats in which they live. The ancestral pattern of structure that an animal inherits fixes its habitat in a general way, and animals that are not of close genetic relationship often show convergent similarity in their structural adjustments when they live in the same habitat. McClendon (1918) noted that Alpheus and Typton, two crustaceans that live in the canals of sponges, are very similar in form and coloration, and cited this as a remarkable case of convergence associated with a peculiar habitat. From an evolutionary point of view it is not permissible to say that peculiar environmental complexes cause animals to assume particular structural adaptations, but the ecologist recognizes many peculiarities of structure that enable him to say with some assurance in which habitats the animals possessing them belong. Fishes from various systematic groups have a ribbon-like form which permits progress by lateral undulations of the body (in the more specialized fishes of this type dorsoventral flexure is not possible), and these are associated with quiet water where they lurk among crevices in rocks or vegetation and burrow in mud. Freshwater mussels show a tendency to greater obesity as one leaves the headwaters of a stream and goes into the waters below. Many investigators have shown that the forms of plankton animals vary according to the condition of the water in which they live, and some species by their structure even indicate the locality and the season of the year at which they were collected. By the direction of the hair on the dried skin of a mammal, a naturalist can form an opinion of the postures, resting positions, and habits of the animal when alive. Animals show unending structural adaptations for nourishment, respiration, excretion, movement, reproduction, protection, and distribution. These are properly read by those who understand as signs of habits and habitats. Homology faithfully serves the taxonomist and evolutionist; scientific, critical analogy is a valuable aid for the ecologist.

Symmetry and Environment.—Child (1915) has attempted to determine the causes of the forms assumed by animals and he has shown that they are associated with gradients in metabolism along axes. If there is only one principal gradient the parts of an animal are arranged in a lineal series and the end of the chief axis that has the most rapid metabolic rate is the anterior end. If there are gradients along several axes, the animal is radially symmetrical. Child frankly states his opinion that the stimulus that determines the direction of the first gradient in an animal must come from the environment—perhaps at the point of entrance of a spermatozoön into an egg, from the point of attachment of an egg in an ovary, or from some other early determining influence. From an ecological point of view, however, environment plays a small part in determining the forms of most animals; heredity is the chief molder.

Perhaps the most apparent relation between structure and environment is in the fact that most animals that live attached or lead a sedentary life show a tendency toward radial symmetry, while those that move about are, as a rule, bilaterally symmetrical. It is apparent that some animals, like barnacles, that are now essentially radial in their symmetry, so far as their relations with the outside world are concerned, have been derived during their evolution from bilaterally symmetrical ancestors. On the other hand, some animals, like the spatangoids, that apparently come from radially symmetrical ancestors have a bilaterality superimposed on their primitively radial plan and at present move freely about. There are many instances where a change from an active free-living life to a sedentary one has been associated with a tendency toward radial symmetry, and many where a change from sessile to active life has been associated with the taking on of more or less bilaterality.

Variation in Structural Adaptations.—If structure kept constant pace with every change in habitat there would be no stability—and no species. But adjustment does not go so far as that. Most animals are able to make temporary minor adjustments, like calloses on carpenters' hands and variations in the lengths of Daphnia crests, but heredity apparently does not permit any fundamental permanent change in response to stimuli received from the environment. In some cases different species show gradations in structure in relation to variations in habitat, but on the whole such cases are rather rare. Dodds and Hisaw (1923) have recently accumulated some data in relation to the area of the gills on the may-fly nymphs of alpine streams and find that there is a rather definite relation between area and swiftness of current—the swiftest current being associated with the least area. Rhode (1912), on the other hand, collected larvæ of the flies of the genus Pelopia from a great variety of habitats and found that they were essentially alike in structure, but when he bred out adults from the larvæ he found that various species were more or less segregated in different habitats. Some sessile marine animals (sponges, corals, etc.) show forms that are correlated with the turbulence of the water—being flat and encrusting on wave-beaten shores and growing into branching, tree-like forms in quiet water.

Uses of Various Types of Structure.—Multicellularity, the presence of tissues, antimerism, metamerism, and colonial life give animals certain advantages in their relations with environment by allowing injury without incapacitating all units of the body system and by permitting division of labor. Chetverikov (1920) compares the plans of structure in insects and vertebrates, pointing out that, according to the principles of mechanics, it is to be expected that vertebrates, with endoskeletons and masses of muscles on the outside of the body, would be big, slow, and comparatively awkward, while insects, with exoskeletons and enclosed muscles, are at their best as small, active animals.

Size of Animals.—Environment limits the size of animals in various ways. The size of snails confined in small containers show direct relation to the amount of water surrounding them. Colton (1908) has shown that under such conditions dwarfing in *Limnaea columella* is due chiefly to limitations in food and oxygen, and to the presence of excretory products. Abyssal animals often grow to very large size and Solokowsky (1910) has advanced the view that this is possible because the perfect quiet at the bottom of the ocean enables them to spread out without risk of injury. Gravity is, of course, an important factor in limiting the size that animals may attain.

Numerical Variations in Parts of Animals.—Environment may also influence the parts of animals numerically. The number of vertebræ in certain species of fishes varies more or less regularly with variations in seasonal temperatures, altitude, and latitude. Zeleny (1923) has been able to control the number of facets in the eye of Drosophila by varying the temperature at which the flies were reared and finds that a logarithmic constant expresses the relation between the germinal and environmental factors.

PHYSIOLOGY

The reactiveness of organisms enables them to make adjustments to the environment. Animals show many adaptive physiological responses, the majority of functional changes being beneficial. There are continual adjustments to temperature, salinity, poisons, and other variable factors in the environment. The chemistry of protoplasm is extremely complex and not as yet thoroughly understood, but doubtless chemical differences will be found to be concerned with such subtle differences in susceptibility as animals show to disease and infection by parasites and in ability to utilize various substances for food. Some animals are able to reduce greatly their total amount of metabolism when living conditions become unfavorable. The sea-cucumber, *Thyone briareus*, when in stagnant water throws out most of its visceral organs (including the greater part of the enteric, nervous, and circulatory systems) and regenerates these when the surroundings again become favorable.

Types of Adjustment to Environment.—Reference has been made in another connection to the paper by Pike and Scott (1915), which points out that animals have three general types of adjustment to environment: (1) those animals that live in an essentially unvarying environment—the ocean—have little need for adjustment and make little; (2) those that live in a variable environment—land or freshwater—may vary with it more or less and often have remarkable powers of adjustment; and (3) those that are to some extent independent of environment because they make adjustments that keep their internal condi-

tions constant. In all the habitats of the earth it is essential that
animals function properly and if the environment varies so that
they are not able to do so, it is "unsuitable" for them. Living
things must function, for a certain amount of chemical activity
is one of the primary characteristics of protoplasm. Physiology
is the keystone of ecology. Plants usually show the effects of
their physiological condition by their growth form to a greater
extent than animals do, and they therefore often serve well as
indicators of the conditions of environment.

Metabolism.—Davenport (1908) says "metabolism is life,"
and points out that it is limited by two sorts of conditions: (1)
structural, such as broken parts or changed chemical compounds,
and (2) dynamical, such as absence of light, water, and proper
temperature. In adjusting itself to environment an animal must
acquire food to maintain metabolism and convert foodstuffs into
assimilable substances. In such processes bacteria are often
important aids, particularly in the digestion of cellulose. The
bacterial flora in the digestive tracts of carnivorous and herbivorous animals is radically different, anaerobic putrefactive
forms being abundant in the former and not in the latter.
Metabolic processes furnish energy for the accomplishment of
the work necessary for normal activities. The chief source of
energy is from oxidation and one of the important relations of
animals with environment is the securing of a continual supply
of oxygen. There must also be opportunity in the environment
for the disposal of waste products. Living things are continually
producing acids and buffers are necessary to neutralize these
within their bodies. Crozier (1923) has cited evidence that
indicates that active protoplasm is acid in reaction. Metabolism
is related to size and small animals metabolize more per gram
than large. Animals have more or less automatic mechanisms
for adjusting metabolism to changes in environment. The evaporation of perspiration in man is a means for cooling the body.
Planarians are unable to increase their oxidative processes to
maintain their usual metabolic rate when they are in a medium
that is deficient in oxygen, but if changed to lower temperatures
will gradually increase their rate of metabolism until it reaches
that before the change. Recent investigations concerning the
relations between the temperature of the bodies of various invertebrates and the media surrounding them showed temperatures
of 0.05 to 2.44°C. above the medium. The earthworm reached

a temperature within 0.05°C. of that of its surrounding medium within two minutes after a change. Animals show considerable individuality in their ability to adjust themselves to changes in environment. Child (1915) states that an individual is to be interpreted in terms of rate of reaction and of transmitted changes as manifested by the relations between protoplasm and the external world.

Circulating Body Liquids.—The circulating media within the bodies of animals have important relations to metabolism as carriers of nourishment, oxygen, and waste products. According to Dakin (1912), invertebrate marine animals have internal liquids that closely resemble sea water and that vary more or less as the surrounding medium varies, but freshwater and land invertebrates do not have blood that is like diluted sea water, and vertebrates, even in the ocean, have blood which differs from the surrounding water in salinity and (except in elasmo-branchs which have considerable amounts of nitrogenous sub-stances) in osmotic pressure. Iron and copper are usually important constituents of the respiratory pigments in blood. Among invertebrates hæmoglobin is frequently characteristic of mud dwellers or animals living in poorly aerated water. It will hold thirty times as much oxygen as water. It is derived by many animals from the four pyrrol groups of chlorophyll and that pigment is, therefore, often essential as a food in the environment.

Respiration.—While oxygen is essential for all animals, there are many that are able to live indefinitely without free oxygen in their environment. Recent investigations show that several marine invertebrates, including the lobster, can endure pro-longed sojourns in water containing little or no oxygen. Plana-rians are not able to live in water that contains one-third its saturation capacity of oxygen. Many animals breathe through the outside of the body, but some have gills of various types for securing oxygen from the water, and those that breathe air commonly have lungs. Various other means are employed by certain animals for securing oxygen: certain fishes and amphibians swallow air and absorb oxygen through vascular areas in the alimentary tract; dragon-fly nymphs and certain sea-cucumbers breathe through the specialized walls of the cloacal chamber. Some aquatic animals pass large quantities of water through their bodies and this serves for respiration. The amount thus flowing through finger sponge is 78 liters per day; Ascidia, 173 liters; Stichopus, 20 liters. Some aquatic insects carry air below the surface; others utilize bubbles from aquatic plants and get oxygen in other ways. The animals that live in sandy beaches have many interesting adaptations for keeping dirt out of their respiratory chambers.

Tides and Respiration in the Atmosphere.—Flattely (1921) has suggested that the rise and fall of the tides played an important part in the development of life on land, some of the animals becoming gradually adjusted to air breathing by being periodically left out of the water. Along the seashore there is an interesting series of crustaceans, snails, and fishes—some living always below low-tide mark, some frequenting the 'tween-tide zone, and others living always above the water. These animals show gradations between gill breathing and lung breathing. Some crabs and snails can breathe through either gills or lungs. A barnacle high up on a beach may be out of water nineteen-twentieths of the time, and retains a little bubble of air inside the apex of its tightly closed shell.

Aquatic Air Breathers.—Racovitza (1904) states that air breathers in water usually develop the following rhythm: (1) long inspiration, (2) long submergence, (3) return to surface, (4) long expiration, (5) rapid inspiration and expiration, etc. A duck shows outstanding resistance to the effects of submersion when compared with a hen. A duck with a ligated trachea is able to stay under water twenty-three minutes while a hen dies after three and a half minutes. If only the head of a duck is submerged, the heart and the respiratory rate slow down and the resistance is normal, but a duck with a ligated trachea that is kept wholly in air will live only seven minutes (Huxley, 1913). Some aquatic insects are believed to absorb oxygen from the water and to visit the surface only to expel waste gases. Noble (1925) has shown that hairy frogs are adapted to cutaneous respiration and that lungless salamanders have no left auricle because they breathe largely through the skin.

Growth.—Growth may result from metabolic processes. It is increase in size—not development, or increase in mass. It may be determinate, and cease when the animal attains adult size, or indeterminate, and only become slower in the adult. A blue crab molts fifteen times between the megalopa stage and the adult, increasing the diameter of the shell about one-third after each molt. Animals that do not shed their exoskeletons usually grow gradually, though all parts of the body may not increase proportionally. The weight of a crab may double in an hour after molting on account of the rapid absorption of water. The blood before molting may constitute only 5 per cent of the body weight and 50 per cent after.

Rhythmical Rest and Activity.—Metabolism is not only limited by appropriate temperatures and other conditions, but it takes place in a more or less rhythmical way. Many insects and vertebrates, and even simple animals like corals, have regularly recurring periods of rest and activity that are commonly correlated with the alternation of day and night. The butterflies belonging to the family Lyncænidæ (Frohawk, 1914) are said to rest with the head downward from about four o'clock in the afternoon until sunset, then sleep with the head up throughout the night. Certain animals kept continuously in comparative darkness appear to suffer no particular injury. For example, animals in mines may remain in good condition for years.

Regeneration.—Animals are in continual danger of disturbances in their physiological balance through injury by actual loss of parts or through chemicals that incapacitate certain functions. Regeneration helps many animals to adjust themselves to such difficulties. A Difflugia can reunite with parts of its body that have been separated from it, but cannot fuse with fragments from other individuals. Many animals can grow parts that their bodies may lack. Autolysis also enables them to absorb injured parts that cannot be separated from the body. Child (1915) has shown that the ability to regenerate certain missing parts of the body, like the head of a planarian, depends upon the rate of metabolism in the body mass that remains after mutilation. Certain limiting factors, like low temperature, may so operate as to prevent regeneration of parts that require high metabolic rates.

Excreta in the Environment.—The excreta of animals often constitute an important factor in the environment. Excretory products are usually toxic to the producer and by their presence may constitute a basis for succession. Trouessart (1901) says that animal hygiene has four chief aspects: (1) removal of fæces and excretions, (2) removal of dead bodies, (3) aeration of habitats, and (4) preservation of provisions. Many animals cleanse themselves carefully before producing eggs or young. Honey

bees leave the hive to defecate and produce air currents for
ventilation by waving their wings.   A pocket gopher has a latrine
pit at one side of its burrow where it buries excreta.   Birds
usually remove fæces from their nests, probably both to keep
them clean and to prevent the droppings from giving notice to
predaceous animals of the nests' positions.   Some bees have
definite places for the deposition of fæces, cadavers, and other
undesirable matter; others cover foreign bodies, such as dead
insects, within the hive, with a heavy coating of wax.   A lion
does not eat the intestines from animals that it kills, but cleanly
removes them from the body and buries them.   Some animals,
like termites and certain bees, are unusual in that they use their
own excreta in the construction of dwellings.

PROTECTION

Animals are continually beset with dangers: the environment
may change beyond their limits of toleration; there may be
a less pronounced change that does not actually make it impossible to exist but makes it more difficult because conditions
become more favorable for some competing animal; predatory
species continually devour a certain percentage of the population;
and insidious parasites wait for opportunities to invade the bodies
of their hosts.   Marked changes in environment may completely upset the established balance in a habitat—some species
may decrease or die out completely and others increase.   The
animals in any habitat usually have means for adjusting themselves to usual changes.   When the water in a pond dries up
certain planarians roll up, especially so as to protect the anterior
end, and, surrounded by mud and secretions from their own
bodies, are thus able to survive for a time.

Predaceous Animals.—The world of preying animals has
various means of capturing its food.   The archer-fish shoots
drops of water; the crocodile lurks immobile and drags its prey
under water; the python hangs waiting in a tree; the vulture
circles a mile above the earth and with its keen eyes patiently
watches for something to die; the angler displays baits to attract
little fishes; the spider spins elaborate snares.   Predatory
animals continually watch for an animal that is at a disadvantage.
Wolves follow a sick or injured buffalo and wait for it to die; agile
dragon-flies are easy victims when they are emerging from their

nymphal skins. Ants frequently eat their injured fellows (Hingston, 1920); it is well known that elephants, cattle, and other animals often turn on weak or wounded individuals in their herds.

Escape from Enemies.—The following are the most important means employed by animals to escape from predators: agility or speed in flight; habits of resting in open places, so that approaching enemies may be readily seen; hard shells on the outside of the body (insects, turtles, molluscs, hermit crabs, armadillo, etc.); electricity (torpedo, electric eel, etc.); distasteful or irritating odors or flavors (skunk, millipeds, various insects, etc.); autotomy (lizards, crustaceans, brittle starfishes, etc.); death feigning (walking-stick, many bugs, opossum, etc.); spiny or slippery exterior (spiny lobster, sea-urchins, eels, etc.); alarming or startling appearance(puss moth larva, etc.); concealing or warning coloration and mimicry; active resistance (clawing, scratching, biting, etc.); the association of two species together, one or both having some protective qualities (hermit crab with anemone, etc.); the defense of colonies by special protective individuals (soldiers among ants and termites, stinging individuals in hydroid colonies, etc.); the use of protective devices taken from other animals (nematocysts of cœlenterates used "second hand" by molluscs and flatworms, etc.); resorting to isolated or inaccessible places, such as burrows, houses, islands, cliffs, etc.; luminosity (possibly of protective value to some pelagic, marine animals); behavior by parents that simulates injury and attracts predators away from eggs, young, or mates. If such measures as the last are not effective, some species of birds stage a mock combat among themselves to attract attention.

Means of Defense.—The dependence of animals on some of these means is remarkable. A walking-stick or a giant water-bug while in a death feint will not move, even if its body is cut in two. The latter assumes two death-feigning attitudes, both unlike the position assumed in actual death. By appropriate stimulation it has been made to feint thirty-eight successive times for a total of about eight hours. The scallop's chief danger is the starfish, and it swims precipitately away if a dilute extract from its enemy is squirted into the water about it. Certain beetles of the genus Stenus escape from floods by "skimming" on the surface of the water. This they are able to do by secreting a substance at the posterior end which, on account of

differences in surface tension, forces them rapidly forward.
Such animals as horses, deer, and house flies depend largely on
the acuteness of their senses and their speed for escaping from
enemies.   Birds hastening south in their migrations may attain
a speed of over 100 miles per hour.   Sometimes slow stupidity
has better survival value than agile astuteness.   Animals do
not fall into two classes, protected and non-protected, but protective devices are rather to be classified as more or less efficient.
Animals are not protected from all dangers, but are usually
suited particularly to escape those of certain types.   It is believed
that the elephant is limited in numbers chiefly by the harassing
of little insects, and of course cattle and men are absolutely
unable to live in certain parts of Africa on account of the parasites carried by tse-tse flies.

Homes.—The dwelling places of animals serve as refuges for
the development of the young, as prisons to prevent the young
from wandering, as places for the training of the young, for the
storage of food, etc.   Homes are often concealed or placed in
inaccessible places, but may be conspicuous, particularly in
gregarious or social species.   The home and its situation are
more or less distinctive for each species.   In some cases homes
are merely spots that appear much like other similar places.
Birds choose a secure roosting site with considerable care and
often return to the same spot night after night, apparently to
avoid the trouble of finding a new place.   A nighthawk builds
no nest but lays her eggs on the surface of the ground, and yet
she recognizes this place as home.   Some coliad larvæ rest on
the under surfaces of leaves near the center.   They go to the
edge of a leaf to feed, but spin a thread in order that they may
return directly to their resting spot.   Spittle insects live in
masses of froth that they whip up on plant stems.   The dromi-
ads cut out pieces of sponge that they hold over their backs
and are thus concealed.   Caddis-fly larvæ live in portable or
attached tubes that they make by spinning threads and fastening various materials together.   Hermit crabs commonly live
in snail shells, but may inhabit holes in corals or sponges.   Ship-
worms and some crustaceans make holes in piles and thus destroy
much property; timbers on land are also seriously injured by
boring insects.   Certain sea-urchins and clams even bore into
rock.   Many animals dig burrows in the dirt.   Gophers have
elaborate tunnels with compartments for the storage of food,

the burying of excreta, and other purposes. Many marine worms line their burrows with secretions from their own bodies and often include foreign materials. The tubes of some of these worms have collapsible ends that are closed by valves which prevent the entrance of enemies; other tubes close up by having the ends roll like a young fern frond. The ant-lion has a burrow at the bottom of a sand pit and every windy day is one of hard labor, for sand must be thrown out of the pit continually. Among insects there are many expert home builders— workers with silk, mud, paper, and other materials. The larva of Bucculatrix when ready to pupate not only spins a cocoon but surrounds it with a stockade of spikes. Birds exhibit a great variety of homes; that of the magpie is roofed over and the doorway surrounded by thorns; that of the oriole, pendant and safe at the tip of a branch; that of the flamingo, a mud tower in a muddy flat, etc. Birds have two types of young: (1) *altricial*, which are usually reared in safe places, are carefully cared for by their parents, and show no fear for some time after hatching; (2) *precocial*, which show fear soon after leaving the egg and soon shift for themselves. The beaver prepares for a home by damming a stream. The resulting pond furnishes a place for a lodge and for the storage of winter food; it also is a highway that remains passable throughout the winter and gives opportunity for a quick escape from an enemy or for the transportation of materials under the ice.

Protective Behavior.—Holmes (1922) has given a tentative classification of the forms of behavior used by animals for self-protection. He makes two subdivisions: escape and defense, and subdivides the latter into passive and active. Passive defensive behavior includes such measures as closing, rolling up, erecting spines, and emitting odors; active measures employed are biting, clawing, kicking, stinging, hunting for parasites, etc.

Defenses within Animals.—Animals have certain inherent defenses within their bodies. Injuries are repaired to a greater or less extent. Antitoxins, phagocytes, or other bodies neutralize or destroy substances that enter the body of an animal and threaten to do it injury. Different species of animals show varying degrees of resistance to diseases and poisons. Poisonous animals are usually immune to their own venoms and many animals have natural or acquired immunity to particular poisons.

BEHAVIOR

Interaction with environment is a fundamental property of protoplasm. The behavior of animals consists of movements that cause rearrangement of parts or of whole animals so as to assume different positions in relation to the environment. The most common cause of reaction is a stimulus, or change in the environment, though some are brought about by stimulating changes within the animal itself. Reactions are fundamentally regulatory, or adaptive, in that they usually tend to make an animal continue to exist, but they are not necessarily performed in the best possible manner, and sometimes they may actually injure the animal that performs them. Animals with simple organizations are usually able to perform only a few rather stereotyped reactions in response to stimuli; those with specialized nervous systems are able to exercise more or less choice in the time, degree, and nature of their responses. More specialized animals also react more and more to representative stimuli—not for the actual effect that the stimulus may produce, but as a sign of the order of events that experience has shown that such a stimulus presages. It might be expected that, if an organism was subjected to the same type of stimulus on two different occasions, its behavior would be the same. While this holds true in general, it is not always so. The physiological state of an animal varies and causes an animal to respond now in one way and now in another. The more complicated the mechanism in an animal's body is the more possibilities of response it has. A Paramœcium swims ahead until it encounters a stimulus that causes it to swing about, or swim backwards, or stop. Encountering hundreds of stimuli, it has less than a dozen methods of response. On the other hand, a rabbit that is resting under cover and hears a twig snap has many possibilities of response —it may remain motionless; bound away on a tortuous course, astutely "doubling" to throw off a pursuer; stand up and look for the cause of the sound; or perform countless other acts. Acts that give pleasure, or satisfaction, or cause the animal better to continue to exist are apt to be repeated and habits of activity are thus formed; acts that lead to discomfort, pain, or injury are apt to be avoided and habits of inhibition are initiated. All animals are able to profit by experience more or less and intelligence, which is the logical outcome of the specialization of such ability, is not the ability to form associations, but a high degree of ability to make profitable use of associations that are already formed. Learning is not something new, but the facilitation through repetition of fundamental movements and activities.

Behavior and Choice of Habitat.—The behavior of animals often accounts for their distribution in the environment. Shelford (1914) made careful comparisons of the modes of reaction between animals in pools and rapids. He found that there was general agreement among the animals in each habitat. Animals by their behavior tend to find the environment that is best suited to their peculiar types of activities.

Behavior of Sessile and Motile Animals.—Probably the most fundamental distinction in behavior is between that of sessile and motile animals. The former tend toward radial symmetry, and it is undoubtedly advantageous for a sessile animal to be able to receive stimuli with equal facility from all directions. Radial symmetry from a psychological point of view is inherently diffuse and unprogressive because different radial axes of the body are more or less of equal importance and it is, therefore, difficult to have great centralization in control. The animal remains a "republic of reflexes." Animals that move about freely are usually bilaterally symmetrical and have a tendency toward cephalization. Control becomes more and more delegated to the central nervous system, which in the most specialized types exercises nearly absolute authority and is finally able to think of many expedients for adapting various means to particular ends.

Adaptability of Behavior.—For movements to be directed with adaptive relation to the environment there must be stimuli coming to an animal from the outside. A complete living mechanism, if supplied with adequate energy, may give an adaptive, orderly response to such stimuli. Protozoans select proper food from a varied assortment of materials in the environment. A young silversides minnow avoids all large objects; hence spends its youth in open water far from shore and thus generally avoids large predaceous fishes. Animals receive stimuli from their environment and generally respond so that they may continue their activities, but different animals in the same environment do not necessarily respond to the same stimuli. This is where the remarkable adaptiveness of animals is most apparent. Different species are suited by hereditary qualities to receive particular stimuli and individuals of the same species form various habits of reacting on account of peculiarities in receiving organs or differences in past relations with environment (experience). Emphasis is placed now on impulses initiated by a receptor for one type of stimulus and now on those from another. A bullhead feeds at night, largely through stimuli received by smell, taste, and touch organs in its nostrils and on its barbels. The stickleback feeds by day, depending on stimuli received through its eyes. It chases and tentatively takes into its mouth every bubble or other small object that moves. A dog's world is largely a smelling and seeing world; a man's world is more a seeing and hearing world. Though most animals can perceive a variety of stimuli, each species and individual usually depends primarily on those of one or of a few kinds in making adjustments in order to fit in with changes in the environment.

Responses to Touch.—Touch stimuli play a leading rôle in the lives of many animals. Whether a hydroid stem develops into a stolon or a hydranth depends, in some cases, on whether it encounters a solid object or not. The ichneumon, Thalessa, is able to bore through a considerable thickness of solid wood with its ovipositor and reach the larva of its host, Tremex. An earthworm is said to be stereotropic because it is usually restlessly active unless its body is in contact with the walls of its burrow or with some similar surface. Stereotropism, geotropism, and to some extent rheotropism are all responses called forth by pressure against objects. Lyon (1904) in his admirable paper on rheotropism shows that so-called rheotropic responses are brought about by optical or tactile stimuli. Rheotropism is a form of compensatory motion that tends to keep animals in the same spatial relation to certain objects in their environment.

Responses to Sounds.—Auditory stimuli produce pressure on appropriate receptors, but stimulation differs from touch in that it is concerned with vibrations in ponderable media. Sounds are of value to animals as: warnings; call notes, particularly as signals during mating and for keeping groups together; and as a medium for language expression. Hartridge (1920) has advanced the view that bats are able to fly about in total darkness by emitting high sounds which are reflected back to their ears from obstructions, which thus may be avoided.

Responses to Thermal Changes.—Temperature is effective for many animals as a limiting environmental factor through its influence on the rate of metabolism, but differences in temperature are also received as stimuli. Cases are rare where temperature serves as a directive sitmulus, however. Animals tend to rest near their optimum in cool or warm places, but usually do not go directly toward or away from such situations unless they have a high order of psychic development.

Responses to Chemicals.—Chemical substances are often important stimuli. Animals use tastes and odors for judging the suitability of foods; for the recognition of particular individuals, foods, places for depositing eggs, etc.; for keeping predaceous animals away; and for other purposes. The life of a honey bee is dominated by odors and each individual produces those that are characteristic of its hive and sex. The primary basis for the social life of bees, ants, and certain other insects is in the odor sense. A filtered solution from a Paramœcium culture will cause a Didinium to emerge from its cyst and take up an active life, though it cannot find sustenance, for its food consists of living protozoans. There has been some discussion as to whether aquatic animals have distinct senses of taste and smell. Recent experiments demonstrate that smell serves fishes, as it does land vertebrates, for the perception of very dilute solutions and taste is used for the discrimination of those of greater strengths.

Responses to Light.—Light may be a non-directive stimulus, merely exciting an animal to activity, or cause animals to assume definite orientation with relation to it and perhaps also cause them to move directly toward or away from it. The skin of many animals is sensitive to light, but many others have special pigmented areas and eyes of various sorts for light perception. The simpler eyes merely allow an animal to perceive with more or less accuracy the direction from which light comes, but the more complicated types enable animals to perceive images and distinguish colors. The camera eyes of vertebrates give very good images of objects, but the compound eyes of arthropods are probably superior to them as organs for perceiving motion in the environment. It was long a dogma that Paramœcium is absolutely insensitive to light, but recent experiments show that, if this protozoan is in motion and the light intensity is suddenly increased, the rate of locomotion is also increased.

Some animals are very sensitive to changes in light intensity. Thyone and Hydroides will contract at once if a glass rod is passed between them and a window. The moth larva that lives on coffee leaves is apparently sensitive to the absolute amount of light. It never comes out into the direct sunlight, but frequents the upper surfaces of leaves on cloudy days and on bright days is found underneath.

Most animals that commonly respond to light as such are stimulated, as far as quick reactions are concerned, by the time rate of change in the intensity, but the absolute amount of light is chiefly responsible for the periodic activities of animals that are markedly diurnal or nocturnal. For example, if the amount of light is decreased very slowly Hydroides does not withdraw into its tube, but if the decrease is rapid, it snaps back at once; chickens usually will go to roost when the light is decreased during an eclipse. Changes in the amount of light serve as signs for many animals and influence behavior accordingly: A hermit crab avoids shadows as indications of passing enemies; leeches wave their bodies or swim in the direction of movement of shadows and thus often gain attachment to hosts. There is a general migration of plankton animals up and down with the daily changes from dark to light, but all species do not rise or descend when the light has reached the same degree of intensity.

Animals that can make use of light to perceive images and that can distinguish different wave lengths have unusual advantages in adjusting themselves in the environment. A jumping spider or a tree frog can judge distances with great accuracy and is thus able to leap on its prey with certainty. An animal like a vulture that habitually soars high above the earth must depend for a livelihood chiefly on its eyes. The ability of the honey bee to discriminate colors and patterns is of great value in seeking food in flowers. The remarkable resemblances of many animals to the colors and patterns in their environment is to be taken as evidence of the sharp vision of predators.

Homing Behavior.—Animals often show place association, particularly those that have more or less permanent homes. The snail Patella rests on rocks along the shore of the ocean. It remains in one spot so long that it sometimes wears a little scar and if moved a few inches away will return. Arey and Crozier (1921) studied the homing of Onchidium, a pulmonate that lives in colonies of about a dozen individuals in crevices along the shores of Bermuda. Each snail leaves its home crevice for about an hour each day to feed. It returns to its own crevice and cannot be induced to enter any other. Arey and Crozier believe that Onchidium recognizes its home by "contact odor" and that their observations give no evidence of associative memory. Crabs that live in burrows and similar habitations often show pronounced homing habits. In the Philippines the writer once moved a fiddler about 30 feet from its burrow and the crab returned to the same spot after twenty-eight days. The old burrow had long been filled up by the tides, but the little crab dug a new one beside the stake that had been set to mark the place. Many insects resort to particular places. Certain butter-flies have resting spots and they attempt to dislodge any intruder that may have squatted on the property during their absence. Bees, wasps, and ants have nests that are the center of their activities. There has been considerable controversy as to which senses are most used by ants and other insects that have pro-nounced homing habits. Wasps and bees depend much upon landmarks. According to Pieron (1913), different kinds of ants return home by the use of different senses, Formica and Cam-ponotus depending mostly on landmarks, Lazius using odor trails, and Messor utilizing "muscular memory." Various fishes, amphibians, birds, and mammals have homing habits. It has been determined by banding birds that they return to the same spot to nest year after year; even the penguins in the Antarctic resort to the same rookeries. Noddy terns are able to return quickly over the open ocean for distances of 800 to 1000 miles; just how is uncertain (Watson and Lashley, 1915). It is known that homing pigeons can return from greater distances if they are allowed to observe the route over which they are taken from the home cote.

Classification of Behavior.—Melrose (1921) has recently classified the behavior of animals according to psychological levels and makes the six following groups:

I. Lowest Animal Learning:
    A. Organic Fixation. Defining and fixing inherited behavior by practice. Fixation depends on trial and action. System attains stability by discharge.
    B. Organic Spatial Accommodation. Learning by repetition of direct sense stimuli and assimilation of the result. Depends on location of stimuli, and environment must be roughly uniform.

   C. Organic Choice.   Shortening at once of a series of reactions and most useful parts of series are retained.

II. Higher Animal Learning:

   D. Organic Association (Association by Contiguity).   Not mere change of given emotions and not necessarily analysis, but learning by associations with objects.

   E. Organic Conception.   Responses to new situations in such a way as to show contributions of past "concretes" of experience, and yet show that experience does not absolutely determine behavior.   No "ideas" are necessary; the whole is not a set plan but the parts are.   Concept comes from integrating on the basis of the law of averages of a class of similars.

   F. Organic Judgment.   Association between complexes; between relations.   Responses to problems of environment.

Melrose also suggests another grade:

   G. Reflective Judgment, which is accompanied by consciousness.

Tropisms, Habits, Instincts.—Protozoans and many other animals respond to stimuli largely by tropisms, which are repeated over and over without much modification whenever the appropriate stimulus is repeated. A Paramœcium that is dropped into a toxic solution keeps on giving "avoiding reactions" until it dies; a moth will fly persistently against a lamp, showing maladaptation of a tropism that under normal conditions would be generally useful. *Tropisms* are for whole animals somewhat like the reflexes of parts of animals. If acts are repeated they are usually performed more readily and thus grow into *habits*, which are useful because they enable an animal to save some of the time, attention, and labor that is necessary without learning. Memory is important in the relations of animals with environment, enabling them more readily to avoid dangers that are encountered repeatedly and to find food more easily through experience. *Instincts* are complicated acts that are characteristic for each species and that an animal is able to execute with some degree of perfection without learning. They have been defined as "inherited" or "racial" habits, the supposition being that they have been fixed by repetition during phylogeny and are now a part of the specific inheritance of each species. Instincts concerned with the procuring of food, locomotion, defense, escape, homing, and social life are usually more or less continuously active; those concerned with reproduction are often cyclical or periodic—like those for migrating, mating, nesting, and incubating; some instincts are transitory and usually appear irregularly at certain periods in the life cycle—like play, the climbing period of certain young birds, etc.

Levels of Response.—Animals that have only a few simple reflexes, tropisms, and instincts must lead very simple lives and have limited relations with environment. They spend their time seeking food, eating, digesting, avoiding danger, resting. Animals that have attained enough complexity, so that they do not have to respond to every stimulus, but exercise some degree of choice in their methods of response, can conserve energy and have more leisure for practice and hence may attain perfection in complicated acts. Animals that can reason may go beyond the reflex and instinctive endowment that they inherited. They invent new methods of procedure, and have leisure for the intellectual enjoyment of living—recalling the past and anticipating the future for pleasure—playing for mere pleasure and not only because the skill attained gives better chance of survival. They may even acquire many purely mental standards for living that have no reasonable basis, but are dependent on custom.

COMPETITION

Animals are racially always "between the devil and the deep sea." If they are taking part in the affairs of the world and struggling for a better type of existence, they must carry on a continual fight and are in constant danger of defeat or death; if they have found a quiet eddy in the slack waters of the evolutionary current and are enjoying more or less immunity from competition, they cannot hold a dominant position and, though perhaps secure and more or less at ease, take little or no part in shaping the affairs of the world. A lion takes his chances from day to day and, though the evidence is lacking, everyone would like to believe that as the ages go by his eyes become sharper, his leap longer, his muscles stronger, and his brain more cunning. Sometimes an elephant tramples the life out of a lion, sometimes a buffalo strikes one down, but there are more lions and more lions—fighting, preying, breeding. The ant-lion sits in his pit and waits for game. He is voracious and strong compared to his prey and he rests well protected from enemies by his burrowing ability and caving sand. Which of these animals has the best of it? I say the lion because he does not hide away from anything, but struggles and (thus, I hope and

believe) improves.   He is to some degree specialized as a preying
animal, but he goes abroad among the others—jackals, foxes,
hyenas, cheetas, leopards, even tigers—and is the greatest of them
all.   But, scientifically, it is not proper to say that the lion is
greater, or better, than the little ant-lion.   One survival is as
good as another.

Numerical Balance in Nature.—The animal world is full of competition.   There are continually more animals produced than can
survive, and many require a continuous supply of other animals
for food.   The barnacles on the rock beaches have an abundance
of food supplied in the ever-flowing tidal water, but conditions
are never such that every young barnacle can find a place for
attachment and grow to maturity.   So it is with every species.
To keep a balance and maintain its numbers, each must find
enough food, escape from enemies or other dangers, and produce
enough offspring to hold its own.   Some animals, though apparently successful in their efforts to continue to live, are never
abundant—*e.g.*, the osprey.   When animals are unusually successful for a time and increase in numbers far beyond the usual
limits of their species, they usually pay the penalty.   Their
abundance leads to an increase in the predatory animals that feed
upon them, leads new animals to seek them as food, and renders
it more easy for diseases to spread among them.   Climatic
changes usually favor one species and a competing one that is
handicapped by the change falls behind.

Competition is most keen among individuals of the same
species—because they need and strive for almost the same things.
Species within a genus are usually protected more or less from
competition by differences in habits.   If an animal can attain new
styles of living, it may be able to invade habitats where there are
no competitors.   Vestal (1914) has summarized the characteristics that may remove animals from competition as: (1) structural
(the fossorial fore limbs of the mole enable it to live underground);
(2) physiological (the clothes moth lives on keratin, which is
indigestible for most animals); (3) psychological (one mouse
prefers to live in the forest, another in the meadow); (4) biographical (the butterfly hunts by day, the moth at night); (5) numerical
(two species that use practically the same resources cannot be as
numerous as if there was only one).   Warming (1909) states the
results of competition as: (1) the establishment of natural
communities, (2) unceasing changing and adjustment, (3) the

production of rare species because suitable habitats are not to be found, because a species is new in a locality, or because it is a relict, and (4) perhaps also the origin of species. He also says that dominance depends upon: (1) ability to obtain a foothold, (2) hardihood or endurance, (3) capacity for assimilation or rate of development, (4) reproductive capacity, and (5) freedom from enemies.

CHAPTER IV

SUCCESSION

Mill (1848) in his classical work on the Principles of Political Economy, said:

Of all truths relating to phenomena, the most valuable to us are those which relate to their order of succession. On a knowledge of these is founded every reasonable anticipation of future facts, and whatever power we possess of influencing those facts to our advantage.

Many of the changes on earth take place in an orderly manner and some of them are rhythmical. When such changes are not too extreme in range or rate, animals are often "adapted" to them and may show correlated variations in metabolism or behavior.

Geological Succession.—During geological succession there has usually been a sequence of species, some types of animals being exterminated by changes and others arising by evolution to live under new conditions. Orderly physiographic changes, such as accompany the wearing down of elevations or the filling up of depressions, are also accompanied by a consecution of succeeding species. Some species enter habitats soon after they are formed, as pioneers, some live in habitats when they are in their maturity, others frequent habitats that are undergoing the senile changes that lead them toward the ends of their careers and perhaps transform them into new types. A young stream, as represented by a torrential brook, has quite a different group of animal inhabitants from an old river. The species that invade a stream in its youth do not persist in the same locality, but migrate back with the headwaters as the land surfaces are worn down, and new species come into the quieter waters near the mouth (Shelford, 1911a). After a change in environment there is a gradual succession of species until a climax formation is established and this group of species usually persists until there is another change.

Life Zones.—In connection with ecological succession the horizontal distribution of animals in space often recapitulates their past distribution in time. Klugh (1921) found that the lower beach pools along the Bay of Fundy, which were exposed for a shorter time at low tide, contained a more stenothermic fauna than pools at higher levels.   Mayer (1917) in his review of the medusæ of the world found 77 species that were confined to tropical, 22 to temperate, and 7 to frigid regions; 16 species ranged from tropics through temperate zones and only 2 from tropical to polar seas.   Klugh's observations indicate that the animals in beach pools have come from the ocean and that some have been able to go farther than others because they had, or were able to develop, greater toleration for variations in temperature. Mayer's summary may be interpreted as indicating that medusæ spread from the equator toward the poles.   Glaciation caused many animals to migrate southward and. when the glaciers retreated toward the north those species that were most tolerant of cold followed close behind, while those that required higher temperatures moved more slowly.   Thus a general zonation was established and it is still more or less apparent across the continents and oceans from north to south.

Rhythmical Changes.—When changes are periodic and occur within a comparatively short time, many species readily become adapted to them.   Seasonal succession is annually accompanied by regularly recurring migrations, periods of rest and activity, and sequential changes in life histories. Periodic monthly changes, associated with the rotation of the moon about the earth, are correlated with particular activities in certain animals, like the Palolo worm and grunion.   The rhythmical recurrence of day and night is correlated in many animals with physiological rhythms, usually as an alternation of periods of rest and activity.

ECOLOGICAL SUCCESSION

Ecological succession is related to environmental evolution. In general, it progresses toward a condition of stability as represented in a climax formation; it is a movement toward an equilibrium which is in a sense the optimum for existing conditions. Yet throughout the more or less orderly series of changes that constitute succession the power of adjustment of animal systems to radical changes in the environment is often retained. At certain times in life cycles stages are often produced which tend to spread into new habitats, where better conditions for existence may be found when the original environment changes or becomes overpopulated. In the origin of new habitats, geological, geographic, and physiographic changes lead the way. Vegetation is usually of prime importance in giving character to particular habitats.

Order of Succession.—When a change in environment opens up a habitat, pioneers invade the new field from adjacent regions. These pioneers are often young animals and are usually few in species and numbers. Their struggle to keep a foothold is, as a rule, largely with the physical and chemical features of the environment. After the pioneers become established one or more transition periods follow. These are usually characterized by more or less variety of conditions and a considerable number of species. During transition periods there remains more or less of the strife with the physical and chemical conditions in particular habitats and there is also competition between different elements of the biota. As the climax group for a particular habitat is established, species usually again become fewer and the conditions of the habitat simpler and more monotonous. Certain types dominate the habitat and others are largely excluded from it (Adams, 1909). Of course, the conditions that make possible a series of successional changes are in a sense the "cause" of the particular types of conditions that follow. But causes and conditions are often difficult to understand, and the two terms are often interchangeable.

Pioneers.—Pioneers in new habitats often show their relationship to adjacent regions and have qualities which fit them primarily for their old habitat, but which also permit them to invade the new. Frequently they have a considerable ability to resist certain unfavorable conditions in the environment. Pioneers on clean, dry sand must be able to resist desiccation and the fact that many are able to burrow also enables them to escape extremes of heat and cold. Many of the marine animals that invade the habitats available on clean rock beaches have hard shells, which protect them from desiccation and the beating of waves, and are firmly attached, so that they are not easily dislodged. The occupation of a habitat is often more easy after vegetation has made a cover and is established so that it furnishes a dependable supply of food.

As was mentioned in the introduction to this chapter, the order of invasion of new habitats is often represented in the horizontal arrangement of the biota. Along the margins of forests, above the shores of ponds, and along ocean beaches animals are found in more or less definite zones. Those with aquatic affinities that live farthest from the water are for the most part those that first came from water and established their residence on land; those typically terrestrial animals that live closest to the margin of the water are, as a rule, those that first became associated with water.

Spreading to New Habitats.—Among animals there is continually more or less effort to invade new habitats. Many species through their particular means for spreading are continually taking chances in the environment and are thus perhaps able to gain a foothold in new habitats and localities. In some instances species when once established can take some part in transforming the environment, so that it comes closer to their own optimum of conditions for existence. When one group of animals is being replaced by another, the succession is usually due to one of two causes: (1) the environment is changing, or (2) the increasing group of animals is better able to take advantage of existing conditions—*i.e.*, these animals are actually "better" animals or they have certain inherent qualities that make them better fitted to the particular conditions that exist at the time. Kennedy (1922) states that at present there is continual "pressure" for pond dragon-flies to invade lake habitats. He says: "The lake species are specialized remnants of a preceding fauna, of which the pond species have been already very largely displaced by the very modern *Libellulinæ*." As ponds, with their quiet waters and abundance of food, afford the best habitats for most dragon-fly nymphs, the progressive species have there first displaced their archaic predecessors, and the archaic species that have remained have become "improved" by shortening their life histories to meet competition. Among many animals there is a tendency, at certain seasons or at particular stages in life cycles, to wander far from the usual haunts of the species.

Sporadic Spreading Movements.—Besides the spreading into new localities that is more or less characteristic of all species of animals, there are at times great movements that involve many individuals. Introduced into the United States at New Orleans about 1891, the Argentine ant in 1918 had spread over an area of about 1000 square miles, averaging about 300 to 400 feet per year. Shelford (1911*a*) observed that two river snails (Campeloma and Pleurocera) spread upstream at the rate of about

a mile per year.   These two instances are probably typical of
the normal spreading of animals through favorable areas.   Movements of another type are at times performed by such animals
as the sand grouse, gray squirrel, Scandinavian lemming, locusts,
butterflies, dragon-flies, etc.   In such cases there are great
emigrations at irregular intervals from usual areas of distribution.
Large numbers of individuals together make stampedes into new
areas which may be wholly unsuited to their needs and where
they are seldom able to become permanently established.   The
reasons for such movements have been assigned to lack of food,
overpopulation, prevailing winds, humidity conditions, etc.
Apparently, there is no general explanation that will apply to all,
and, indeed, the "causes" of most of them are little known
(Tutt, 1902; Anthony, 1923).

Succession on Coral Reefs.—The growth of coral reefs brings
about a peculiar type of ecological succession.   The accumulations which give rise to enclosed lagoons are due primarily to the
presence and activities of living organisms.   Darwin and Dana
were early advocates of the subsidence theory of reef formation
by the upgrowth of fringing reefs while a coast was sinking.
Semper advanced the view that fringing reefs might be formed by
the dissolving away of the interiors of massive formations, thus
leaving lagoons or channels surrounded by fringing reefs.   Recent
evidence has largely given support to the subsidence theory, and
also brought in glaciation as an important factor.   During
glacial times much water was lost from the ocean and this
furnished material for the glaciers.   On this account the surface
level of the ocean was lowered and platforms were worn at the
edges of exposed land areas.   As the ocean gradually rose, reefs
were built up on many of the submerged platforms (Vaughn,
1919).   Pioneer corals and other animals that become established
on exposed reefs differ markedly in form of growth and other
qualities from those that live in sheltered lagoons, the former
usually growing as flat encrustations and the latter forming
tree-like growths.

Summary.—Shelford (1911a) says:

Ecological succession is the succession of ecological types (physiological types, modes of life) over a given point or locality due to changes
of environmental conditions at that point.   From this point of view
we have nothing to do with species except that names are necessary
. . . If the habits of a species are a part of a definition of that species,

as they must sooner or later come to be, then species are significant
. . . Ecological succession is one of the few biological fields in which
prediction is possible.

Such succession is usually a succession of species or groups of
species, each of which attains more or less dominance when
habitatic conditions approach its optimum and is succeeded by
another when conditions change beyond its limit of toleration
or to such an extent that another species or group of species can
attain dominance.

ANNUAL SUCCESSION

The annual revolution of the earth about the sun and the inclination of the earth's axis to the plane of the ecliptic produce a
regularly recurring series of seasonal changes which are most
pronounced near the poles and least near the equator.

Adaptations of Animals to Seasonal Changes.—The activities
of many animals are closely correlated with the annual succession of seasons. In temperate and frigid regions hibernation is
common during periods of cold; in the tropics animals often
æstivate during dry or hot periods. The annual cycle of many
species of animals is made up of a series of stages in a characteristic life history or of a characteristic series of periods of rest and
activity which are closely correlated with seasonal succession.
Long-established correlations operate in such a way that seasonal
environmental changes serve to stimulate animals to appropriate
activities or inactivities, and cyclical physiological changes
within animals prepare them to react properly with recurring
seasonal events. The development of different species begins at
different times in the general climatic rhythm, and there is thus a
progression throughout the year. The time of activity of each
species must conform more or less with environmental opportunities for feeding, the presence of optimum temperatures,
proper conditions for reproduction, etc. Particular species may
vary markedly in numbers at different seasons. This is strikingly shown by plankton organisms. As the season advances,
each species reaches a maximum, then declines, and may be
succeeded by another species. Herdman (1909) has classified
the factors that influence the numbers of plankton organisms as
follows: (1) sequences of stages in normal life histories, (2)
irregularities introduced by interactions of different organisms,

and (3) more or less periodic abnormalities, as to time and abundance, caused by physical changes in weather. Johnstone (1908) gives diagrams that show the seasonal appearance of the eggs of certain marine fishes and of various planktons off the west coast of England. Diatoms, which are the chief source of organic food for animals, decrease in May, but increase again in November and remain abundant through the colder months. There is the greatest quantity of plankton in winter, but the greatest variety in summer.

Seasonal Variations in Animals.—The chemical characteristics of the water in Lake Mendota vary considerably with seasonal successions (Birge and Juday, 1911). Such variations are brought about chiefly by fluctuations in temperatures and gases, but the activities of living organisms also exert a considerable influence. The yellow perch in Lake Mendota accumulate stores of fat within their bodies during the summer and these are used up in winter (Pearse, 1924). Juday (1922) made quantitative catches of the fauna in the deeper waters of Lake Mendota and found that some of the animals showed striking variations in numbers at different seasons. The larvæ of the midge, *Corethra punctipennis* Say, varied from about 1000 per square meter in August to as high as 25,000 to 30,000 in December. Birge (1897) studied the variation of plankton animals in Lake Mendota and described the seasonal maxima for various species. The chief factors causing seasonal variations were said to be: (1) quantity and quality of food, (2) temperature, and (3) competition. In 1895 Cyclops varied from about 25,000 per square meter of lake in January to about 1,000,000 at the end of May. In his studies of the prevalence of acanthocephalans, Van Cleave (1916) observed that some species occurred in their appropriate hosts throughout the year and that others were found only at certain seasons. He states that important factors in determining the seasonal range of these parasites are: (1) the longevity of their adult hosts, (2) time during which infection may occur, (3) time required for larvæ to develop in intermediate hosts, (4) migrations or seasonal changes in food habits of hosts.

Light and Annual Succession.—On account of the relation of light to photosynthesis, the length of day is the dominant factor in the seasonal periodicity of most plants, though temperature and water are also important. Most animals are directly or indirectly dependent on vegetation and their development is often closely correlated with that of food plants. Vestal (1913) in his report on Illinois sand prairies says:

Plant and animal associations are coextensive and to a large extent interdependent, the animals being entirely dependent on the plants, speaking broadly, and the plants being partly dependent upon the animals. If this be true, the boundaries of the animal associations are those of the plant association.

Vestal points out that grasshopper succession is closely related to the development of vegetation and, once vegetation and grasshoppers are established, there is during each season a progressive change in species and in habits.

Temperature and Annual Succession.—Temperature, directly and indirectly, is an important factor in seasonal cycles. The maxima in numbers of certain species are closely associated with high or low temperatures. The rate of metabolism and behavior are often influenced by temperature. Perhaps no other factor so manifestly sets off such a variety of seasonal activities or states as does rising or falling temperature. In the ocean adjacent to northern Europe, seasons of low temperatures are associated with the penetration of light to greatest depths, and consequently with maximum production of food in deep water. Many marine animals in that region spawn during the cold season (Ekman, 1920). As has been stated elsewhere, Orton (1920) has pointed out that most marine animals fall into general groups which spawn (1) when the temperature of the ocean falls or (2) when it rises. Cooke (1913), while admitting that the migration of such birds as the American robin is influenced largely by average temperatures, shows that "the temperature under which the birds[1] are migrating is about four times as variable as the date of arrival of the birds." He points out that it is rather difficult to judge of the effects of temperature on bird migration because the temperatures at which birds leave distant localities may be quite different from those at which they arrive at points of observation, and it is difficult to determine how far birds have travelled. A favorable temperature may stimulate a bird to start off and the bird may then encounter unfavorable temperatures while migrating. In many localities in the tropics there is little annual variation in temperature and little variation

[1] American robin, fox sparrow, towhee, brown thrasher, rose-breasted grosbeak, ovenbird, Baltimore oriole, scarlet tanager.

in the seasonal rhythms of animals. In temperate regions a season of low temperatures may retard the growth of animals and prolong their life histories, thus causing those that are annuals to become biennials and producing other aberrant conditions.

Annual Variations in Available Water.—Seasonal variations in the amount of available water are often concerned with successions. Morgan (1907) believes that the seasonal dimorphism of certain butterflies is largely due to varying conditions of humidity. Wolcott (1918) points out that prairie animals are apparently most abundant in spring, and he believes this to be due largely to the fact that moisture conditions then permit more isopods and earthworms to frequent the surface layers of the soil. Cummings (1918) observed that migration "waves" of frogs to aquatic habitats for spawning were coincident with periods of high relative humidity, when the temperature ranged from 16 to 26°C. Sanders and Shelford (1922) state that the animal population of the sand dunes near Chicago during summer, in general, varies directly with the evaporating power of the air, and, therefore, with the amount of water available for animals.

Animals of Various Seasons.—The chief physical variants during annual cycles of seasonal changes are light, temperature, and available water. These, directly or through their influence on vegetation and available food, are the most important environmental factors that are concerned with succession. In the temperate regions of the earth there are characteristically "winter" and "summer" species. Certain apterous insects and amphipods reach their numerical maxima during cold weather; the fairy shrimps are present in the cool, temporary puddles formed by melting snow and early spring rains; frogs and toads are active only during the warmer months. Some animals, like the ptarmigan and varying hare, change their coats and are white in winter. Morgan (1908) maintains that cool climates tend to make butterflies lighter in color and that warm climates bring out richer and deeper shades. Many of the so-called winter and vernal animals of temperate zones have relatives that are found in arctic or alpine habitats, and those that are active in summer often show affinities with the animals of the tropics. Ekman (1920) believes that the relict faunas of Scandinavian lakes and fiords show their relationship to marine ancestors by breeding during the cold season, which, for the species concerned, is apparently the best time of the year for obtaining food and rearing offspring.

Relations of Reproduction to Annual Succession.—Among the varied activities of animals, those connected with reproduction perhaps show the most striking adjustments to usual annual rhythms, but in this connection it should be said that the cyclic, physiological, successional phenomena related to reproduction often persist when the external environmental conditions that are usually associated with them are lacking. Schultz (1912) cites instances where plants and animals that were transferred from the Southern to the Northern Hemisphere bred at the same season as before their transfer. He points out that, though all animals do not breed at one season, many species do breed at a particular season and that the particular time, though it may be correlated with favorable conditions in relation to season or to a favorable environment in general, is in most cases fixed by cyclical physiological activities. These activities may continue to cause a periodic ripening of the gonads when usual environmental succession is absent, and this may be true even when environmental conditions are not well suited to reproduction. On the other hand, some species of animals readily change their season for breeding, particularly under conditions of domestication. The wild hog breeds in November and domestic strains breed at any time of the year. Schultz shows that related species may be able to occupy the same territory and that each may exist in greater numbers because it breeds at a different season from its relative. Along the Amazon, *Caiman niger* breeds during October and November and *Caiman sclerops* in May and June. Adams (1907) states that crayfishes fall into two groups in regard to time of breeding: (1) cold-water species, breeding more or less throughout the year, and (2) warm-water species, mating in the autumn and laying eggs in spring. Reproduction is apparently the chief driving force behind the annual migrations that many animals make to and from their breeding grounds. Among some species of animals certain types of reproduction are associated with particular seasons. Many cladocerans and aphids reproduce by parthenogenesis during the warmer months, when there is an abundance of food, but produce fertilized eggs, which are usually quite hardy, in the autumn.

Papanicolaou (1923), in discussing the reproductive activities of certain animals, says:

Considering the phylogeny of mammals, we find that the earliest living types actually display the polyœstrous rhythm just as do the somewhat more recent and modified types, such as the insectivores or the rodents, among which polyœstrus prevails especially in tropical climates. But in the still earlier or lower animal a type of sexual activity exists which we may call monœstrous or seasonable, since the reaction shows a definite connection with certain seasons of the year. Birds, reptiles, amphibians, fishes, insects, molluscs, worms, etc., all show the same periodical expression of their sexual activities. The connection between the monœstrous rhythm and certain seasons of the year is equally well expressed in the mammals. The spring and the fall, the two most favorable seasons of the year, are usually those during which most sexual activities are shown, while the two extreme seasons, summer and particularly winter, are characterized by a more or less pronounced sexual quiescence.

TROPICAL REGIONS

In the tropics there is usually no time of year when animals are generally resting, except in regions where there are sharply defined rainy and dry seasons. Thus the annual cycle often lacks marked seasonal periodicity. High temperature is, of course, characteristic of the tropics. This is due to the altitude of the sun, the high temperature of the soil, and the presence of water vapor, which not only serves as a transparent blanket that allows radiant energy from the sun to pass through to the earth, but also absorbs heat that is lost from the soil and at night by condensation into dew gives up heat so that air and soil temperatures are maintained. The warm surface of the tropical ocean continually supplies moisture to air currents and warm winds help in keeping temperatures uniform. Visher (1923), however, has pointed out that it is a mistake to say that the tropics as a whole do not have considerable variability in climate. He states that, where large amounts of atmospheric water vapor do not keep temperatures uniform, "night is the winter of the tropics." Thunder showers serve to cool the atmosphere and cleanse the soil. In many localities they occur daily with great regularity.

Varied Biota.—The tropical flora and fauna are extremely varied. A typical rain forest does not consist of a few dominant species of trees, as do the forests in temperate regions, but of many types that struggle with each other for room to spread their leaves beneath the sun. The abundance and the variety of life is due to the general uniformity and permanence of favorable conditions. The light and the heat from the sun are evenly distributed throughout the year and, unless there is drought, photosynthesis can supply basic foodstuffs at a uniform rate. Tropical forests do not wholly lack periodicity that is more or less correlated with seasonal changes, and, indeed, some tropical forests are not evergreen, but, in general, there is no time of the year when most of the vegetation is not actively at work, some plants shedding their leaves only at intervals of several years. An evergreen rain forest, as a representative tropical climax formation, furnishes favorable habitats for a great variety of animals.

Variety of Adaptations.—Tropical animals show many adaptations to special means of existence and their specializations are perhaps more often related to prey, competitors, enemies, and other living constituents of the environment than to variations in physical conditions. The tropics permit variety, and with variety is associated adaptations for competition. The more austere climates of temperate and frigid regions have allowed much less variation and adaptations there often fit animals more for surviving variations associated with seasonal periodicity than for struggles with living competitors. The arctic and antarctic oceans, however, though continually cold, permit an abundance of life to exist because they afford an extremely constant environment.

Productivity of Tropics.—The tropical ocean is less productive of microscopic life than cold seas. Woodruff (1910) suggests that the phytoplankton is probably limited by "excessive" light. The attached algæ do not attain as large size as elsewhere. Cold seas are, of course, unfavorable for the growth of bacteria, which swarm in tropical waters and continually remove nitrogenous compounds. In freshwater and on land, tropical animals flourish in great numbers, and there are many types that are largely confined to, or flourish best in, warm climates. Though there are, of course, many animals that are active in bright sunlight, there are also many that hide continually in the shade of the forest or avoid the sun by hunting at night. The number of nocturnal animals is strikingly large.

These take advantage of the great photosynthetic activity of the tropical forest, but avoid the light and heat.

FRIGID REGIONS

The polar and alpine regions of the earth have much in common. Both have low temperatures throughout the year and an aridity in land and freshwater habitats due to lack of available moisture for plant growth, though freshwater may be abundant in the form of ice. As plants are essential, directly or indirectly, for animal food, the animals are usually few in freshwater and land habitats. The cold oceans, however, have a greater quantity of plant and animal life than those of the tropics. It has been suggested by various writers that this is due to: (1) the slowing of metabolism by low temperatures and the resulting greater length of life for each individual; (2) the greater abundance in tropical seas of bacteria and other microscopic organisms which take nitrogenous compounds from the water so rapidly that there are not enough available to support a fauna like that in the arctic and antarctic; (3) the greater capacity of cold water to hold atmospheric gases in solution. Probably all these causes contribute more or less to produce a greater abundance of life in cold seas.

Bipolarity.—Pfeffer (1901) and others have supported a theory of "bipolarity," which stresses the similarities between arctic and antarctic marine faunas. The adherents of this theory hold that these faunas originated in early Tertiary times from the rather uniform fauna of the temperate and tropical oceans. Pfeffer says:

The arctic fauna shows a zonal development, or, as it has been called, circumpolarity, very perfectly, while in the antarctic fauna, with the weak development and the wide separation of the coast area characteristic of that region, circumpolarity is much less observable . . . In the fauna of the temperate zones circumpolarity diminishes considerably, giving place to local faunas.

Ortmann (1899) and others do not accept the bipolarity hypothesis.

Birds of Cold Regions.—Gain (1913) states that thirty-six species of birds live south of 60°S. All these live in or near the sea and are dependent upon it for food. The five species of penguins show a high degree of specialization for life in the antarctic ocean. A penguin cannot fly, but uses its front limbs for swimming. It is perfectly at home in the water, being able to dive to a depth of 50 feet; its food consists largely of fishes and pelagic crustaceans. The absence of foxes and bears in the antarctic makes it possible for penguins to breed on land. Arctic birds are all able to fly and usually resort to inaccessible cliffs or islands to breed.

Freshwater Fauna.—The freshwater fauna of arctic regions is rather limited in its number of species but often abundant in particular situations. Protozoa, cladoceran and amphipod crustaceans, rotifers, midges, and mosquitoes develop in pools; caddis-flies and may-flies are characteristic of flowing streams.

Land Animals.—Except for animals that depend on the ocean for food, the land animals of arctic and antarctic regions are not abundant. The arctic "barrens," however, support a considerable number of animals. The ice floes are the resorts for the seal, walrus, and polar bear. Stefansson (1922) resents the notion that many persons hold regarding the dearth of life in the arctic:

To sum up, the arctic sea is lifeless, except that it contains about as much life to the cubic mile of water as any other sea. The arctic land is lifeless except for millions of caribou and of foxes, tens of thousands of wolves and musk oxen, thousands of polar bears, billions of insects and millions of birds. And all these go south in the fall except the insects which die as they do in temperate lands, and except the ptarmigan, caribou, foxes, wolves, musk oxen, polar bears, lemmings, hares, weasels, owls, and ravens, all of which we have named in approximately the order of their decreasing numerical strength.

The flora on land in the antarctic is nearly non-existent. There are a few algæ, lichens, and mosses. Insect visits to plants are rare in the arctic; anemophily and autogamy are common (Schimper, 1903). True bulbs and tubers are rare, and many arctic plants have dwarf, prostrate, or rosette habits of growth, and most plants are perennials (Warming, 1909). Flowers and fruits are commonly formed before the short growing period and appear very quickly when the favorable season arrives. A "plankton," which consists of algæ, podurans, tardigrades, oligochætes, and nematodes, may occur in snow. Johansen (1921) found that land insects decreased rapidly in numbers as he went north in Canada. Forest insects dropped out first; scavengers and predaceous species extended farthest north. Mites and a few spiders persisted as far as land extended. Phytophagous species are rare, but blood suckers and scavengers may be abundant at times. In Canada, mosquitoes are unbearable for ten weeks on the arctic barrens, but they are abundant for only about eight weeks in the spruce forest and for six or seven in the wheat belt. The caribou move north in summer to avoid these pests (Seton, 1911).

Food of Animals in Cold Regions.—The polar Eskimos are said to flourish on a diet that contains little or no plant food. The polar bear, according to Koettlitz (1900), eats considerable amounts of grass and seaweed. The length of the intestine in this animal is remarkable (180 feet), being twenty-two to thirty times that of the body. The wolves, foxes, and weasels prey more or less upon the caribou, musk oxen, hares, and lemmings which subsist on plants. The pinnipeds, of course, depend on the ocean for food, and the same is true of the polar bear. Even typically terrestrial animals, like foxes and wolves, visit the seashore at times to feed. The birds of frigid regions get their food largely from the ocean, particularly in the antarctic, where few wading birds are present. There are, of course, a few scavengers and robber birds, like the skua gull and raven.

Care of Young.—The young of arctic animals are usually attended with great care. A polar bear cub, though foraging for itself more or less, remains with its mother and is suckled for two years. Penguins escape their chief enemy, the sea-leopard, by marching inland to rookeries on wind-swept barrens where loose stones are available for nests. There is great rivalry for building material and the female Adelie guards the nest while the male collects stones. The parents fast for as much as twenty-seven days while mating, building the nest, and beginning the incubation of eggs. The male and female then take turns at fishing and the young feed themselves from their parents' crops. Levick (1914) determined the rate of growth of the young, finding that there was an increase from 3 to 42.5 ounces during the first twelve days after hatching. Later the young are herded together and attended by a few adults, while unoccupied members of a colony feed and play in the ocean. The emperor penguin lays its single egg in the dead of winter and the parents take turns holding it to keep it warm. This species molts in a hole in the snow, where it remains for more than two weeks. Jourdain (1913) has observed that passerine birds in Iceland lay larger clutches of eggs than those in England.

Adaptations of Animals.—Outside the ocean the arctic and antarctic faunas consist of a comparatively small number of highly specialized species which show unusual adjustments to the rigorous environment. A number of birds and mammals (bunting, ptarmigan, hare, ermine, etc.) shed their coats twice a year, so that they are white in winter and pigmented in summer. The accumulation of fat for insulation and storage is common in the bodies of animals. Many animals are able to withstand inanition for considerable periods of time. Arctic Diptera are covered with a heavy covering of bristles. Certain of the mammals, birds, and fishes make seasonal migrations. Penguins are covered with a thick layer of fat, can dive and feed under water with great skill, and have peculiar social instincts which are important for their survival. The caribou's hoof has a very wide expanse, so that it does not readily sink into snow; its frog is resorbed during the winter and the sharp edge then prevents slipping on ice.

Alpine Regions.—In alpine regions the mean annual temperature is not so important in relation to life as the degree of warmth during, and the length of, the summer season. Such regions throughout the world have similar faunas which consist of: (1) true alpine animals, like the lemming, chamois, and mountain goat, that are not found in the lowlands but may have relationships with the animals of polar regions; and (2) ubiquitous species that usually have a wide range and have invaded alpine regions since glacial times. The temperature in all alpine habitats is always low and food resources, as represented by plants, are not produced rapidly. In general, there is a period of renewed activity and multiplication at the time when snow melts. On account of the scarcity of food and continual low temperatures, dwarfs are common. There is a tendency to the prolongation of life, because animals are active for such a short time each year. Many poikilothermal animals are viviparous. The gestation period of the alpine salamander is three to four years; the eggs of crustaceans develop slowly and may winter over before hatching (Schultz, 1912). Hesse (1921) states that the eggs of alpine animals are often laid in sunny places; whereas comparable animals in the tropics usually deposit their eggs in shade; also, that the bodies of alpine animals contain and require less water than those of animals in the tropics. The size of the heart is large and respiratory capacity is comparatively high in alpine land animals.

As in the polar regions, annual plants are rare in the alpine zones. Lakes are free from ice for only two or three months out of each year and their temperatures are seldom above freezing. Yet they have a characteristic, though scanty, fauna. Dodds (1917) observed that alpine species of plankton crustaceans, like *Diaptomus shoshone* Forbes, did not become established in mountain or lowland lakes, though they were constantly carried into them by streams. Sarcodinans persist in lakes at higher altitudes than other protozoans (Edmondson, 1912). Steinmann (1908) has given an excellent account of the animals in alpine brooks, which maintain a low and more or less constant temperature throughout the year. The commoner brook animals in the Alps are amphipods, may-flies, caddis-flies, mites, leeches, and planarians. The land animals in alpine regions are highly adapted to stand exposure and some of them migrate to lower levels or latitudes during the coldest weather. Schimper (1903) noted that bees and bee-fertilized flowers decreased at higher altitudes and that there was a corresponding increase in Lepidoptera and the flowers pollinated by them. Alpine animals in temperate zones may be relicts or be derived from adjacent lowlands, but those in the tropics are usually derived altogether from neighboring regions (Gadow, 1913). A part of the food of alpine animals is derived from animals that wander upward from the lowlands and perish. Caudell (1903) identified seventy-eight species of insects from a snowbank on Pike's Peak, and he stated that most of these apparently came from levels below.

DORMANCY

Hibernation and æstivation are resting states during which animals exist in a more or less torpid condition. The former is usually associated with cold, but many animals become inactive at particular seasons or at certain periods in their life cycles, even when the temperature remains high.

Æstivation is usually associated with warm, dry periods and is characteristic of many tropical animals, particularly in localities where there are sharply defined rainy and dry seasons. The environmental conditions that are most often associated with the assumption of resting states by animals are lack of food, low temperature, and drought.

Hibernators among Animals.—Throughout the animal kingdom there are hibernators. Protozoans, rotifers, annelids, and copepods commonly rest within cysts; snails close the mouths of their shells and remain dormant; certain fishes enclose themselves in cocoons of mud and slime; and many poikilothermal land vertebrates seek aquatic habitats or burrow in order to remain torpid through certain seasons. According to Folsom (1922), insects commonly hibernate (1) as adults, when they can deposit their eggs early in the following spring on proper food for their young; (2) as larvæ, when they are protected from cold and are able to feed late in the autumn; and (3) as pupæ or eggs, when non-feeding, resistant stages are necessary on account of environmental conditions. Among mammals hibernation is limited to representatives of the insectivores, bats, rodents, and certain carnivores.

Stimulation of Resting States.—There is apparently some variation in the different types of the stimuli that bring about resting states in animals. Simpson (1912) states that the woodchuck hibernates more because of lack of food than because of decreased temperature. Cartier (1910) is also emphatic in his statement that hibernation in animals is an adaptation for avoiding starvation and that it is, therefore, a response to lack of food. He points out that among the species of jumping mice in the genus Zapus, some hibernate and others migrate when food becomes scarce. Pike (1923) observed another type of adaptation characteristic of homoiothermal animals—as the surrounding temperature increases less carbon dioxide is given off. There is thus a compensation by decreased heat production at higher temperatures. Lusk (1917) says that warmth is not the cause of metabolism, but one of the conditions for it. Knauthe (1907), and various observers since his time, have found that many fishes cease to feed when the temperature of the surrounding water falls below 6 to 9°C. Schoenichen (1903) believes that the length of time to which certain animals are exposed to critical temperatures determines whether they hibernate or not. Barbour (1921) has shown that decreased temperature brings about a transference of water from the blood of certain mammals. The amount of blood in woodchucks decreased 30 per cent before hibernation and increased gradually during the period of dormancy. On waking, the woodchucks that had least fat showed the highest percentage of blood (Rasmussen, 1917). Cleghorn (1910) claims that rodents may delay their time of hibernation on account of high temperatures, but, if hibernating, will continue to do so at high temperatures. He believes that they remain active only until they have acquired their "full coating" of fat, even if the temperature is high. It is known also that rodents like pocket gophers and ground squirrels may awaken at intervals when the temperature is continually low, and that they do so to void excreta. Tiger beetles prepare for hibernation during a period of three to ten days by the evacuation of the intestine and Malpighian tubules, and before hibernating these insects lose 30 per cent of the body weight, the loss being largely due to water elimination. The beetles prepare for hibernation in a rather variable way at certain stages in their life histories, even when the temperature remains high (Tower, 1907). A grass-hopper, *Chartophaga viridifasciata*, hibernates rhythmically at certain stages in its life cycle (Bodine, 1922). Slonaker (1901) observed that a captive toad burrowed into the ground just before cold periods, but Hargitt (1912) found that tree frogs remained active as long as the temperature was high. Darwin (1920) noted that certain desert animals hibernated but emerged from the sand when the temperature reached 51 to 58°F. Haupt (1915) kept a rattlesnake and some turtles in a cage together for three years. The former never hibernated and the latter each winter refused to eat and "fell into a stupor until spring." Shaw (1921) states that dryness and high altitude cause Townsend's ground squirrel to emerge early (Mar. 22) and begin its period of æstivation by July 4, while ground squirrels only a few miles away, at lower altitudes where there is greater humidity, do not emerge until May 10 and become dormant much later. Ground squirrels were taken from localities where they would have æstivated early and dormancy was accordingly postponed (Shaw, 1921). During drought periods in South Africa fishes and crocodiles burrowed into mud and æstivated (Marais, 1915). Many bottom animals in Lake Mendota pass through an æstivation period from July to October, when the deeper parts of the lake contain no oxygen (Birge and Juday, 1908). Clams (Pisidium) from the bottom remain dormant in oxygen-free water, but at once become active if oxygen is admitted (1911). Buchanan (1923), after pointing out that anæsthesia may be readily produced by reducing the oxygen supply to the vertebrate brain, suggests that animals use this method to go into a state of hibernation when their food supply fails.

Physiology of Dormant Animals.—There has been much discussion concerning the physiological state of animals during hibernation and æstivation. Hibernating mammals show heart block (Buchanan, 1923) and a peculiar type of respiration in which there are a few rapid respiratory movements alternating with long breathless periods. The mechanisms for maintaining a high, constant body temperature are not functional, the tissues become more or less like those of poikilothermal animals and retain their ability to respond for some time after being removed from the body (Cleghorn, 1910). There is often an assumption of an orbicular position, a clenching of jaws, closing of the eyes and dilation of the pupils, a congestion of the spleen, and other characteristic physiological conditions. Metabolism, of course, takes place at a very slow rate, and yet may not cease altogether; Van der Hyde (1921) gives $20°C$. as the critical point below which a frog's rate decreases. Rasmussen (1923) has investigated the so-called hibernating "gland" of the woodchuck and concludes that it is not a true gland, as it secretes nothing, but is a mass of adipose tissue that is largely used up during hibernation. He had previously shown (1917) that hibernating woodchucks lost an average of 3.25 grams per kilo of body weight during a dormant period of 110 days. In his later paper (1923) he reports that the "gland" constitutes 3 per cent of body weight before hibernation and 0.75 per cent after. It contributes only a twentieth to a thirtieth of the substance lost during hibernation. There is an increase in calcium content during winter in the bodies of marine crabs, ascidians, brachiopods, crayfishes, and land snails (Giard, 1898). Such calcification is believed to give animals an increased resistance to low temperatures. In preparing to become dormant, animals commonly lose water from their bodies. In mammals the water content of the blood increases somewhat during hibernation (Rasmussen, 1917); in insects, water is reduced in preparation for and during hibernation, but increases rapidly when activity is resumed. An insect's resistance to minimal temperatures is increased in proportion to the degree of desiccation that its body shows (Bodine, 1922). More carbon dioxide is given off by hibernating grasshoppers than by those that were growing and this fact has been made the basis of a suggestion that these insects are metabolically young during hibernation.   Desiccation appears to have an effect similar to low temperature in many animals and tends to throw them into a dormant state.   Schmidt (1919) believes that catalepsy plays an important rôle in the hibernation of insects.   He describes a partly contracted condition of the muscles which is characteristic. Perennial bee colonies store food and remain more or less quiescent during cold weather, but the bodies of the bees are kept at rather high temperatures in winter by exercise and the insulation furnished by the walls of their abodes.   The temperatures of bee clusters may be 20 to 30°C. when the temperatures outside the hives vary between −9 and +11°C. (Phillips and Demuth, 1914). Animals when ready to hibernate often choose a retreat where, though perhaps very cold, they will be protected from actual freezing.   Frogs and salamanders commonly go into ponds, toads burrow below frost, bears and bats enter caves, and many animals resort to hollow trees.   Blanchard and Blatin (1907) found that a marmot could not be infected with trypanosomes, spirochætes, or trichinæ during hibernation, probably on account of the low temperature of the body.

Duration of Dormancy.—The dormant states of animals may continue for years.   Semper (1881) kept some land snails in paper for three years and found them alive when unwrapped.   He states also that trichina cysts remained alive in flesh for ten years. Van Beneden (1876) observed that tapeworm cysts remained alive for years.   Bodine (1923) found Colpoda cysts alive after three years and kept cysts in a desiccator for six months without killing them.   He states that the resistance of such cysts to cold and chemicals is proportional to the degree of desiccation they have undergone.   The cysts of Didinium were viable after a rest of five years Mast (1917a).   Shaw (1925) has studied the æstivation and hibernation of the columbian ground squirrel.   He says:

It has long been known that a regular order of sex precedence exists among migratory birds.   That a corresponding precedence should exist among æstivating and hibernating mammals is not surprising . . . Adult male squirrels were the last to go into æstivation, and the first to come from hibernation.   Adult males were from four to six days later in going to æstivation than adult females; and were from seven to fifteen days earlier in returning from hibernation.   The average duration of hibernation for adult males was 204 days, and that for the adult female was 220 days, or a difference of sixteen days.   The longest hibernation period was that of a young female, 238 days.

Functions of Encystment.—Encystment is a means by which many animals are able to increase their chances of survival when the environment fluctuates beyond their normal limits of toleration. Protozoans, rotifers, annelids, molluscs, and crustaceans commonly employ this means to pass through unfavorable periods. Colpoda cysts are better able to endure gradual than sudden changes in temperature of the chemical constitution of the surrounding medium (Bodine, 1923). The more cysts are desiccated the greater is their resistance. In cultures of Didinium conjugation is usually accompanied by encystment and Mast (1912) therefore concluded that either process might be of service in preparing for an unfavorable period. Hopkins (1921) asserts that encystment restores the power of conjugation to run-down strains of Paramœcium. Mast (1917*a*) was able to make Didinia encyst at any time, by cutting off their food supply, but he also observed that they often encysted when food was plenty. These protozoans could be induced to emerge from their cysts by adding Paramœcia (their usual food) or even a filtered extract from a Paramœcium culture, to the medium containing them. Mast concluded that encystment served to carry Didinium over unfavorable periods and as a favorable state for distribution to new habitats, particularly when cysts were dry. He found that ex-conjugants often became encysted, but could not do so unless food was available. In later studies Mast and Ibara (1923) discovered that Didinium encysts most often at temperatures between 25 and 30°C., which are also the range of the optimum for growth and fission, and that it does not encyst at injurious temperatures, low or high. They found that there was most encystment when most food was present and believe that it is probably brought about by the presence of waste products. Though it is a protection from starvation and supra- and suboptimum temperatures, it is not necessarily directly induced by such conditions. In Lake Mendota, Birge and Juday (1908) found *Cyclops bicuspidatus* enclosed in cocoons for about four months each year during the season when the deep water was without oxygen. Yet the period of encystment did not exactly coincide with that of stagnation, for many of the crustaceans were found encapsuled and resting on the bottom mud by June 1 (stagnation period about July 1 to Nov. 1) and many emerged from their cocoons before oxygen returned to the deeper water. In this case lack of oxygen is apparently not the sole and immediate cause for encystment. In certain European lakes *Canthocamptus micro-staphylinus* forms cocoons and rests at the bottom during the winter (Lauterborn, 1909). An oligochæte in Bohemia forms "slime cysts" during drought periods and multiplies within its cyst wall (Mrázek, 1913).

Conclusions.—From the foregoing discussion it is evident that dormant states in animals are usually associated with (in certain cases apparently caused directly by, or a preparation for) periods during which there is lack of food, cold, heat, drought, accumulation of waste products, lack of oxygen, or other unfavorable conditions. Metabolism is reduced and an animal perhaps survives until the environment again reaches a condition that is favorable for renewed activity. The stimuli that bring about dormancy are apparently not the same for all animals, or in some cases even for all individuals of a single species.

ANNUAL MIGRATIONS

Many animals make more or less rhythmical migrations that are correlated with the changing conditions brought about by the annual succession of seasons. Wodsedalek (1912) speaks of the Heptagenia nymphs in Lake Mendota as follows:

All summer these insects occupy a narrow strip, about 3 feet wide, along the lake shore . . . . Along in the latter part of October as the water turns cool the nymphs slowly begin to migrate into deeper water and practically all desert the shallow water before the ice begins to form. A careful search was made on the day the ice broke up in the spring, but not a single specimen was seen. A few days after the ice disappears, however, the nymphs begin to make their appearance.

Phryganea larvæ in a European lake were observed to ascend Potamogeton plants and make cases from them in summer, but in January retreated to the bottom and used the accumulated leaves there for building (Wesenberg-Lund, 1911). Along the shores of the ocean such animals as crabs, prawns, lobsters, and squids go into deep water in winter and return to the shore in spring. Two brackishwater snails, Ilyanassa and Littorina, migrate up streams during summer and retreat to deeper and saltier water in winter (Batchelder, 1915). Migratory marine and freshwater fishes fall mostly into one of two classes: (1) anadromous species migrate inshore and often ascend rivers to spawn, (2) catadromous species spawn in deep water at favorable seasons and move into shallow water or streams at other times. Meek (1916) divides marine fishes into three groups: (1) midocean spawners that produce pelagic or bathypelagic eggs and the young of which frequent open water (eel), (2) coastal or subcoastal spawners with pelagic eggs and denatant (swimming or drifting with currents) larvæ, and (3) coastal or subcoastal spawners with demersal (on or near the bottom) eggs. Whales, walruses, seals, turtles, snakes, and other marine animals also make seasonal migrations. On land, there are various types of seasonal movements: Birds and certain bats go north or south; monkeys, deer, and wolves move up or down mountain slopes; caribou move from woodland to tundra or *vice versa;* buffalo and antelope follow the green grass as spring moves north and retreat again when cold drives them south; land crabs go down to the ocean to deposit their progeny in the ancestral habitat of their race. Certain mammals, like the hare, woodchuck, bushy-tailed wood rat, and muskrat, are accustomed to wander far from their usual ranges and habitats at certain seasons (Anthony, 1923).

Reasons for Migrations.—Stubbs (1912) states that the present balance of life on earth is made possible by the existence of a mobile mass that is shifted twice yearly from hemisphere to hemisphere. Animals depend on plants for food; plants require sunlight, water, minerals, and carbon dioxide. When sunlight or necessary food materials fail, most animals must follow the sun, die down with the plants, or hibernate. During the northern winter the land and freshwater habitats have their productivity greatly decreased. Food, temperature, and breeding are the factors to which animals are able to make better adjustments by migrating. For example, a bird that goes to the arctic regions to breed in summer finds abundant food, long hours of daylight for foraging and attending to its young, and temperatures that, while often low, are not near its limit of toleration. When the arctic winter begins, many animals migrate south to escape the long night and the covering of snow and ice that makes food hard to obtain.

Causes of Migrations.—Though migratory animals obtain certain advantages, it cannot be said that unfavorable variation in any one factor (such as a failure of food, or a shortening of the hours of daylight) is the cause of all migrations. In his book on bird migration Coward (1912) says:

Isepipteses and magnetic meridians, coast lines and river channels, food supply and sex impulses, hunger and love, homing instincts and inherited or acquired memory, thermometer, barometer, and hygrometer may all be factors in the problem; but none of them, and not all such together, can satisfy the whole equation.

Migration is not due to temperature alone—swallows leave for the south when temperatures are high; herring gulls remain as far north as they find open water which contains fish or other food. Migration is in some cases due directly to a lack of food, but in other cases animals leave abundance and invade regions where there is as yet little to sustain life. With a few exceptions, birds breed where they can find long days and an ample supply of food for their nestlings; salmon leave the ocean and, after fasting and traveling for weeks, lay their eggs and die.

Origin and Evolution of Migrations.—There has been much discussion concerning the origin and evolution of the annual migrations of animals. In general, migrations are between breeding grounds and feeding areas, and the former are often more localized than the latter. Some individual animals return to the same spot to breed year after year. There is evidence to show that, though particular flocks of birds from the same breeding area commonly migrate to particular feeding grounds at certain seasons, there is a tendency to make exploratory movements and species often become established on new feeding grounds, which they then continue to visit each year (Leopold, 1923). It is a noteworthy fact that most migratory birds move north in the spring and nest in the cooler parts of their ranges. Attempts have been made to explain this by the supposition that birds were forced to move south during glacial times and later followed the glaciers north as they retreated. Having thus established relations in the north and south, a semiannual migration was supposedly developed. Another theory emphasizes the fact that the continents in the northern hemisphere expand toward the north, while those in the south taper off toward the antarctic. With this in mind, it is plain that more nesting areas in land, marsh, and freshwater habitats will be available during the open season in the north. Some believe that the great feeding and breeding areas available in the north have attracted birds and led to the establishing of regular spring and autumn journeys. Walter (1908) gives a condensed but rather complete review of the numerous attempts to account for bird migrations.

The well-established migrations of fishes may take place annually or only once when a certain stage in the life cycle has been reached. The adult yellow perch migrates into shallow water and spawns annually for several years; the salmon and eel migrate to their breeding grounds and spawn only once. The migrations of fishes for spawning are usually to situations where suitable conditions for the development of eggs and fry are found. There are apparently three conditions which influence the migratory movements of the spiny lobster—cold causing retreats into deep water and molting or mating inducing movements toward shore (Crawford and Smidt, 1922). The minnow, *Fundulus heteroclitus*, migrates into marshes in summer to secure food and live at high temperatures, but returns to the ocean and remains near the mouths of rivers during the winter. During favorable seasons it wanders back and forth between the ocean and freshwater (Chidester, 1920).

On the whole, changing temperatures and food supplies exercise a general control over the migrations of animals, but they are not necessarily the direct or indirect causes of migratory movements. Sherman (1910) observed that during a mild spring birds nested earlier but did not arrive earlier. Phillips (1913) even asserts that birds have a "time sense," because he found their dates of arrival during migrations so regular in succeeding years. On the other hand, Cooke (1911) makes it clear that the northerly movement of the robin each year is correlated closely with the attainment in any locality of a certain mean daily temperature. Coward (1912) maintains that, though there are numerous exceptions, the average of weather conditions does influence the average time of arrival of migratory birds in particular localities. Smith (1917) finds considerable correlation between the flights of night migrants and meterological conditions. Adams (1909) also finds that bird migrants commonly arrive in "waves" following peculiar types of weather. Migratory fishes are known to be influenced by differences in temperature and doubtless other factors are potent in setting their routes. The mackerel in the Black Sea were very sensitive to temperature variations and a decrease caused them to move inshore (Galtsoff, 1924). In this instance variations in salinity appeared to exert little influence. Powers (1923) observed that carbon dioxide tension was an important factor in the movements of the Pacific herring, this fish frequenting areas where the pH was between 7.76 and 7.73.

Methods of Migrating.—The methods of migration vary greatly among different species of animals. Some birds make a leisurely journey, feeding as they go, and food supplies appear to influence their routes; others make a direct and hurried flight, feeding little or not at all. Some birds (warblers) fly mostly at night during migrations, others (swallows) move by day. The migration routes of some species of birds are broad and those of others are narrow paths. Different groups of birds of the same species may travel by different routes. Salmon hatched near the headwaters of rivers may move to the ocean after six months and other young of the same species may remain in freshwater for eighteen months. The sea-run salmon probably often remain near the mouths of the rivers where they hatched (Cobb, 1921) and even come into the rivers to feed (Rich, 1920). After spending from two to seven years in the ocean, salmon migrate up rivers, fasting and maintaining their energy from reserves of fat stored in their bodies. There is an increasing body of evidence (Robertson, 1921) that each race of salmon returns to breed in the river in which it hatched. Prince (1920) suggests that these fishes have continued to go back to gravel beaches that were originally on the seashore but have gradually migrated inland with the development of rivers. Southwell (1905) maintains that the races of mackerel remain distinct. Those that hatch on a particular spawning ground swim together in a school, that maintains its identity for years. Along the Atlantic coast of America cod travel along rather definite routes to and from shore (Smith, 1912). Among many species of animals (fishes, birds, seals) the males generally precede the females on the migration to the breeding grounds, and often protect certain areas while awaiting the arrival of their mates.

Pathfinding.—The means by which birds and fishes find their way to the spot where nesting or spawning is to take place have excited much speculation. There have been more or less superstitious advocates of "instinct," magnetism, semicircular canals, "sixth" senses, and other rather unscientific explanations. Birds certainly have a homing instinct and many individuals of many species are known to return to the same spot year after year to breed. Certain fishes migrate to particular breeding areas. How birds find their way during migrations is still somewhat of a mystery, though some are known to follow coast lines, to make use of landmarks, in certain cases to follow leaders to some extent, and to receive more or less aid from favorable winds. Ward (1921) affirms that the red salmon in migrating up the Youkon River chooses the coolest water at each fork, but, according to Huntsman (1920), Roule maintains that the amount of oxygen in the water is the primary factor in determining which branch of a stream salmon ascend.

Extent of Migrations.—The extent of animal migrations varies within wide limits. Douglas (1917) divides the woodcock in Ireland into three groups: (1) resident birds that remain for several years in the general region where they hatched, (2) birds that migrate south, and (3) those that come from the north to spend the winter. Coward (1912) classifies all birds as follows: (1) permanent residents, (2) summer residents, (3) winter residents, (4) birds of passage that are in localities where this name would apply for only a short time as they pass back and forth between breeding and feeding grounds, (5) irregular migrants, (6) stragglers. The golden plover travels about 15,000 miles each year and the arctic tern about 22,000 miles. The European eel (Schmidt, 1922) spawns in a rather limited area north of the West Indies and the larvæ during three years travel over a quarter of the earth's surface in order that adult eels may inhabit favorable habitats from the Nile to the regions about the Baltic Sea. In 1917 in Wood River, Alaska, 1,081,378 red salmon passed upstream to spawn; these were accompanied by about a hundred humpback salmon and thirty king salmon. Some animals move very short distances during their annual migrations. The brackishwater snail, Ilyanassa, makes a journey of 5 to 60 yards downstream in autumn, hibernating in deep water, and returns upstream again about the middle of April (Batcheler, 1915).

Speed of Migrations.—Migrating birds travel at heights of 1400 to 5400 feet above the earth and attain speeds of 80 to 130 miles per hour (Coward, 1912). Meinertzhagen (1922) believes that most birds migrate at speeds below 50 miles per hour, unless pursued by enemies, when they may attain 60 to 100 miles. The American robin takes ninety days to make about the same journey that the blackpoll warbler accomplishes in thirty days (Cooke, 1911). The king salmon moved 62 miles per day for thirteen days and on its whole journey traveled 1500 miles at

an average of 42 miles per day. The sockeye salmon in the
Frazier River averages 10 to 17 miles per day for 470 miles
(Gilbert, 1922). O'Malley and Rich (1919) observed that this
species showed no retardation in speed in moving from salt
into fresh water. The chinook salmon moves upstream at a
rate of 15 miles per day. Smith (1912) published a record of
a cod that moved at the rate of 16.5 miles per day.
A spiny lobster off the California coast traveled 6 miles in fourteen
days, but all the individuals observed averaged 1.4 miles during
twenty-two days (Allen, 1912).

Spreading Movements.—Many animals at certain seasons
make rather irregular migrations that are spreading movements,
not rhythmically recurring journeys to and from breeding and
feeding grounds. Great flights of butterflies, locusts, dragon-flies,
and other insects have frequently been recorded. Tutt (1902) gives
a general review of insect migrations and concludes that they
are all irregular dispersal movements. Uvarov (1921) made a
very careful study of the migratory locust in Russia and says:

The development of air sacs compels the insects to fly, and this
impulse is strengthened by their gregariousness, that is, by some kind of
tropism that makes each individual keep close to its fellows and follow
their movements . . . Thus, the periodicity of locust invasions is
caused entirely by the transformation of a swarming locust into a
solitary, harmless grasshopper.

The spreading movements of lemmings, squirrels, millipedes, and
other animals, though they may occur at certain seasons, are
not to be classed as annual migrations. The young of many
species are often particularly inclined to wander and thus invade
new localities and habitats.

LUNAR SUCCESSION

The moon produces two rhythms in earth environments that
are of considerable importance to animals: (1) the tides flow
up and down twice each day, (2) the height of the tides varies
rhythmically, high tides occurring about every two weeks when
the pull of the sun and moon reinforce each other and low tides
when the forces from these two bodies act at right angles. The
results of the first of these rhythms will be considered in the next
chapter and the discussion here will, therefore, relate only to the
influences exerted in the height of tides that are associated with
different phases of the moon.

Rhythms Related to the Moon.—Thomson (1911) states that a correlation has been demonstrated between the amount of plankton in rivers and the phases of the moon. The noteworthy instances of rhythmical lunar influences that relate to animals, however, are to be found along the shores of the ocean, and among these perhaps the palolo worm is most famous. The Pacific palolo, particularly along the shores of Fiji and Samoa, comes to the surface when the moon is full in October and November and sheds its eggs. The Atlantic palolo, which has been studied by Mayer (1902) at Tortugas, swarms within three days of the time of the moon's last quarter between June 29 and July 28. The hinder portion of the worm crawls out of the burrow and breaks loose from the anterior. It darts to the surface, rapidly swims backward while shedding its eggs or sperms, and the whole ocean becomes milky. Other polychæte worms besides the palolo show a correlation between their spawning and the phases of the moon. Grave (1922) says:

The cause of this type of periodicity must be fundamentally the same in all cases, although it is exhibited in a variety of ways and at different times relative to the phases of the moon.

In speaking of *Amphitrite ornata*, Scott (1909) says:

The egg-laying reflex is closely associated with the time of spring tide; the height of any period of egg-laying always occurs within two days of the time of new or full moon. Periods of oviposition occur in June, July, and August. The moon does not have any direct influence in producing the period of sexual activity. It is probable that the tide also has little, if any, direct effect on the process. At any spring tide, the worms feed more actively, the food supply is more abundant and the sand flats have a higher temperature. As this period approaches we also find a more rapid growth and development of immature eggs and sperm. Therefore the period of sexual activity is closely associated with a synchronous period of greater bodily activity, and this greater vigor of the animal is induced by conditions that depend upon the tide. In this way we may explain how oviposition in Amphitrite has become a sort of reflex habit associated with the time of spring tide.

The Atlantic palolo gives off more carbon dioxide as the time for spawning approaches (Treadwell, 1915).

The Grunion.—Thompson (1915) has described the very interesting behavior of a smelt, the grunion (*Leuresthes tenuis*), along the California coast. The little fishes of this species come on the second, third, and fourth nights *after* the highest tides during April (March, May). They come exactly at high tide and wiggle out on sandy beaches above the water. The females bury their posterior ends in the sand and the eggs are deposited 2 to 6 inches below the surface, each female producing about 2200. Each is attended by a male that exercises his fertilizing functions. The eggs are protected from enemies and are able to stand rains or considerable desiccation. After two weeks the eggs are ready to hatch but will not do so unless the egg pod is washed out of the sand by the tides occurring at the next full moon. The fry within the eggs will live for a month if they are not exposed by the first high tide.

The grunion offers a remarkable instance of adaptation to lunar rhythms as represented by tidal fluctuations. If spawning occurred just before the highest tides, when the high beach was being eroded, instead of just after, when the beach was being built up, the eggs would be washed out of the sand before they had developed for a fortnight. If spawning occurred at the very highest tides (dark of the moon) the eggs might not be exposed for a month, or even for two months. If grunions laid their eggs during the day, they would be exposed to the attacks of gulls and other predaceous animals.

DAILY SUCCESSION

Most animals on the earth show more or less adaptation to the daily rhythm, often being known as diurnal or nocturnal because they are active during day or night. Daily succession is brought about chiefly by the variety in times of activity in different species of animals. A physiological rhythm of rest and activity is correlated in various ways with conditions associated with the alternation of day and night. Some animals are active very little and others much. Nelson (1921) showed that an oyster works about twenty hours each day. A barnacle high up on a beach may be able to feed only one hour out of every twenty-four. A phasmid spends nine-tenths of its life in a "state of perfect stillness" (Schmidt, 1919).

Examples of Daily Activities.—Certain marine copepods retain their tendency to migrate upward at night and downward during the day when they are kept continuously in water having a constant illumination (Esterly, 1919). Franz (1912) maintained that daily plankton migrations were "Fluchtbewegungen," due to the avoidance of light by the animals concerned. The shrimp, *Hippolyte varians*, normally assumes a blue color at night but continues its rhythmical color changes for a time at approximately twelve-hour intervals when kept continuously in light or dark (Keeble and Gamble, 1904). Animals on the Indiana sand dunes show a tendency to "migrate upward during the first half of the day and downward during the later portion" (Sanders and Shelford, 1922). An orb-weaver in India is said (Hingston, 1920) to repair its web once each day, taking in the spirals in the morning and spinning them all anew. Annandale (1902) states that phasmids are not active and out in the open except during the middle of the day. In Ireland the long-eared bats fly all night, but the hairy-armed bat flies only at twilight, morning and evening (Moffat, 1905). Insects commonly sleep at night and some species are gregarious at such times but solitary during the day. Miss Hintze (1925) has recently shown that the white grub, *Cotinis nitida* Burmeister, commonly emerges from its burrows and creeps over the surface of the ground at night, when it would be least subject to attack by predaceous enemies. She found that the grubs continued to come out rhythmically at night periods when they were kept in soil at constant temperature and continuously in light or dark.

Plankton Migrations.—The daily migrations of plankton animals have excited much interest. Juday (1904) in his studies of freshwater plankton crustaceans showed that their migratory movements were not simple, that some species do not migrate, and that the movements of the same species may vary in different lakes. The whole body of crustaceans does not move upward or downward together. Each species had its own time for arrival at the surface, copepods generally preceding cladocerans, and the order of return to deep water was much the same as that for movements upward. The extent of movements varied from 0 to 35 meters. Juday states his belief that light is the most important factor in influencing migrations and he found certain species at higher levels on cloudy days. In a later paper Juday (1921) describes his observations on a fly larva (*Corethra punctipennis*) that burrows into the bottom mud of deep lakes (where it is protected from fishes) soon after sunrise and comes to the surface for air at night. Esterly (1919) has reviewed the knowledge of the daily movements of marine plankton organisms. At night there is a greater abundance of many species at higher levels and the opposite is true by day. "One form may have a vertical range from the 100- to the 200-fathom level and another may range from the surface to 100 fathoms." Esterly concludes that: "Owing to specific differences in behavior, no general explanation of diurnal migration can be given at present." He found a physiological rhythm in certain copepods, and a "change in geotropism with change of light intensity" in Sagitta. He cites light, gravity, temperature, and changing behavior as influences that are important in inducing plankton migrations.

RHYTHMS

Reynolds (1920) says: "The formation of overtones from Nature's rhythms seems the only hypothesis capable of explaining the chief methods of Nature." This writer argues that rhythms are universal—all natural phenomena are concerned with changes from stability to instability and returns to stability. He claims that evolution has been regarded as relating mostly to matter and that the assortment of forces has been neglected. Definite steps in assortment are recognized as colloidal, enzymatic, biotic, and psychic. Flattely (1920) also discusses rhythms in nature and distinguishes two types of biologic rhythms: (1) periodic rhythms correlated with such rhythms in environment as day and night, seasons, tides, etc.; (2) rhythms inherent in the organism and independent of the environment—all of which are correlated with age cycles. In temperate climates age and seasonal cycles usually coincide in a general way. In a tropical forest each species has its own separate time for breeding or breeds through long periods at any season.

Metabolic Rhythms.—There is no question that rhythms play an important rôle in vital phenomena, and that animal activities are readily correlated with rhythmical environmental conditions. Periods of rest and activity or of definitely varying activities are correlated with the ebb and flow of tides, the periodic succession of day and night, lunar succession, the cycle of the seasons, and perhaps with rhythms having longer periods. The same species may vary in its rhythms in different localities in order to conform with environmental conditions. The majority of the human race sleep each night and eat during the day, but the polar eskimos, who live where nights are six months long, have very irregular periods of activity, eating, and sleeping. Some mammals breed only once a year at a particular, favorable season; others, in which breeding is not closely dependent on environmental conditions, breed at any time. A red-legged locust lays its eggs in the autumn; a flour beetle lays eggs at any time. Willey (1920) has described a nice dovetailing of periods of rest and activity in Ceylon. Certain palms served as roosts for crows at night and for fruit-eating bats by day.

Reproductive Rhythms.—The rhythmic activities of animals that are not closely correlated with environment are, as Flattely (1920) says, commonly associated with attainment of a certain age or stage in a life cycle. Some such activities, like the resorption of tadpoles' tails (Swingle, 1922a), the development of broodiness in fowls (Pearl, 1914), and menstruation, are associated with endocrine secretions. Hisaw (1924) discovered that female gophers cannot bear young without resorbing the pelvis in the region of the public symphisis, and such resorption normally takes place through the action of ovarian secretions when females have attained the proper age. By injecting ovarian extracts, Hisaw was able to bring about the resorption of the pubes in castrated males. When secretions that normally induce qualities that develop at certain stages in life cycles are absent, animals fail to make the usual progress. Castrated animals retain juvenile characteristics and do not develop adult characteristics. An eunuch has separate epiphyses on his long bones and does not develop a beard or a deep voice.

CHAPTER V

ANIMALS OF THE OCEAN

The ocean constitutes 72 per cent of the surface of the earth. It has apparently contained animals longer than freshwater or land habitats. The antiquity of the ocean is also indicated by the fact that the fossils from the earliest known geological ages are all marine. At present the distribution of a considerable number of great groups of animals is limited to the ocean (Cteno-phora, Brachiopoda, Echinodermata, Polychæta, Cephalopoda, Tunicata). All types of animals that are found in land and freshwater habitats are also found to some extent in the ocean, except the Myriopoda and Onychophora. The sponges, cœlen-terates, and bryozoans, though represented by many species in the ocean, are few in freshwater. Such facts have led to the rather general belief that life originated in the ocean and later invaded freshwater and land habitats. Many speculative evolutionists have believed, and still believe, that life came into being along the seashore, but Heilprin (1887) and Brooks (1893–1894) advocated the view that life first appeared in the open ocean. Most marine animals are poikilothermal and those that are homoiothermal have apparently, judging from palæonto-logical evidence, been derived rather recently from freshwater or land habitats. Murray (1898) thinks that the ocean has long constituted a rather uniform, favorable dwelling place for animal life. Because the animals near the poles of the earth show greater similarity to each other than to those in intervening tropical and temperate regions, several writers (Murray, 1898; Pfeffer, 1901; and Pratt, 1901) have supported a theory of "bipolarity." These writers postulate an ocean of rather uniform temperature from pole to pole during Tertiary times, and a corresponding uniform distribution of animal life. The remnants of the Tertiary fauna are believed to persist today near the poles, but have changed or been displaced by other animals toward the equator.

The Ocean as a Habitat.—As a dwelling place for animals the ocean offers unusual stability in temperature, salinity, and gaseous content. The general chemical and physical conditions of life vary slowly and to a less degree than in freshwater and on land. The average salinity of the ocean is about 3.5 per cent. Freshwater seldom has a salinity of 1 per cent and its fauna, according to Hirsch (1915), is usually not able to tolerate a salinity greater than 2 to 3 per cent. Johnstone (1908) believes that in the past calcium and potassium have been decreasing and that sodium and magnesium have been increasing in sea water. He suggests that vertebrates and certain other animals use such a large percentage of lime in building their skeletons because they established their metabolic habits long ago when the ocean was rich in calcium. Many marine animals (corals, etc.) can survive a 20 per cent decrease in salinity and Vaughn (1919) believes this is evidence that the ocean is growing more salty. Flattely and Walton (1922) state that the primordial ocean contained no salts or nitrogen that was available for living things, but that the modern ocean is an "ideal medium for life." Lime-secreting organisms are more active at present in warm oceans and their presence in Tertiary deposits led Pfeffer (1901) to conclude that the tertiary ocean had a higher and more uniform temperature than now. The salts in sea water are mostly chlorides and sulphates, with smaller (but for certain animals no less important) quantities of bromides, carbonates, and other compounds. At least twenty-four metals are present, but those in largest quantity are sodium, magnesium, calcium, and potassium. Small amounts of copper and zinc are found in many marine animals. The ratio between the different salts in the ocean remains rather constant with variations in salinity, except that the amount of calcium increases with depth. Murray (1914) gives averages for the salts in sea water in parts per thousand:

Sodium chloride	27.213
Magnesium chloride	3.807
Magnesium sulphate	1.658
Calcium sulphate	1.260
Potassium sulphate	0.863
Calcium carbonate	0.123
Magnesium bromide	0.076
Total	35.000

Oxygen and carbon dioxide vary in amount. Except in rare cases, such as deeper water of the Black Sea, there is enough oxygen at all depths to supply the needs of plants and animals. Oxygen, on account of its solubility in sea water, has a higher ratio (34:66) to nitrogen in the ocean than in the atmosphere (21:79). Atkins (1923, 1923a, 1923b, 1923c) has recently studied the dissolved chemicals in the sea near Plymouth. He found that there were seasonal variations in alkalinity; that algæ rapidly used up phosphates and that the water contained little of free phosphates from May to August; that diatoms required and used silica; and that traces of oxidizable organic matter were present. Vaughn (1919) has demonstrated that the precipitation of lime to form coral reefs is due to bacteria more than to corals. Danois (1924) showed that the movements of the haddock were influenced by salinity, the fishes ranging where the variation was between 35.4 and 35.5 parts per thousand. He divides the ocean into four general regions according to temperature and salinity: Arctic, −1°C., 35 to 35.5 parts; Abyssal, +4°C., 35 parts; Continental, temperature variable, 33 to 34 parts; Equatorial, warm, 35+ parts.

Depth in Relation to Marine Life.—Life occurs at all depths in the ocean (Murray, 1898), but the photic zone, where the manufacture of living substance through photosynthetic activity is possible, extends down to only about 3000 feet and the number of species and individuals decreases steadily at greater depths. Only 5 per cent of the ocean has a depth of over 3000 fathoms. The pressure increases about 1 atmosphere for each 33 feet, so that abyssal animals are subjected to enormous pressures. Water is not absolutely incompressible and it has been estimated that, if gravity should cease, the ocean level would rise about 200 feet. Murray (1914) gives pressure above that of the atmosphere at various depths as follows: 33 feet, 15 pounds; 99 feet, 45 pounds, 100 fathoms, 270 pounds; 1000 fathoms, 1.2 tons; 5000 fathoms, 6 tons per square inch.

Light in Relation to Marine Life.—The living plants in the ocean are, of course, dependent on light, and hence are confined to the upper 3000 feet. Most of them are algæ, but Zostera is often abundant along shores and a few other phænerogams occur. Light and plant life occur at greater depths in tropical waters than elsewhere. Huntsman (1920) says: "The depths of the sea experience a never-ending, starless night and the intermediate waters enjoy a brief daily bluish twilight." Shelford and Gail (1922) working near Seattle found that in calm, clear weather 25 per cent of sunlight was cut off by the surface of the ocean; in rough weather such loss reached 60 to 70 per cent. The penetration of light is, of course, not only limited by roughness of the surface but also by turbidity. Along the shore a zone of brown algæ usually occurs at depths between 5 and 20 meters, where shorter wave lengths are about 10 per cent of those of total sunlight and where red wave lengths are about 99 per cent. The red algæ usually occur between 10 and 30 meters.

The red algæ begin where the red and orange light is reduced to about 1 per cent and extend to where the red light is approximately 0.0032. They are most abundant where the shorter wave lengths are approximately 2.9. The depth at which the red algæ grow, when compared with these wave lengths, probably gives a clew to the reason for the red color of the algæ growing in deeper water.

Temperature in Relation to Marine Life.—The minimum temperatures of the ocean vary in polar seas from -2.22 to $-16.7°$C. and the maximum of those of the tropics from 26.67 to 32°C., yet the ocean shows less variation than the atmosphere, which ranges from -45 to 50°C. The ocean absorbs and loses heat only one-fourth as rapidly as land, hence has greater thermal stability. Below depths of 600 feet there is little or no seasonal variation in temperature, the mean being about 2.5°C. Cold sea water will always sink through warmer water of equal salinity. Dense water, produced at the surface by evaporation, may sink and warm deeper strata. Temperature is the primary cause of the vertical and horizontal zonation that animals show in their distribution. Huntsman (1920) makes twelve climatic zones in the north Atlantic, and in another paper (1918) shows that the fishes and other animals in the Gulf of St. Lawrence are arranged in vertical strata according to temperature. Setchell (1922) questions the value of such terms as eurythermal and stenothermal as indicative of the actual range of marine plants. He studied thirty-four species of marine algæ and found that twenty-six were stenothermal in zones having an amplitude of 5°C.; six were somewhat eurythermal, and two were broadly eurythermal (15°C. range). He points out that plants may have a wider range than their ability to reproduce would indicate. For example, *Zostera marina* grows well between 10 and 20°C., but usually reproduces only between 15 and 20°C. Stenothermal plants are said to be particularly characteristic of the tropics

(Setchell, 1920) and in all seas plant zonation is believed to be closely related to temperature. Danois (1924) has shown that the cod frequents cold water (-2 to $+6°$C.). In warmer seasons it deserts the banks and fishing is accordingly poor. The herring is known to swim at greater depths in summer. Orton (1920) affirms that temperature largely controls distribution and reproduction of life in the ocean and points out that breeding usually starts at the beginning of periods of maximum or of minimum temperatures and continues as long as conditions are favorable.

Tides and Currents.—Tides and currents, especially in shallow water, exercise important influences on the ocean, particularly in regard to temperature. Flattely (1921) has suggested that the ebb and flow of the tides have led to the development of terrestrial habits in certain types of animals through rhythmical exposure to air and desiccation. Animals living in the intertidal zone must also have considerable resistance to rapid thermal variations. Huntsman (1918b), in speaking of the fishes along the Canadian coast, says:

Our major conclusions are that the absence of heavy tides makes the Gulf of St. Lawrence, and in particular the Magdalen shallows, an important spawning ground for many species of fishes with pelagic eggs, and the presence of heavy tides prevents the Bay of Fundy serving in a similar capacity, excludes from it the mackerel, and is of prime importance in the fishery for young herring or sardines.

Movements in ocean water are much more limited in rate and extent than those in the atmosphere, but the great currents have important influences on climate and serve to distribute animals and transport food. Seasonal succession and general marine stabilization are often related to vertical circulations. Many currents show cyclical variations, often correlated with seasonal changes.

Strata in the Ocean.—The stratification, or zonation, of marine habitats is striking. Such arrangement of animals in appropriate habitats is due primarily to variations in temperature, light, and bottom. A photic zone extends down to nearly 3000 feet, and below that is the aphotic ocean. The temperature near the surface is comparatively warm and variable; that at great depths is constant, and the water is nearly immobile. Near land, the ocean bottom may consist of various types of deposits. In deeper water there is a uniform substratum of ooze, lime shells extending down to a depth of 2 miles and being succeeded at great depths by fine red clay. Pfeffer (1901) divided the ocean into three regions:

1. Surface—light, plants, currents, often a warm surface stratum down to 50 to 150 fathoms.
2. Subsurface—cool, homothermal, no light or plants, food from above, 600 to 1000 fathoms.
3. Deep sea—no light, no temperature variations, no plants, food from pelagic region, bottom of ooze or clay.

Murray (1898) distinguished seven regions:

1. Littoral and Shallow Water—littoral down to 20 fathoms; sublittoral 20 to 100 fathoms.
2. Surface Oceanic Fauna and Flora.
3. Mud-line Fauna—just below 100 fathoms.
4. Intermediate, or Twilight, Fauna of Open Sea.
5. Archibenthal Fauna of Continental Slope—100 to 1700 fathoms.
6. Deep-water Intermediate Fauna—below 1700 fathoms.
7. Abyssal Benthoic Fauna—below 1700 fathoms.

Flattely and Walton (1922) make four divisions of the ocean: (1) Strand or Tidal Zone, (2) Shallow Sea, (3) Pelagic, (4) Abyssal. They also differentiate the marine plant zones as

1. Free or floating plant—plankton.
2. Fixed plants—benthos:
   a. Littoral—to low-water mark.
   b. Sublittoral—to lowest limits of seaweeds.
   c. Elittoral—no vegetation.

These diverse classifications make it apparent that there has been no uniformity of usage in regard to the regions in the ocean.

Marine Food Resources.—Brooks (1893) stressed the fact that the great food resources of the ocean were in the plants of the pelagic region. He said:

We may regard the great primary food supply as made up of two simple protozoa, Globigerina and the radiolarians, and some five or six unicellular plants.

He also pointed out that the pelagic food resources must be very old because such a large part of the ocean fauna is adjusted to and dependent upon them. Brant (1901) likewise dwelt upon

the importance of plants as the source of marine food and pointed
out that nitrogen compounds were not abundant in sea water,
probably because they were broken up by denitrifying bacteria.
He noted that there were relatively more of nitrogenous compounds in cold seas because there were fewer putrefying bacteria
there.   He also believed that both nitrifying and denitrifying
bacteria were present in the ocean, but Lipman (1922) has
recently produced evidence that the former are absent from or
cannot function in sea water.   If Lipman is right, it follows that
marine organisms are dependent to a considerable degree on land
and freshwater habitats for their nitrogenous compounds.   This·
is what Johnstone (1908) and others have long maintained.
Osborn (1917) takes the position that life could not have originated in the ocean because enough available nitrogen was not
present.   Herdman (1907) made it clear that available calcium
and nitrogen were essential and limiting factors[1] in the development of life in the ocean, and that these compounds are continually taken into and excreted by marine organisms.   Ritter
(1918) has shown that the Pacific has less of Sargassum and Globigerina than the Atlantic and is, in general, more barren.   The
life in the ocean, on the whole, grows more abundant toward the
surface, and animals living below are always dependent directly
on the organic material that is manufactured there, largely
through the use of solar energy.

The Ocean as a Favorable Environment.—Animals living in
sea water are continually surrounded by a medium that is quite
similar to their own body fluids.   The blood of many marine
invertebrates is like sea water in its salt content and osmotic
pressure.   The blood of marine vertebrates resembles sea water
less closely, but still shows a general similarity to it.   In many
respects the ocean is perhaps the most favorable realm in which
animals live.   It is relatively constant in temperature, and in
oxygen and carbon dioxide content.   It is a solution of the
chemicals from which protoplasm is readily built up.

PROVINCE A. LITTORAL ANIMALS

Perhaps the most important factor on marine beaches is the
tidal rhythm, and littoral animals show more or less adjustment
to it.   Animals living in the intertidal zone lead a hard life.
They are subject to the impact of waves and endure alternating

[1] Atkins has recently shown that calcium is never a limiting factor, phosphorus usually is, and nitrogen may be.

periods of wetting and desiccation, which are often associated with striking changes in temperature. When the tide flows, it brings food, and with its advent barnacles, mussels, and other shore animals begin to feed on the myriads of microscopic organisms that are swept in from the open sea. The rising tide also gives a band of voracious predators an opportunity to migrate up the beach and devour helpless shore animals. Fishes, crustaceans, snails, starfishes, and others periodically come inshore to seek food. Probably on this account such animals as mites (King, 1914), fiddler crabs (Pearse, 1913), and podurans (Davenport, 1903a) remain inactive or safely enclosed in burrows while they are covered with water. On the other hand, such animals as Renilla (Parker, 1920), Actinia (Crozier, 1921c), worms, Lingulas, and clams contract when exposed to the air and expand when they are immersed. Some animals find refuges in pools at low tide or hide under vegetation. When the tide ebbs, a resident and foreign army seeks food in the intertidal zone. Gulls, crows, rats, sandpipers, crabs—even lizards and frogs—come to forage. The drift line is picked over by crabs, amphipods, beetles, and other scavengers.

Fecundity and Growth of Littoral Animals.—The animals on ocean beaches have many opportunities to die and usually have great propagative powers. Field (1922) observed a mussel that laid twelve million eggs in a quarter of an hour. He found that mussels grew more rapidly if they chanced to rest in sheltered situations, where they had opportunity to feed from tidal water and were also protected from some of the vicissitudes of littoral life.

Coloration of Littoral Animals.—Among shore animals protective coloration is often developed to a striking degree, and many species have variable patterns that closely resemble the backgrounds on which they rest (Keeble and Gamble, 1904), and some, like the flounder (Mast, 1916), are able to change their colors and patterns to match changing backgrounds. Decorator crabs cover their backs with bits of seaweed and other objects so that they resemble their surroundings closely (Pearse, 1911).

Littoral Temperatures.—Temperatures in littoral habitats are variable. An animal attached to a rock may be baked in the rays of a summer sun and the next moment deluged with cool water. Many littoral animals are able to endure wide and sudden variations in temperature, and stenothermic species are usually found in habitats where there is little change. Recent experiments by the United States Bureau of Fisheries show that lobster fry will not develop in water below 11°C., though adults will live and eggs hatch at lower temperatures. The Pismo clams of the west coast of North America live above low-tide mark during the first three years of their lives. A case has recently been described (Ecology, 4:45) in which these clams during a cold wave were numbed to such an extent that they could not burrow. They were then washed out of the sand by the waves and devoured in great numbers by gulls and pelicans. Shelford (1916) tested the resistance to high temperatures as shown by crustaceans of the same species from deep and from shallow water. He found that those from deep water (100 meters) died more quickly. In polar seas the temperature is never warm and there is little distinction between littoral faunas and those below. The upwelling of the Humboldt Current along the western coast of South America permits Antarctic animals to range farther north than they would otherwise be able to do (Murphy, 1923). Temperature is an important factor in limiting the local and geographic range of many littoral animals.

Littoral Vegetation.—The shore vegetation is distinctive and differs from that of the open sea in being larger and attached. Cowles (1902) states the plants growing above freshwater and ocean beaches are strikingly alike. There are the following strata: (1) a barren zone just above the water; (2) pioneer plants, such as sea-rocket, sea-spurge, and beach pea; and (3) a higher zone where sand reeds and other plants are characteristic. Warming (1909) points out that submerged marine plants that grow on loose bottoms are ribbon-like and become narrow in shallow water. Martin (1922) states that eel grass is the most important plant on soft bottoms, that the brown algæ (Fucus, Ascophyllum, etc.) characteristically cover exposed rock surfaces, and that Ulva and Enteromorpha typically occur on "flats" in rather quiet water. Red algæ are commonly found below low-tide mark and many of them form calcareous coverings over their own surfaces. There are more bacteria in littoral waters than in the open sea (Johnstone, 1908). Shore diatoms have resting spores and those in the pelagic province do not. The attached shore vegetation is a source of food for many animals, but sometimes does injury by overgrowing and smothering such animals as mussels (Field, 1922) and barnacles. Allee (1923a) found that there was usually more oxygen over beds of attached vegetation than elsewhere.

Littoral Zonation.—Though there are numerous transitional areas the littoral animal formations and associations are rather clearly defined according to the character of the bottom. Those of hard bottoms (rock, piles, and to some extent clay) are, as a rule, quite distinct from those on shifting bottoms (sand, mud), but the propagative phases of the former are so abundant in shore water that they usually occupy every firm surface, however small or isolated from other suitable areas. Allee (1923) found that mud flats constituted a remarkably independent habitat, many of the typical animals there being rare or wholly absent from other situations. Among all littoral formations there is a more or less characteristic assortment into horizontal zones. In Puget Sound Shelford (1916) found four zones: (1) shore, between tides, about 3 meters wide; (2) laminarian zone, from low-tide mark to a depth of about 20 meters; (3) coralline zone, 20 to 100 meters; (4) subcoralline zone, 100 to 165 meters. King and Russell (1909) on the shores of England at Millport describe the following zones: (1) *Fucus platycarpus* and *Pelvetia canaliculata*, 24 feet wide; (2) *Ascophyllum nodosum*, 30 feet; (3) *Fucus vesiculosus* and *F. serratus*, 26 feet; (4) laminarian zone; (5) coralline zone. Murray and Hjort (1912) advocate the recognition of a littoral region where there is strong light, 0 to 30 to 40 meters in depth, and a sublittoral, 35 to 150 meters. In his study of the Woods Hole region Sumner (1910) found that depth, as a rule, had little influence in the distribution of littoral animals. He cites one instance, however, where a snail (*Crepidula fornicata*) was confined to the sublittoral zone, although the hermit crab to which it was commonly attached ranged into shallow water. Allee (1923a) also working at Woods Hole found the hermit crab, *Eupagurus longicarpus*, in all types of associations, regardless of the character of the bottom. Huntsman (1918) has shown a very interesting control of vertical migration on the Canadian coast. He found that where tides ran high Littorina, Balanus, and Mytilus did not extend *below* 4 feet above low-tide mark, and that this line was about the upper limit of their predaceous enemies, Buccinum and Asterias.

The starfish and whelk are enemies of the mussel and it may well be that their presence in abundance near and below low-tide mark at St. Andrews is the determining factor for the lower limit of the distribution of the mussel in that region. The zone of common distribution is quite narrow—about 3 feet—and does not contain any of these species in abundance. It is to be considered the area of struggle—by the starfish and whelk against the effects of heat and exposure and by the mussel to obtain a foothold in spite of depredations by the whelk and starfish.

In localities where tides were low the snail, mussel, and barnacle extended considerably below low-tide mark. Huntsman also found that barnacles were most abundant where sea-urchins were few or absent. Probably rockweeds attracted the urchins, and localities where they occurred were not particularly favorable for barnacles.

Littoral corals are largely confined to warm seas where they live in rather shallow water with a mean temperature of at least 20°C. Reef builders require higher temperatures.

The most abundant reef builders at moderate depths are madrepores, astræids, porites, and meandrines. At depths of 90 to 120 feet the millepores and seriastopores predominate. The great field for coral development lies between low water and 120 feet.

Corals are most luxuriant in protected lagoons and channels. McCaughey (1918) described five zones: (1) beach or inshore waters, (2) partially submerged rocks, (3) pools, (4) lagoons, (5) reef rims.

Adaptations of Littoral Animals.—The adaptations of littoral animals to various peculiar modes of life present an endless variety. There are structures for adhesion, burrowing, resistance to impact, etc. There are animals that feed by spreading a radially disposed group of tentacles, by swallowing mud, by straining microscopic organisms from flowing water, by everting the stomach about the soft parts of some unlucky animal, etc. There are those that escape from watchful enemies by concealing their bodies with coverings of foreign objects or the cast-off shells of other animals and by living in burrows. Sessile animals are protected by hard exoskeletons, nematocysts, avicularia, pedicellariæ, and often have special cleaning devices to keep their bodies free from sediment. For reproduction there are adaptations that serve to spread a species or to keep it from being swept out to sea: swimming larvæ, adherent eggs, special spawning places, etc. The species of Littorina that live on beaches show an interesting series, those that live near low-tide mark giving off eggs containing earlier veliger stages, and those that live near high-water mark giving birth to small snails. Murray (1895) states that animals beyond the mud line (100 fathoms) have no free-swimming larvæ and that this fact constitutes a distinction from shore animals.

On the whole, littoral animals are resistant and capable of enduring wide ranges of variation. Fulton (1921) kept a Bermudan tide-pool anemone in a corked bottle of sea water without access to the atmosphere for more than eleven days and the animal was apparently uninjured. He also dried individuals for as much as six days, until they had shriveled into a raisin-like mass, but these soon became active when replaced in sea water. Hausman (1920) studied the shore anemone, *Sagartia luciæ* and says:

It seems remarkable that so soft and relatively defenseless a creature should have so greatly increased its numbers and extended its range in our waters. Its success in meeting the unusually numerous vicissitudes of a littoral existence may perhaps be attributed to the following: (1) an ability to withstand considerable differences in temperature, (2) its ability to withstand buffeting by the waves because of the yielding and resilient character of its body, (3) its ability to contract tightly and to survive through a period of foul water, or of dry conditions exposed to the sun and wind, (4) its apparent disregard of the differences in the salinity of water, (5) its protective coloration, (6) its defensive acontia, (7) its rapid rate of reproduction and growth to maturity, (8) its several methods of reproduction, (9) its ability to withstand annihilation through laceration, and (10) its ability to regenerate lost parts.

Some of the active shore animals are very sensitive to slight variations in environment. Shelford (1915) found that there was usually more hydrogen sulphide on sandy bottoms in the Puget Sound region and that herring usually avoided such localities. Sometimes a storm changed the chemistry of the water and Shelford believed that herring died on account of such changes.

FORMATION 1. HARD-BEACH ANIMALS

A firm substratum gives littoral animals opportunity to attach themselves. They are thus able to withstand the action of waves and tidal currents and at the same time secure food from the shore algæ or from the microscopic life that swarms in littoral water. Hard bottom is usually associated with much movement in the water. The ocean continually sorts over its movable bottom materials, depositing the finest muds at the head of bays and its sands where there is an intermediate degree of molar activity. Thus the immovable, rocky headlands are left standing out into the open ocean where they receive the maximum of water movement.

ASSOCIATION *a*. ANIMALS OF ROCK WALLS

The animals on the unbroken rocky shores of the ocean offer an excellent example of zonation. Highest is the barren transitional strip (Stratum 1), where neither land nor sea dominates. Here birds, ants, and spiders forage over the rock surfaces; swallows, dragon-flies, and butterflies sail through the air. The rocks in this stratum are not lichen-covered, like those farther inland, but are for the most part bare, thus showing the influence of the ocean. In pools among the rocks little flies (*Coelopa frigida* Falle, etc.) commonly breed. Larvæ are often abundant in the water and the adults may be seen floating about on the surface, often in such numbers as to form veritable miniature rafts. Other insects, such as aquatic bugs and beetles, occur in limited numbers. Earwigs hide in crevices during the day and come out at night to forage.

Intertidal Zone.—The abundant population of the intertidal zone (Stratum 2) shows an arrangement into horizontal, but more or less overlapping, consocies. Barnacles extend in a white band above other marine animals. The water level covers some barnacles only at the time of spring tides and such individuals have no chance to feed except when, at intervals, food-laden waves dash over them. Yet they cannot move and are able to persist within their calcareous armor. Mussels and snails (Littorina) extend almost as high as the barnacles on bare rock surfaces. In the bands of rockweeds (Fucus, Sargassum, Ascophyllum, Chondrus) many animals find food and shelter. There are chitons, snails (Littorina, Purpura, the limpets, Acmæa, and Patella; nudibranchs, etc.), clams (Mytilus, Modiola, etc.), sponges; sertularian and campanularian hydroids, anemones, bryozoans, flatworms, annelids (Spirorbis, etc.), amphipods, isopods (especially Caprella and other sedentary types), crabs, sea-urchins, starfishes, attached ascidians, fishes and other animals.

Even some crinoids are found between tides (Clark, 1921). Arey and Crozier (1921) have described an interesting mores on the Bermuda coast where snails (*Onchidium floridanum*) live in little crevices and only come out for about one hour out of each twelve to feed on algæ. The three species of snails of the genus Littorina that live on rock beaches, though much alike in structure, occupy separate zones—being assorted according to their adjustments to plants, crevices, and sunlight (Hazeman, 1911; Flattely and Walton, 1922).

Laminarian Zone.—In the Laminarian Zone (Stratum 3) below the low-tide mark there is a characteristic group of species. Here lobsters and other animals that do not migrate up into the intertidal zone are often associated with barnacles, mussels, snails, and other species that also live at higher levels. Certain species move up somewhat with each rising tide (sea-urchins, starfishes, crabs, carnivorous snails) and drop back with the ebb. Murray and Hjort (1912) have pointed out that *Laminaria hyperborea*, which has stiff stalks, shelters many animals, while other laminarians with thin, pliant stalks have few attached species.

Shorewater.—The shorewater (Stratum 4) has a characteristic fauna and flora which is in many respects distinct from that of the open ocean. Some of the animals are free-swimming stages of species that live on the shore during parts of their lives. Crabs and starfishes have swimming larvæ; many attached hydroids bud off sexual medusæ, which, in turn, often produce swimming planulæ. The organisms of the shorewater constitute the sole food of many of the attached animals along beaches.

Adaptations of Animals on Rock Beaches.—Marine rock beaches furnish an abundance of food, but conditions of life on them are severe. Many of the animals are firmly attached in order to withstand the continual movement of waves and tides. Radial symmetry is usually associated with attachment and many of the animals show it. Even animals that are able to move about do so very little. The writer (1914) once found a sea-urchin that had rested so long in one spot that a sponge had grown up and enclosed it in a living nest. He also mapped a colony of anemones in a beach pool, carefully plotting the position of each individual, and found that after two weeks not one could be observed to have moved. Some limpets remain on one spot so long that they wear scars in the rocks. Many rock-beach animals are protected by the hard shells that cover their bodies.

Parker (1917) found that a beach anemone (Cribrina) held bits of shell about its column by means of sucking discs to protect itself from the beating of the waves. Other animals escape the impact of waves through their small size, which enables them to creep into crevices. Arey and Crozier (1921) found that Onchidium never emerged from its home crevice when the tide was in. Hamilton (1903) observed an interesting type of behavior in a chiton that lived in cavities in coralline rock on the coast of Cuba. These molluscs crouched against the rock when a wave came in, but raised their bodies and allowed the water to run over their gills when it receded. Their eyes apparently served to give notice of coming waves. Some animals escape wave action by boring into the rock itself. An isopod (Sphæroma) and clams tunnel into rocks on the coast of Australia (Stead, 1900); a clam known as the piddock establishes itself for life in the rocks along the Pacific coast of North America (M'Curdy, 1902); in the Atlantic, rocks are excavated by sea-urchins and clams. Even some of the classic buildings along the Mediterranean have been bored into by clams at times of high water.

The animals remaining above low-tide mark show various adjustments to resist the drying action of the atmosphere while they are exposed. Barnacles and molluscs are protected by their calcareous shells and opercula; anemones are turgid with water when the tide goes out and gradually become flaccid; many smaller animals hide under the rockweeds; some secrete slime which serves as a covering for the body; certain crabs, starfishes, and other motile animals cannot long endure desiccation and therefore must migrate downward when the tide ebbs.

Rock-frequenting littoral animals have various means of adjustment to the temperature changes. Skeletons, slime, water loss, nocturnal habits, and instincts to seek shelter serve to mitigate the heat of summer. During the winter many unattached shore animals move into deeper water. Some of these are able to respire from either water or air.

Origin of Littoral Fauna.—The invasion of littoral habitats has not come altogether from the ocean. King (1914) described several species of mites that are adjusted to rocky shores and show varying degrees of ability to endure submergence. Podurans and halobatids have also been derived from the land. The strenuous existence that shore animals are obliged to lead apparently has some compensation. Hubbs (1920) affirms that reef fishes usually have few parasites and he believes this is "a fact apparently due to the strength of wave and tidal currents."

Feeding of Animals on Rocky Shores.—The feeding of the animals on rocky beaches is more or less characteristic. Those that are attached spread sweep nets (barnacles) or tentacles (hydroids, anemones, bryozoans), or siphon water through their bodies (clams). It is not safe for any microscopic organism to come near the living blanket on a rocky shore. Snails, sea-urchins, and other algal feeders search over the rocks or lurk in favorable nooks. Ribbon fishes, sculpins, small crustaceans, crabs, drills, and starfishes commonly seek their prey when the tide is high and hide away when conditions for feeding are not favorable. Cribrina captures food with special tentacles which are provided with sucking discs. Onchidium emerges from its home crevice for only an hour each day when the tide is out, but in that time rasps enough algæ off the rocks to sustain it. Crozier (1921) summarizes estimates concerning the amount of water siphoned daily through certain rock-beach animals as follows: one sponge "finger," 78 liters; Ascidia, 173 liters; Stichopus (for respiration), 20 liters.

Animals in Pools on Rocky Shores.—Rock pools are frequently carpeted by living animals. Certain sponges, hydroids, anemones, bryozoans, crustaceans, clams, snails, ascidians, and fishes flourish in such situations. The shanny, blenny (viviparous), lumpsucker, gunnell, fifteen-spined stickleback, and five-bearded rockling, which live in pools along the British coast, produce many eggs or young because so many are destroyed, particularly by predaceous enemies (McIntosh, 1900). The young of the Californian viviparous perch leave the lower beach pools soon after hatching and remain in those at higher levels, where they are secure from predators and are inundated only at high tide (Hubbs, 1921a). Klugh (1924) has made a careful study of six beach pools on the rocks of the New Brunswick coast. These were much alike except for their elevation, constituting a comparable but graded series. There was a change in salinity in the higher pools on account of evaporation. The chemical nature of the water was found to be influenced largely by the plants present. Temperature varied widely. In the lower pools it was never above 3°C.; in the highest, it rose to 15 to 28.5°C. A fauna characteristic of the laminarian zone was found in the three lower pools, but was absent from those above.   This was associated with coralline seaweeds.

ASSOCIATION *b*.   ANIMALS OF PEBBLY BEACHES

Loose pebbles on a rock beach may change the character of the fauna.   Usually, there is an increase in the number of animals that frequent crevices.   Sumner (1910) found that the distribution of *Thuiaria argentia* was confined to situations where there were loose stones.   The Basque coast lacks the zonal arrangement characteristic of that along Brittany on account of the presence of pebbles and warmer water.   On the former nullipores, sea-urchins, and anemones are dominant types (Beauchamp, 1907).

ASSOCIATION *c*.   PILE, WHARF, AND SHIP ANIMALS

The wooden structures introduced into the ocean by man are populated largely by animals that frequent rocky shores.   Wood, however, is frequented by certain boring animals that do not work in rock.   On the exposed surfaces (Stratum 1) are barnacles, hydroids, corals, sponges, oysters, amphipods, isopods, spider crabs, mussels, snails, ascidians, and tunneling in the wood (Stratum 2) are shipworms (Teredo, etc.) and the crustaceans, Chelura and Limnoria.   These animals are very destructive and cause great economic losses.   The shipworms are highly adapted to the life they lead.   They are probably able to digest the cellulose from wood (Dose and Miller, 1923), but also feed on plankton, which is drawn through their incurrent siphons. Their burrows are lined with calcareous secretions.   Both boring crustaceans and molluscs are more abundant in the lower half of the intertidal zone.

FORMATION 2.   ANIMALS OF SHIFTING BEACHES

The beaches which have shifting substrata form a graded series with firm clays at one end and at the other the soft muds that occur on shores where sediment is accumulating.

ASSOCIATION *a*.   ANIMALS OF CLAY BEACHES

While clay bottoms are hard enough to give a firm foothold for clinging animals, they do not permit permanently attached animals, like barnacles, sponges, and hydroids, to exist. There are, however, creeping types, such as snails and chitons, which are often common, particularly in crevices and eroded holes.

The drift line (Stratum 1) here supports the usual group of scavenger insects, but the small amphipod crustaceans are not abundant, as on sand beaches. The intertidal zone (Stratum 2) is usually dominated by crabs, which find an excellent place for their burrows in the clay because it does not cave in readily. The zone below low-tide mark (Stratum 3) is similar to that on rocky shores, but patches of mud and eel grass often occur.

Association *b*. Animals of Sand Beaches

Sand beaches occur where there is considerable water movement, and therefore, while they are made up of particles that are less transportable than the fine sediments that are found in mud, are the most unstable of shore bottoms. Few algæ can maintain themselves, though there are some that live in or on the sand. Spermatophytes which are provided with roots or rhizomes are quite characteristic in certain situations, though usually not abundant. Both plants and animals are more abundant on sheltered than on exposed beaches. Many of the latter live below the surface of the sand and special adaptations for respiration and feeding are often present. In speaking of adaptations that certain crustaceans have for keeping sand from entering their branchial chambers Garstang (1896, 1898) says:

It is both remarkable and interesting that the same function in relation to the process of respiration should be discharged by organs and parts so dissimilar from one another as are the first antennæ of *Abunea*, the second antennæ of *Corystes*, the frontal area of *Platyonichus nasutus*, the five lateral spines of *Atelecyclus*, the crests of the chelipeds of *Calappa granulata*, and the orbits of *Matuta victor*.

Drift Line.—High up on the beach in all warm parts of the earth live the crabs of the genus Ocypoda. They are well protected by their resemblance to the sand and, as they scuttle for their burrows in the twilight, are well named "ghost crabs." Along the drift line (Stratum 1) there are myriads of sand hoppers (Orchestia, Talorchestia, etc.), and scavenger insects (flies, beetles, ants). Sand spiders, tiger beetles, and robber-flies seek their prey on the smooth stretches of sand.

Intertidal Zone.—The intertidal zone (Stratum 2) shows a variable stratification depending on the exposure of a beach to the open ocean. Very often there is a rather steep slope where there is little life below the drift line. Below this there is a rather flat, ripple-marked zone where the tortuous tracks left by the little isopod, Chiridotea, are found. Chiridotea is extremely flat and can slide in and out of or through the sand with great ease. Where there are plants growing so that roots hold the sand together, the burrows of fiddler crabs may be found. Below the flat there is often a little barren ridge that is covered with small pebbles. On the seaward side of this are little V's made by the antennæ of the mole crabs (*Emerita talpoidea*, etc.), which protrude above the sand into the receding waves. Beyond that ridge a gentle grade leads into deep water. On this slope there are many characteristic sand-dwelling animals. When the tide is in, shrimps swim about or scamper over the sand and burrow, so that their bodies are partly buried. In the tropics the crabs of the genus Mycteris dig their holes near low-tide mark and remain buried while under water. Hermit crabs and isopods (Idothea) move up and down with the tides. Haustorius and other burrowing amphipods share the sand with sea-cucumbers (Synapta), enteropneustans, lancelets, worms (Arenicola, etc.), sand dollars, spatangoids, sand snails (Lunitia, Fulgur), and clams. In some parts of the world the beautiful Renilla buries itself when the tide is out and expands when it is again covered with water. The snails slide through the submerged sand and burrow in when waves begin to shift it about. Several make peculiar egg cases by fastening the sand together with slime. Some annelids also anchor cocoons of agglutinated eggs in the sand. Perhaps the clams (Venus, Cardium, Ensis, Solen, etc.) are as characteristic as any group on sand beaches. Their heavy, well-protected bodies and burrowing ability enable them to live in the shifting substratum with little danger of injury and their siphons permit them to obtain food from the water. The sand-dwelling echinoderms are also highly adapted; the synaptas lack respiratory trees and burrow at some little distance below the surface; the flatness of the sand dollars enables them to slide through the sand and offer little surface for wave action; the spatangoids can remain largely below the surface and feed through the activities of the "brushes" on the petaloid ambulacra which lie on the upper side.

Below Low-tide Mark.—Below low-tide mark (Stratum 3) lurk rays, flounders, sand eels, and other animals which move up the shore with each tide in search of food. On sandy shores there is a rather gradual transition into deep water, and many of the littoral animals (Venus, sand dollars, spatangoids, etc.) extend to considerable depths. Allee (1923) notes that in the Woods Hole region a worm, *Scoloplos fragilis*, is the dominant species on sand bars that lie off the shore. The shorewater (Stratum 4) contains the usual store of floating and swimming organisms which are, living and dead, the most important source of food for sand-beach animals.

ASSOCIATION c. ANIMALS OF MUD BEACHES

Mud is deposited on beaches where the action of molar agents is not pronounced. The animals that live in the mud itself are chiefly burrowers which, on account of the stagnant medium in which they live, are commonly provided with special means for creating respiratory currents. Many have hard exoskeletons or build tubes. Sumner (1910) in his extensive survey of the Woods Hole region found a greater number of species on rock and gravel bottoms than on mud. Allee (1923) asserts that the fauna of mud flats differs markedly from that on other types of beaches. He says: "The associations of the flats are highly independent of others."

Drift Line and Flats.—The drift line (Stratum 1) on mud beaches has a population of scavengers, with fewer amphipods than on sandy shores. Below this the bare mud flats (Stratum 2) are spread out. The surfaces of these get very hot in the sun, but colonies of mussels, by attachments to each other, often form great rafts and appear to flourish. In the mud, worms, the clam, Mya, and the brachiopod, Lingula, are characteristic. The Japanese Lingula never invades sandy or plant-covered areas (Yatsu, 1902). This animal retreats as deeply as possible by contracting its peduncle when the tide is out. The peduncle is not attached, but is so firmly imbedded in the mud that it is often broken when the body is pulled out. Lingula makes burrows by squirting water and rubbing slime along the walls of the cavity thus formed. It has great resistance to stagnation. One colony described by Yatsu survived when all molluscs were killed. Where stones or drift are present on flats, worms or other animals commonly burrow under them; barnacles, snails, and other hard-beach animals may also find attachment.

Low-tide Mark and Below.—Near low-tide mark sea-lettuce (Ulva) and eel grass (Zostera) begin, and a little below this the latter forms a dense growth (Stratum 3). The mud snails (Nassa, etc.) and often fiddler crabs are found somewhat above the vegetation zone and many nematodes, annelids, and clams flourish among the roots. On the coasts of Japan a small cuttle-fish adheres by its ventral surface to the under side of Ulva fronds. It holds its tentacles together and keeps turning its head about to observe passing animals that it may capture for food (Sasaki, 1923). There is an abundant population among the eel grass leaves. Along the borders of open spaces starfishes pursue scuttling scallops and holothurians (Thyone, etc.) wave their tentacles. Hermit, rock, spider, and panopeid crabs scamper about seeking food. The eel grass serves to support snails (*Littorina minuta*, etc.), tubicolous worms (Spirorbis), and certain hydroids. According to Parker (1917) the hydroid Corymorpha imbeds its stalk in the mud. Where there is a current, passing particles are captured for food, but in quiet water the stalk is bent over and the tentacles are scraped over the bottom. On the Australian coast, according to Dexler and Freund (1906), the dugong does not frequent estuaries, but browses on eel grass along the borders of muddy shores. Fishes like Fundulus, the pipefish, eel, and stickleback migrate back and forth with the tides. Jackson (1922) says that eels, Funduli, and young flounders burrow into the mud at the bottom of puddles when left stranded by the tide, and thus survive until the water covers them again. The toadfish nests in such situations as old cans and hollow logs on mud beaches. The male clears off his nest and continually fans it to keep the eggs clean. He induces as many passing females as he can to deposit eggs. When the tide is out herons, gulls, snipes, crows, and other birds often resort to the flats to feed. On shores where there is an intermediate degree of wave and tidal movement there may be a sand beach in the upper strata followed by eel grass and characteristic animals of Stratum 3 of mud beaches.

Lagoons.—Lagoons (Stratum 4) usually have a muddy bottom and have a characteristic fauna of anemones, holothurians, worms, molluscs, and other animals. Crozier (1918) has esti-mated the amount of mud (dry) that passes through a Stichopus at 6 to 7 kilos each year. The digestive secretions of this holothurian are acid enough to dissolve some calcium carbonate, but little grinding action is exerted on particles that pass through the gut. McClendon (1910) found that many of the animals in the lagoons behind coral reefs were negatively phototropic and positively thigmotropic.

Shorewater.—The shorewater (Stratum 5) near mud beaches varies considerably in its temperature and gas content. When the tide is out, the water standing over vegetation may become very warm and supersaturated with oxygen, while that over masses of drift may have an unusual amount of carbon dioxide. The rising tide, however, usually mixes the water and soon brings it to a condition of chemical and thermal uniformity. The eel grass that is out of water at low tide serves as a mat to protect animals beneath it.

Association *d*. Estuarian Animals

The vegetation of brackish water is closely allied to that on marine shores but, depending on its salinity, "also includes other species and genera, such as Chara, Zannichellia, Batrachium, Naias, *Potamogeton pectinatus*, and Myriophyllum, which reappear more bountifully in freshwater" (Warming, 1909).

Murray (1914) estimates that about 3.7 cubic miles of suspended and dissolved material are carried into the ocean each year by rivers. At this rate the whole of the present land volume would be carried away in 6,340,000 years. The salts in rivers are principally carbonates and the salinity averages about 0.018 per cent (ocean, 3.5 per cent).

Stratification.—At the mouths of rivers there is usually a transition in temperature and salinity which leads to a stratification of the water. At the mouth of the St. Lawrence River Huntsman (1918*b*) found three layers: (1) a warm surface layer— a mixture of river water and warm ocean; (2) an intermediate layer (18°C.); and (3) a cold (0°C.) layer near the bottom. The fishes were arranged in five zones: (1) in deep channels were few fishes, rockling, angler, skate, sole, etc.; (2) banks were covered with ice-cold water and were resorts for plaice, sole, skates, cod; (3) the warm surface water contained dogfish and mackerel in the open, and alongshore cunner, grubby, eel, sand flounder, pipefish, young sand flounder, butterfish, smelt; (4)

in the intermediate zone herring ranged in the open, and on the bottom were haddock, hake, dab, adult flounders, muttonfish, wolffish, sculpin, and skates; (5) in the estuarial transition from shorewater to fresh were the smooth flounders, white perch, sand smelt, Fundulus, and stickleback. The important zones for food fishes were the third and fourth.

Murray and Hjort (1912) describe the "pools" at the mouths of rivers in Norway as ranging up to 30 meters in depth. The surface is covered by a layer of more or less freshwater. "About 1 to 2 meters below the surface the temperature in some summers may rise to 30°C., or even more, while that at the surface does not rise above 18 to 20°C." In such pools live oysters, scallops, anemones, starfishes, crabs, and mussels—the fauna as a whole being "decidedly southern" in its relationships.

At the mouth of the Caspian Sea Tschugunoff (1921) finds three strata: (1) an upper layer with less than 0.75 gram of sodium chloride per liter, (2) a brackish layer, ranging up to 3 grams per liter, (3) a salty layer, ranging up to 4 to 16 grams per liter. In this case the plankton organisms are assorted according to salinity. Fifty-two of the ninety-two species recorded are characteristic of freshwater. The salinity of Chesapeake Bay increases downward, with a rapid rise at a depth of about 10 meters (Cowles, 1923).

Zonation of Estuarian Animals.—Ferronnière (1901) made extensive studies of the distribution of the plants and animals at the mouth of the Loire. He found that in going upstream representative marine plants and animals dropped out in the following order: *Arenicola marina, Lineus gesserensis, Carcinas mœnas, Sphœroma serratus, Fucus* and *Lichina, Balanus, Amphitrite, Cardium edule, Heterochœta, Vermiculatus, Phragmites communis, Boccardia ligerica, Nereis diversicolor, Palœmon edwardsi.* This writer notes that when salinity changes there may be various responses, which he lists as follows: (1) immediate death, (2) autotomy, (3) violent contractions or irregular movements, (4) tropisms, etc., (5) exaggeration of certain natural functions, (6) establishment of a new equilibrium, or (7) acclimatization without observable change.

Variations in Salinity.—There have been many studies upon the ability of estuarian animals to survive changes in salinity. Packard (1918) investigated twenty-three species of lamellibranchs and twelve species of snails in San Francisco Bay. He concluded that depth had little influence on distribution, but the character of the bottom was of great significance. Low salinity and wide ranges in salinity were unfavorable. The shipworm, Teredo, readily survives rapid changes in salinity (Blum, 1922). It will remain active in water that contains nine parts of salt per liter, but dies when there are five. It may close its burrow with its pallets and thus retain salty water within for a time.

Oyster Typical in Estuaries.—Nelson has written a number of papers on the oyster. He has found (1921) that oysters eat a variety of plankton, 80 per cent of animal food being taken at times. An oyster strains about 6 quarts of water per hour, or 120 quarts per day. It is active about 20 hours out of each 24; 73 per cent of shell closures are during ebbing tides, and 50 per cent between 11 p.m. and dawn. When the density of the surrounding water reaches 1008 the shell closes, but opens again if the density is raised to 1010. In a later paper Nelson (1923) states that there is a sudden decrease in ciliary action between 4 and 6°C., and that below 4°C. there is no feeding. There is active feeding as the tide rises and little as it falls.

For oysters which have been living in water of fairly constant saline content there is a definite minimum salinity below which the bivalves become inactive. This minimum salinity is lower for oysters grown in brackishwater than for those matured in waters of higher salt content. Oysters continue to feed when the water surrounding them is very turbid.

Fishes of Estuaries.—The male gaff-top-s'l catfish carries eggs in his mouth and goes without food for eighty days (Gudger, 1912). "The habit is common to estuarine catfish in all tropical and warm temperate regions." The eggs are thus protected from predaceous enemies and are in no danger of being smothered in mud.

Bays Resemble Estuaries.—What has been said of estuaries often applies in a general way to bays. Nelson (1917) noted that oyster larvæ were numerous at the heads of bays and, though they were swept back and forth by tides, few were carried out to sea. He (1923, p. 33) has advanced the theory "that oyster larvæ work back toward the headwaters and away from the sea by rising on the flood tide and sinking on the ebb." Murray and Hjort (1912) note that in Norwegian fiords the limpet and Purpura are absent and hydroids decrease away from the ocean.

They believe this to be due largely to decrease in salinity, which is especially marked along the shores and less in deeper water.

Association *e*. Marsh Animals

Marshes resemble estuaries in that they are transitional regions between salt and freshwater. Warming (1909) says that marshes "are not only floristically, but also anatomically and morphologically so peculiar, that they differ widely from freshwater swamps."

Mangroves.—Perhaps the most characteristic and extensive of the marshes in tidal waters are those formed by mangroves on flat, muddy shores, especially in lagoons near the mouths of rivers and in estuaries. Mangroves are specially adapted to live on soft, mucky, poorly aerated bottoms. They possess prop and respiratory roots. Their seeds germinate into a spike while still attached to the stem on which they grew and, when ripe, fall and plunge into the soft substratum where they are not readily dislodged. Mangroves are usually densely populated by crabs which dig burrows among the roots. Their branches are favorite roosts and nestling sites for herons and also shelter deer, raccoons, and other animals.

Animals of Marshes.—Marshes in temperate regions furnish habitats for characteristic birds, such as bitterns, rails, snipes, grebes, and ducks. Their seaward margins are inhabited by sand hoppers, fiddler crabs, marine snails, and clams (Nassa, Mya). Where their inner margins grade into freshwater there may be such types as cat-tails and pond snails. Areas like those along the coasts of Carolina, Florida, and Louisiana extend over many miles through which transitions from salt to freshwater faunas may take place. Probably animals in such areas are acquiring new limits of toleration and perhaps through the ages such new modes of life may become hereditary. Certain mosquito larvæ and dragon-fly nymphs are known to be able to live in brackishwater. Perhaps after a few millions of years such types may, like Halobates, be living in the ocean itself.

In speaking of the marshes along the shores of New Jersey, Martin (1923) emphasizes the importance of land and organisms from land-locked waters as sources of food for oysters. He says:

The marshes adjoining Barnegat Bay are covered with a dense growth of *Spartina glabra* and associated plants and scattered among them are numerous shallow salt ponds, the larger of them connected by creeks with the lagoons or the bay. The striking feature of these ponds is the extreme abundance of plankton in them, even as compared with the rich waters of the bay, which makes them important sources of oyster food. The bearing of this fact upon the adjoining waste land to the oyster beds, and especially upon the possibility of increasing the supply of oyster food by appropriate treatment of the land-locked waters, is obvious.

PROVINCE B. PELAGIC ANIMALS

The flora and the fauna of the open ocean are at the same time primitive and specialized. The plants are all algæ and microscopic species greatly exceed in quantity the multicellular types. Indeed, all the multicellular pelagic algæ are derived from the shore. The gulfweed, *Sargassum bacciferum*, and the rockweed, *Ascophyllum nodosum*, which cover great areas in the middle of the Atlantic, grow to some extent after they separate from their shore attachments, but they do not form new bladders; hence gradually sink and after a time contribute their substance to bottom sediments or furnish food for animals below the surface (Murray and Hjort, 1912). Arnold (1901) affirmed that of the hundred odd species in the genus Sargassum only *S. bacciferum* is found in the open ocean.

Types of Plankton.—Pelagic organisms are often divided into plankton, which includes those that float or swim feebly and are carried about by currents, and nekton, which consists of large animals that can make progress against currents. This scheme includes such species as the animals attached to sargassum and the goose barnacles attached to floating logs under plankton, which to some persons seems illogical. All pelagic plants belong to the plankton. Lohmann (1911) divides the plankton into megaloplankton, the constituents of which are large enough to be readily seen from the deck of a vessel, and nannoplankton, which includes small organisms 1 to 20 or even 25 micra in length. He also divides phytoplankton into euflagellates, and aflagellates. The former make up the bulk of the nannoplankton. Peridinians are abundant near the surface, diatoms reach their maximum at greater depths, and coccolithophorids occur at intermediate depths with diatoms or peridinians. Hjort (1911) has shown that the plants in the open Atlantic are most abundant between depths of 10 and 50 meters, where they average 3000 individuals per liter, and that coastal waters contain more than the open sea. The marine floating algæ are mostly brown, with a few green and blue-green representatives. They are characterized by thin shells and by various structures for suspension or flotation. Diatoms are more abundant in muddy water near shore, probably on account of the presence of dissolved silica, which they require for their shells. Lohmann (1911) found that there were about 100 bacteria per cubic centimeter in the open ocean·and 880 or more in harbors. These produce food, but are not able to manufacture new organic matter as green plants do. Murray (1914) believes that there are all types of bacteria (putrefactive, fermentive, ammonifying, nitrogen-fixing, etc.) in the ocean, but Lipman (1922) holds that the presence of nitrifying bacteria is doubtful. Luminescent bacteria are found only in the ocean.

Murray (1897) estimated that 70 per cent of the plankton consisted of plants, but in a more recent work Murray and Hjort (1912) state that, in the Atlantic, plants constitute about 56 per cent of the plankton. Lohmann (1911) found that about a tenth of the volume of the nannoplankton was made up of protozoans, the greater part being furnished by plants. Willey (1920) states that there are four general types of plankton: (1) *peridinian*, which is often luminescent and composed chiefly of dinoflagellates of the genus Ceratium; (2) *diatom*, in which Chætoceras is important; (3) *mixed*, composed of diatoms, peridinians, and copepods; and (4) *copepod*, made up largely of crustaceans. Johnstone (1908, pp. 150–156), following Cleve, gives an elaborate classification of Atlantic plankton types, based primarily on the diatoms present, and points out that proximity to shore and temperature are the chief factors which influence the types in a particular locality. He also states that a comparable unit of ocean usually contains less plankton than one in freshwater. The rate of multiplication of plankton organisims is relatively rapid, so that, while individually small in size, they together maintain a large total bulk because their rate of "overturn" keeps pace with the continual losses.

Animals of Open Ocean.—The animals that live in the open ocean are diverse and specialized in various ways for pelagic life. The Protozoa are represented chiefly by foraminiferans, radiolarians, dinoflagellates (some of which are perhaps to be classified as plants), and tintinnidians. Murray (1895) noted twenty species of foraminiferans from the surface waters of tropical seas.

Among prominent metazoans are medusæ, siphonophores, ctenophores, copepods, ostracods, schizopods, amphipods, decapods,
heteropods, pteropods, cephalopods, tunicates, and fishes.
At times the eggs and larvæ of fishes and other animals may
constitute a considerable part of the plankton. The arrow
worms, Chætognatha, are nearly exclusively pelagic. The
nekton includes whales, seals, sea snakes, turtles, sharks, fishes,
and other animals.

Origin of Pelagic Animals.—Murray (1895) believes that
pelagic animals arose from the "mud-line animals" of Pre-
cambrian seas. He says:

> Whales, seals, pelagic fishes, Halobates, pelagic cephalopods, Ianthina,
> Scyllacea, pteropods, heteropods, pelagic crustaceans, worms, and cœlen-
> terates all appear to bear distinct traces of shore and shallow-water
> origin.

Brooks (1894) also maintained that all large pelagic animals
descended from ancestors that lived near the shore or on the
bottom, but also held that the pelagic was the first fauna and that
bottom animals originally arose from it. The abundance of food
at the surface of the open ocean has doubtless been a factor in the
spread of such animals as the albatross and petrel. Some
animals are found in the pelagic region only at certain stages in
their life cycles. The neritic plankton especially is characterized
by the presence of the larvæ, young, and adult stages of littoral
animals. These are often associated with animals that belong
in the open sea and have no particular connection with the shore.
Murray and Hjort (1912) distinguish between holopelagic
animals, that spend their entire lives in the open water, and
meropelagic, that pass part of their existence elsewhere. They
also point out that the neritic algæ of cold seas do not show
bipolarity, and that those of the open ocean do.

Ranges of Pelagic Animals.—In general, the animals of pelagic
regions have wide geographic ranges because there is such a
general uniformity in the medium in which they live that there
are no real obstacles to spreading. Lohmann (1912) gives a
valuable account of the ranges of distribution of many pelagic
organisms.

Effects of Oceanic Currents on Pelagic Life.—The oceanic
currents produce marked variations in temperature and to a less
extent cause differences in salinity. Such differences, when in

limited areas, act as barriers for the spread of certain animals. The margins of currents are usually marked on the bottom by the bodies of many dead animals and certain species, therefore, come there to feed.   When there is a radical change in the course of an ocean current there is often a very high mortality among animals both in the new area invaded and in the one that is abandoned. A notable instance of this kind was the destruction of the millions of tilefish off the coast of New York, supposedly on account of a shift in the Gulf Stream which changed the temperatures over banks that were usually covered by warm water.   The Gulf Stream reaches its maximum volume in November and dwindles to a minimum in March, each year passing through periodic changes (Johnstone, 1908).

Vertical Migrations of Pelagic Animals.—Animals living in the upper strata of the ocean are subjected to annual monthly and daily cycles of changes and many of them respond by making periodic migrations.   There are fishes and other pelagic animals that move to and from particular breeding and feeding areas or strata.   Some occupy different areas in youth from those to which they resort during maturity.   Of all such movements perhaps the most striking is the general migration of plankton animals toward the surface at night and downward during the day. The different species of plankton animals maintain a certain separateness and stratification but many species move upward, in some cases to the surface and in others simply to a higher stratum, for various distances, which usually range from 30 to 50 meters.   Bourie (1912) says that some fishes come near the surface at night from a depth of 1000 meters.   Such species have eyes that are adjusted to light of low intensity.   Steuer (1910), in discussing the causes of the daily vertical migrations that are so characteristic of pelagic animals, states that changes in light, temperature, responses to gravity, and the chemical nature of the water all play a part.   Light is, of course, the factor that varies most during each day through a considerable stratum of water at the surface, and it is known to be of importance in the migrations of a number of species.   Ditlevsen (1923) tested plankton animals in an aquarium.   He found that they went from areas where light intensity was high into those where it was low, and that they spread out in the latter.   Eyden (1923) maintains that the specific gravity of animals undergoes periodic changes, and that these are the primary factors concerned in vertical migrations.   Ritter and Davis (1903) found that Tornaria larvæ made daily migrations toward and away from the surface and that they were little influenced by light, but responded to changes in the viscosity of the surrounding medium.

Adaptations of Pelagic Animals.—Plankton animals, though derived from diverse groups, show a certain unity in the general nature of their adaptations to pelagic life. They are usually of small size and are thus in close contact with the surrounding ocean which varies little, thermally or chemically, and resembles the fluids in their bodies. Their specific gravity is near to that of the surrounding water. Weight is kept at a minimum by thin shells; heavier substances are buoyed up by bubbles of gas or drops of oil; sinking is impeded by horizontally disposed spines, bristles, or threads; the body may sink slowly because it is helmet- or parachute-shaped; small animals may adhere in masses which do not sink readily. Some pelagic animals, like medusæ, are gelatinous and watery, being really composed of a mixture of substances that have about the same density as sea water. Plankton animals, as a rule, are feeble swimmers, if they are able to swim at all. Often their peculiar shape makes it easy for them to move toward the surface and at the same time renders sinking difficult. In general, pelagic animals are rather simple in structure—life is easy and the environment is uniform. In depths above 500 meters, luminescence is quite characteristic, particularly among fishes. There are some luminescent invertebrates at greater depths. In the "twilight zone," where light is dim but not wholly absent, certain fishes and decapod crustaceans have large eyes and luminescent organs. Fishes that live in depths above 500 meters often have their eyes directed upward. Those living near the surface have rods and cones in the retinas of their eyes, but those at greater depths have only rods, and in this resemble certain nocturnal animals that live on land. The amount of pigment in pelagic animals, in general, increases with depth. Surface species are often transparent; those in the twilight zone, silvery; and those in deeper strata, heavily pigmented.

Nekton.—Many of the larger animals of the open ocean are gregarious (flying fishes, whales, dolphins, birds, etc.), though there are some exceptions. Flying fishes are admirably suited to life on the open sea and, though about sixty-five species are known, the group shows considerable uniformity in adaptation.

The length of these fishes varies from 8 to 18 inches.   Swimming in schools, they feed on a variety of foods and are always ready to rise from the surface to escape from predaceous enemies.   Whales are also adapted to a striking degree for life in the open sea. They lack hair; have the openings for the nostrils far back; have a heavy blanket of fat beneath the skin; their hind limbs are degenerate and the front limbs form flippers; the body has a fish-like form.   Some sea birds are not only expert swimmers and divers, but also have remarkable powers of flight and can endure hunger for long periods.   Gurney (1899) showed that an albatross could live for thirty-five days without food.

Food in Pelagic Province.—The food resources of the ocean depend on light for photosynthesis, which, of course, is limited to a stratum near the surface, and on nitrogenous compounds, which are more abundant near the shore and the surface.   Herdman (1909) affirms that, from an economic point of view, diatoms and copepods are the most important constituents of the plankton. Warming (1909) says:

It is of no slight interest to note that it is not, as in the land flora, starch, with its greater specific gravity, but oil which is the main product of assimilation in the floating plankton community.

Willey (1920) estimates the nutritive value of one copepod as equal to 125 peridinians, or 2500 diatoms, and points out that a newly hatched smelt has thirty times the volume of a copepod. Pütter (1907, 1923, 1924) has maintained that, because the plankton apparently does not supply enough food to maintain the growth of pelagic animals and because sea water does contain considerable amounts of dissolved nitrogenous substances, that marine animals must obtain nourishment from solutions in the water.   Murray and Hjort (1912) and Esterly (1916), who have recently reviewed the evidence for this view, believe that there is not yet enough to support it.   Tintinnidians, radiolarians, pteropods, many species of copepods, Dolidium, and salpas feed largely or exclusively on nannoplankton (Lohmann, 1911). Some of these animals have wonderful straining mechanisms, capable of removing the smallest organisms from the water. Salpas, appendicularians, and copepods feed on algæ.   Pelagic protozoans require an amount of food equal to half their own volume daily, and copepods need about one-tenth (Murray and Hjort, 1912).   Certain copepods feed by drawing a vortex containing diatoms and nannoplankton into their mouths (Esterly, 1916). Ctenophores are a considerable factor in the destruction of oyster larvæ (Nelson, 1923). Mayer (1918) reported that the largest jellyfishes were found in cold seas, where food was most abundant, and he noted various species as feeding upon other medusæ and fish eggs. Lebour (1923) has investigated the food and feeding habits of several plankton animals. She finds that medusæ commonly eat small fishes, which they sting with their trailing tentacles and slowly draw toward the mouth. She also notes that other medusæ prey upon crustaceans and that fishes are eaten by Pleurobrachia, Sagitta, and Tomopteris. Willey (1920) reviews the work on the food of herring at Kiel and states that each of 240,000 captured daily for three weeks contained an average of 10,000 copepods. Flying fishes feed on crustaceans, molluscs, and fishes; and are, in turn, devoured by dolphins, whales, sharks, bonitos, tunnies, albicores, etc. (Gill, 1905). The finback and humpback whales commonly feed on crustaceans (the latter also eating herring and other fishes), while the killer and sperm whales hunt fishes and larger animals. Penguins, gannets, and other divers prey on crustaceans and fishes. The pelagic birds, like the albatrosses and petrels, are in part scavengers and in part most expert fishers. With diatoms and peridinians at one end there is often a long series of steps through various predators to great end products like whales.

Numbers and Rates of Increase of Pelagic Animals.—The pelagic province teems with life, especially near the surface. Johnstone (1908) estimates that there are 457 diatoms and three peridinians per cubic centimeter, one copepod per cubic inch, and (by number of the eggs present) a total of 44,172,000 adult female cod in the North Sea. The productivity of most pelagic animals is great and among species of small size the rate of reproduction is rapid. Murray and Hjort (1912) state that the rate of overturn is more rapid for plants than for animals and affirm that the phytoplankton if unchecked would increase 30 per cent daily. The seasonal maxima of different species come at different times. Off California the appendicularians are abundant from October to April, but very scarce in summer (Essenberg, 1922). Perennial animals spawn at particular seasons, usually once a year, but if conditions are favorable, the productive periods of many invertebrates (amphipods, molluscs) may be prolonged. The production of eggs that float at or near the surface is common among many of the pelagic fishes and other animals. Crustacean, cœlenterate, echinoderm, and mollusc larvæ also often form a considerable part of the plankton, particularly near shore. Certain flying fishes frequenting the Sargasso Sea deposit their eggs in spheroidal masses enclosed in seaweed.

Zones in Pelagic Province.—The organisms of the open ocean are arranged in zones that show similar relations to depth and latitude, some of the species occurring in cool water at great depths in the tropics being found in shallow water near the poles. Though pelagic species in general have wide ranges, Dahl (1896, 1898) has emphasized the fact that many have very limited areas of distribution and appear only in certain localities. Temperature is a potent factor in the limitation of horizontal and vertical zones. Murray and Hjort (1912) divide pelagic organisms into four groups: (1) tropical, (2) subtropical, (3) boreal, and (4) arctic and antarctic. In northern pelagic regions plankton organisms attain their maxima below 2°C.; in the boreal, between 4 and 6°C. The border of the ice forms the limit of the arctic pelagic region. In the tropics there are more species of plankton organisms, but fewer individuals. Organisms secreting lime are more abundant in warm oceans. For example, pteropods in the tropics commonly have heavy calcareous shells, but toward the poles are naked or thin-shelled. The tropical ocean also contains many of what Murray (1895) calls "overgrown and more or less pædogenetic larvæ," while there are few larvæ in the cold pelagic regions. Murray and Hjort (1912) say:

It has been proposed to arrange the pelagic fauna in certain bathymetrical zones, distinguishing between those forms living in profuse light, or in the region of twilight, or in the dark abyssal waters, but such distinctions are arbitrary, because our knowledge of the bathymetrical distribution of animals is limited, because the laws of distribution are imperfectly understood (for instance, the effects of light), and because the bathymetrical occurrence of certain species is subject to great variation in different regions. We shall therefore dispense with many Latin and Greek terms employed to describe such groups of pelagic organisms, and simply use the term "bathypelagic" to denote those animals that live in the intermediate layers.

While the present writer recognizes the difficulties, he feels that progress will be made if definite formations, associations, and strata are established in the pelagic region, even though it may be necessary with more knowledge to change such groups radically.

Steuer (1910) tabulates the temperatures for various depths at three typical localities in different latitudes, and his figures are quoted in Table II. There is a gradual decrease from the surface to the bottom in tropical and temperate regions, but in cold seas the highest temperatures may be in intermediate strata.

TABLE II.—OCEAN TEMPERATURES IN DEGREES CENTIGRADE

Depth in meters	Cocos Islands	Cape of Good Hope	Antarctic
0	27.4	15.6	−1.0
50	27.1	....	−1.4
100	25.1	14.6	−1.1
200	20.8	....	1.4
300	13.2	....	1.7
500	9.2	9.5	
1000	5.5	4.6	1.6
1500	3.3	2.7	1.6
2000	....	....	0.6
4170	....	0.7	
4600	....	....	−0.5
5834	1.3		

The thermal stratification and the limitation of the penetration of light downward are chiefly responsible for the distribution of oceanic animals in more or less definite strata. In discussing the distribution of the solitary and aggregate forms of Salpa near San Diego, Michael (1918) said:

Solitary forms show an increasing preference, so to speak, as the temperature of the surface water increases from 16 to 20°C.; while aggregate forms show a similar preference as the temperature decreases . . . Contrary to the prevailing plankton concept, *Salpa democratica*, a typical plankton organism, controls to a significant extent its own distribution just as certainly as does any fish or other animal commonly included in the term "nekton."

Of course, other factors besides temperature and light vary at different depths. Off the coast of England Atkins (1922) has found a decrease of pH 0.03 from the surface to a depth of 70 meters.

FORMATION 1. SHOREWATER ANIMALS

The shorewater differs from that in the open ocean in that it is more variable in temperature and salinity; it contains relatively more of suspended and dissolved mineral and organic materials, among which silica and nitrogenous compounds are important. There is a greater variety and quantity of life in neritic than in proper pelagic formations. The characteristic plankton plants are diatoms, which are dependent on silica for the formation of their shells, and hence flourish near shore where the supply is most abundant.

ASSOCIATION *a*. ANIMALS ABOVE DEPTHS OF 150 METERS

The shallow waters alongshore are subject to the action of sunlight, tidal currents, seasonal changes in temperature, and reduction in salinity by rains and rivers. The flora and the fauna are varied and abundant. A considerable part of the life consists of the adult, young, and eggs of shore organisms, which at certain periods in their life histories have free-swimming stages.

Stratum 1. Animals Floating, or Attached to Floating Objects. The plankton of shorewaters often contains considerable numbers of larvæ of sponges, echinoderms, annelids, molluscs, crustaceans, and chordates as well as the medusæ and larvæ of hydroids and certain other adult animals. Such meroneritic representatives of shore animals are associated with holoneritic types such as chætognaths and copepods. A number of neritic plankton organisms are luminescent. Murray and Hjort (1912) say:

The peculiar agreement between size, form, and distribution of species and the occurrence of a certain specific gravity and viscosity of the water seems entirely absent in coast waters, where the specific gravity of the water is lower than in the ocean because the inflow of freshwater from continental rivers lowers the salinity. The viscosity, mainly dependent on temperature, should, as a rule, be similar to that of the open ocean outside. We would, therefore, expect to find, for instance, on the coast banks of Africa, similar oceanic forms, or the same faunistic characters on the whole, as in the Atlantic Ocean. On the contrary, we find that the fauna as well as the flora have entirely different features. For unicellular plants as well as for animals, the rule holds good that all forms are much larger than those of the open ocean. Among plants the minute coccolithophoridæ are replaced by peridineæ; instead of the minute Scopelidæ we meet with pelagic herrings and mackerels, animals of quite another size and character.

Schaeffer (1924) states that "the surface water of the Gulf Stream in the Tortugas region contains about 4.56 amœbas per 10,000 cubic centimeters of water."

Stratum 2. Swimming Animals.—There are swimming animals that frequent the shallow waters alongshore. Among these are certain fishes, like the herrings and mackerels mentioned in the last paragraph, seals, whales, gulls, terns, sharks, annelids. Some of these animals live in a variety of situations, like the sharks which range through many shore habitats and with their keen scent seek food on the bottom or near the surface; others, like the mackerels, are characteristic of the open shorewater.

ASSOCIATION *b*.   ANIMALS BETWEEN DEPTHS OF 150 AND 500 METERS

Wave movements extend to a depth of about 500 meters, where the bottom is marked by the edge of the continental shelf and the soft muddy deposits of deep ocean begin. In depths below 150 meters the amount of light in shorewaters is greatly decreased. Thus there is a "twilight zone" formed between the bottom above 500 meters and the warm surface stratum down to 150 meters. In the water in this zone live certain animals that are characteristic.

Stratum 1. Floating Animals.—The plankton below 150 meters is not as abundant as that in the zone above, doubtless on account of the smaller amount of light, but many neritic species are regularly found below the surface stratum. Some of the plankton organisms migrate to, or toward the surface at night and some do not. Esterly (1914) says:

If the behavior of the ctenophore *Pleurobrachia bachei* is compared with that of the chætognath *Sagitta bipunctata* or of the copepod *Calanus finmarchicus*, the most striking difference is in the exceeding rarity of the ctenophore in subsurface hauls. The chætognath named and the copepods in general appear to have well-defined levels below the surface (centers of migration), at which they are more abundant than at the surface, at certain times, and from which they move to or toward the surface at regular intervals during the twenty-four hours. There is no evidence at hand that ctenophores perform these depth migrations.

In a later paper Esterly (1914) also says:

The center of the subsurface region where *Euphausia* is more abundant by day, as shown by winter hauls, appears to be at 300 meters, while *Nyctiphanes* seem to center at 150 meters during the day.

Stratum 2. Swimming Animals.—Like the plankton many nekton organisms migrate toward the surface at night. Murray and Hjort (1912) say:

Recently it has proved possible to trawl successfully for herring along the sea bottom, but only during the daytime. All sailors can tell us that at night numbers of animals gather in the surface waters, which are never seen there in the daytime. While fishing with long lines on the Faroe banks our lines were set for cod along the bottom in about 200 fathoms; the lines were hauled at night and the stomachs of the cod contained squids, which had been eaten during the day, while at night numerous squids were seen at the surface darting into the glare of our electric lamp hanging over the side.

FORMATION 2. OCEANIC ANIMALS

The pelagic flora and fauna consist in part of the same species that occur in the neritic biota, but there are also true open-sea species. There are relatively fewer spore-forming species of plants, and peridinians in part replace diatoms. The free-swimming larvæ of shore animals are, of course, largely or entirely absent. Oceanic animals do not produce swimming larvæ to such an extent as those alongshore.

ASSOCIATION *a*. PELAGIC ANIMALS ABOVE DEPTHS OF 150 METERS

A clearly defined surface stratum in the open ocean is largely confined to a belt that extends on each side of the equator and is poorly defined or absent in cold seas. In this association are certain peculiar resident animals, such as pteropods with heavy calcareous shells, and temporary residents, such as the young stages of fishes which as adults live at deeper levels.

Stratum 1. Floating Animals.—The plankton organisms at the open ocean are typically blue, green, or transparent. Even the blood of young eels is colorless. Haecker (1908) arranged pelagic radiolarians into four zones: (1) an upper Acanthometra layer; (2) a Challengeria layer, 50 to 400 meters; (3) a Pandora layer, 400 to 1000 meters; and (4) an abyssal layer. Those in the first group have skeletons of acanthin and are characteristic of warm oceans; those in the others have siliceous skeletons and are usually found in cold water. Among characteristic animals in this stratum are siphonophores, ctenophores, certain copepods "with wonderful feather or fan-shaped attachments which greatly enlarge the surface of the animals and facilitate their floating," ostracods, amphipods, pteropods, salpas, and appendicularians. The greatest quantity of life is usually not at the surface but at a depth of about 50 meters.

Stratum 2. Swimming Animals.—Many of the nekton animals of the surface layer, like their smaller and feebler associates, are often transparent, silvery green, or blue. Swimming fishes are perhaps as widely distributed and as representative as any animals in this stratum. True pelagic birds, like the albatross, do not usually go near land except to breed. Whales are confined to the upper layer of the ocean, none of them being able to dive deeper than 100 meters or remain under water longer than about twenty minutes (Parker, 1922).

ASSOCIATION *b*. ANIMALS LIVING BETWEEN DEPTHS OF 150 AND 1500 METERS

This region is the "twilight zone" of the open ocean, where there are unusual specializations for light production and extravagantly developed eyes. With some exceptions luminescence and the size of eyes among decapod crustaceans and vertebrates reach their greatest development at about 500 meters. Up to depths of 300 meters the laterally compressed Sternoptychidæ with silvery sides and brownish backs are characteristic fishes, but below 500 meters the fishes are usually black and the crustaceans red. "The occurrence of dark colors coincides with the region where the intensity of sunlight is greatly diminished" (Murray and Hjort, 1912).

Stratum 1. Floating Animals.—There are a number of plankton animals that are rather definitely limited to the twilight zone in their distribution. Among the radiolarians *Aulographis pandora* ranges from 400 to 1000 meters

. . . and is considered specially characteristic of these depths. The Tuscaroridæ are genuine deep-sea forms, having a bottle-shaped shell provided with large strong spikes arranged in rings around the main axis. In hauls with closing nets they have never been taken in less than 400 meters of water; some species, for instance *Tuscaretta tubulosa*, occur in all oceans.

Sometimes more species of copepods are to be found in the twilight zone than near the surface. The gigantic-eyed amphipod, *Cytosoma neptuni*, occurs at depths exceeding 500 meters. Three species of pteropods have been found only between depths of 500 and 1500 meters (*Peraclis diversa, Limacina helicoides, Clio falcata*).

Stratum 2. Swimming Animals.—Many nekton animals that are characteristic of the surface do not invade the twilight zones (whales, flying fishes, etc.). There are, on the other hand, a number of fishes that never enter the surface stratum, though some of the black species from the twilight zone move to the surface at night. Murray and Hjort (1912) captured 286 individuals of the peculiar fish, *Argyropelecus hemigymnus*. They say:

The bulk occurred at depths between 150 and 500 meters; no individuals were caught above 150 meters, and only about 7 per cent were taken at depths lower than 500 meters . . . It seems, accordingly, that a preponderating majority of the individuals of this species are very strictly limited to an intermediate layer situated at a depth of about 300 meters. A close investigation showed that the individuals captured at 150 meters were all caught at night.

Again, in speaking of their work off the Azores, Murray and Hjort remark:

These catches may be classified into three main regions: (1) a region extending downward from about 500 meters characterized by the occurrence of *Cyclothone* and various black or dark-colored fishes, and of many peculiar invertebrates, red prawns being prominent; (2) a region ranging between 150 and 1500 meters, characterized by a peculiar community of silvery or grayish fishes, belonging to the families Sternoptychidæ and Stomiatidæ; and (3) the surface region comprising the upper 150 meters, characterized by transparent or blue-colored animals and juvenile forms, especially the members of the large family Scopelidæ.

ASSOCIATION *c*. PELAGIC ANIMALS LIVING BELOW DEPTHS OF
1500 METERS

Below depths of 1500 meters animals are wholly dependent for food on the strata above, and therefore devour plankton that settles down or feed upon other bathypelagic animals. There is a progressive decrease in the number of animals present at increasing depths. Murray and Hjort (1912) combine all the strata below 500 meters into a single bathypelagic region, and there is much in favor of their point of view. Many of the species that range below 1500 meters are also found above it; the typically black fishes and red crustaceans begin at 500 meters. The fauna of the present writer's bathypelagic stratum consists mostly of types of animals that range from 500 meters to depths greater than 1500 meters, but it seems reasonable to separate those that are able to live in the aphotic zone. The temperature of the ocean below 1500 meters is practically uniform to the greatest depths. The young stages of many bathypelagic animals are often found at higher levels.

Stratum 1. Floating Animals.—Foraminifera are most abundant in the surface waters of the tropics and decrease with depth or toward the poles, but a number of species of radiolarians extend to the deepest parts of the ocean. In regard to the latter Murray and Hjort (1912) say:

They occur in all oceans, but sometimes their distribution is very peculiar, for some species live only in abyssal depths under the equator, others at both poles, others only in Antarctic waters; some species live in the surface waters, others between 50 and 400 meters, others between 400 and 1000 meters, others again between 1500 and 5000 meters.

Some range from the surface to depths of 5000 meters. The Tuscaroridæ and large Challengeridæ are particularly characteristic of the deep sea. Copepods and ostracods occur in the bathypelagic zone. The "Challenger" collected fifty-two species of ostracods below 500 fathoms, nineteen below 1500 fathoms, and eight below 2000 fathoms. Many of these were doubtless associated with the bottom and do not represent true pelagic types. This is true of many animals that have been collected from great depths and the plankton of the deep sea is, therefore, less well known than that of any other region. The "Challenger" collected species of schizopods at various depths as follows: 32 to 300 fathoms, six; 300 to 1000 fathoms, four; 1000 to 2000 fathoms, eleven; below 2000 fathoms, four.

Stratum 2. Swimming Animals.—Hjort (Murray and Hjort, 1912) states that the commonest fishes in the deep pelagic regions are two species of the genus Cyclothone. He says:

We get the result that there were nine times more individuals in the intermediate layer from 1350 meters up to 450 meters than below 1500 meters . . . It may be that there is a layer at the lowest depths where there are no individuals and I, for my part at any rate, cannot help believing that the profoundest deep is far more poorly supplied than the intermediate layer.

Hjort also says:

The smaller and younger individuals live . . . higher up in the water layers than the majority of the largest and oldest individuals . . . Notostomus and several fishes and squids have been taken only in the deepest hauls at 1500 or 2000 meters.

PROVINCE C. BOTTOM ANIMALS

The animals that live on the bottom of the ocean beyond the littoral province and below the photic zone have a remarkably stable environment. They live on or in soft ooze, in cold water and darkness, beyond the limits of the action of waves or shore currents. At great depths the pressure becomes enormous. There is relatively more carbon dioxide and less available lime as depth increases, but there is sufficient oxygen to

TABLE III.—AREA OF SEA BOTTOM OF VARIOUS DEPTHS

Depth in fathoms	Estimated area, English square miles	Percentage of ocean floor
0–1,000	22,000,000	16
1,000–2,000	27,000,000	19
2,000–3,000	81,000,000	58
3,000–4,000	9,800,000	7
4,000–5,000	195,000	
Over 5,000	5,000	

support life at all depths, except in peculiar localities like the Black Sea. Depending on the turbidity of the water, there is no light below 500 to 1500 meters except that from organisms. Bottom deposits are important in determining the character of the fauna, and in sheltered situations deep-sea communities may reach higher levels. In terrigenous deposits there is quartz, but lime, iron, manganese, magnesia, and the alkalies seem in the past to have accumulated in the ocean at the expense of the land, and heavier materials are characteristic of greater depths. Beyond the continental shelves and slopes, the bottom of the ocean for the most part is a flat plain with very gentle slopes.

Murray (1914) summarizes the areas of various depths as in Table III. Eighty-four per cent is deeper than 1000 fathoms, but only 7 per cent is below 3000 fathoms. The Arctic Ocean is shallower than the Antarctic and has a different type of bottom ooze. Johnstone (1908, p. 304) quotes the estimates of Murray and Irvine concerning the total areas of various ocean floor deposits as in Table IV.

TABLE IV.—TYPES AND EXTENTS OF MARINE BOTTOM DEPOSITS

Deposits	Area, square miles	Per cent	Mean depth, fathoms	Mean percentage of CaCO₃
Terrigenous:				
Coral sands and muds.......	3,219,800	2	710	86.41
Others....................	27,899,300	19	1,016	19.20
Oceanic:				
Pteropod ooze.............	887,100	..	1,118	79.26
Globigerina ooze...........	47,752,500	34	1,996	64.53
Diatom ooze...............	10,420,600	7	1,477	22.96
Radiolarian ooze...........	2,790,400	2	2,894	4.01
Red clay..................	50,289,600	35	2,727	6.70

Nearly seven-tenths of the ocean bottom is covered with Globigerina ooze or red clay; only about a fifth is covered by terrigenous sediments.

Distribution of Bottom Animals.—Animals are found at all depths and on all types of bottom deposits, though the density of the population decreases progressively at greater depths. The abyssal plain is scantily populated, and beyond 1000 fathoms the decrease in numbers is very rapid. Both the pelagic and demersal regions in the deeper parts of the ocean are rather barren. Johnstone (1908) estimates that for each edible fish in the North Sea there is an area of about 60 square meters, and that there are, on average bottoms, about twenty to two-hundred animals, ranging in size from that of amphipods to fishes, on each square meter. In mussel beds in shallow water as many as 16,000 molluscs per square foot have been found.

Characteristic Bottom Animals in Deep Water.—The fauna of the ooze bottoms does not consist of archaic types, but apparently has been for the most part derived from other marine provinces in comparatively recent times. The size of some bottom animals is unusual: Certain crabs spread over an area 11 feet in diameter; pycnogonids attain great size; hydroids grow to a length of 8 feet; the isopod, Bathynomus, reaches a length of 9 inches. Many animals like sponges, cœlenterates, crinoids, and ascidians have stalks which enable them to lift their feeding organs above the ooze. There is an ooze-inhabiting medusa that walks over the bottom by means of its tentacles, which serve as stilts and are kept from sinking into the ooze by discs at their tips. This species lacks the marginal sense organs for equilibration that are characteristic of pelagic medusæ. The bodies of crustaceans are provided with spines, long antennæ, and very long legs, which may be fringed with stiff setæ or spines. Such structures as the last enable crustaceans to walk on the soft mud bottom. Deep-water crustaceans are usually red, but other invertebrates are commonly transparent, blue, or violet. The deep-water fishes beyond the littoral region are, of course, either bathypelagic or demersal. They may be with or without eyes. They are usually slender, black (often even including the mouth, peritoneum, etc.), and have small gill lamellæ. Some animals, like barnacles, and certain hydroids that depend on hard bottoms, are found at considerable depths in isolated situations if suitable objects for attachment are present. Generally, animals frequenting soft bottoms produce a few large eggs, but a few produce many small eggs.

Some protozoans are truly abysmal. Radiolarians are small with massive skeletons. Among the sponges there are none with calcareous spicules at great depths and even those with siliceous skeletons are not common. Cœlenterates are represented by hydroids, anemones, and even corals, which do not form reefs. Sea-pens are characteristic forms. Among echinoderms, the crinoids are typical soft-bottom animals. Their stalks may reach a length of 50 to 70 feet. The echinoids are of interest because those in the deeper parts of the ocean resemble Cretaceous genera and those in shallower waters are related to more modern types. Spatangoids are quite characteristic and often occur in great numbers. The asteroids are much like those in the Littoral Province. Many holothurians are adapted to muddy bottoms and one group of them, Elasipoda, are abysmal. Worms and worm-like animals are well represented in shallower waters and a few even occur in red clay at great depths. Phoronis is found at depths between 4 and 200 fathoms. Rhabdopleura, Cephalodiscus, gephyreans, serpulids, and terebellids are soft-bottom forms. Those that occur at great depths, of course, do not secrete lime, but live in leathery tubes. The abysmal Errantia are generally eyeless. Brachiopods are not markedly different from littoral types. Molluscs that range to considerable depths have thin shells and lack pigment. There are few species of clams or snails that are abysmal. The cephalopods that live at great depths are not peculiar. The arthropods are well represented in the abyssal region. There are few entomostracans or amphipods, but some of the latter are totally blind. There are several characteristic isopods, and even some abyssal barnacles. The fishes, though largely teleosts, and hence of the most modern types, perhaps show as characteristic modifications for life in the deep sea as any group. The dark hues, attenuated forms, barbels, fin filaments, and large mouths with long irregular teeth make them unique. Anglers are well represented in the bottom fauna and some species have luminescent lures.

Appellöf states that demersal shrimps and amphipods creep almost as much as they swim. Currents are important in distributing such animals and the pelagic larvæ of others, like those of holothurians, that do not swim at all. Currents also bring food to bottom animals and in places sweep fine deposits away, so that sedentary animals may find firm resting places. The distribution of bottom animals is, of course, "much affected by the character of the sea floor, since whole groups of animals are limited by their structure or mode of living to some particular kind of bottom." This is particularly true of mussels, worms, and echinoderms. Some species of sponges and corals, "belonging to groups most of whose members are attached and therefore confined to rocky bottom, have developed special organs in the way of root-like outgrowths by means of which they adhere to soft bottom and can therefore rest there normally." Sea-pens and crinoids are held above the ooze by their stalks. In the Atlantic most of the bottom animals are on the terrigenous deposits and Globigerina ooze, but a few are found on red clay. In their discussion of demersal fishes, Murray and Hjort (1912) state that:

While the fishes of the continental shelf all live on terrigenous deposits, like blue mud, the Michael Sars results prove that, in the Eastern Atlantic at any rate, *most of the fauna of continental slope live on Globi-*

gerina ooze . . . The results show in any case that the Globigerina ooze in depths of 550 to 1000 fathoms may be a rich ground for animal life . . . At Station 53 south of the Azores, 2615 to 2865 meters, the trawl captured in one haul, besides 39 fishes, about 500 holothurians, and the animals that are characteristic of calcareous oozes are therefore not identical with those that are found on the siliceous, radiolarian, and diatom oozes of the coldest polar seas.

Limits of Abyssal and Shallow-water Animals.—The upper limit of the abyssal region is not clearly defined. Appellöf (Murray and Hjort, 1912) says:

The upper limit certainly presents great difficulties, but I believe that a great many of the forms which characterize the archibenthal belt [steep continental slopes] do not as a rule extend into depths less than 800 meters, though it is possible that certain forms may be met with at 600 meters. We have not yet acquired sufficient knowledge of the factors regulating vertical distribution to be able to divide the different parts of the Atlantic into vertical zones, and a division of this kind will, I fancy, always be more or less a matter of personal opinion. Besides it is undeniable that forms which properly belong to the abyssal fauna [that on the comparatively level, deep, ocean floor] may find their way to the lower parts of the archibenthal zone, and that archibenthal forms may go down into the abyssal region, while, given favorable conditions, certain littoral and sublittoral forms may descend below the upper limits of the archibenthal belt. In any case there is no clearly defined boundary between the archibenthal and abyssal areas.

The associations and strata that the present writer lists on page 16 are not to be taken as rigid, fixed areas, but as over-lapping and variable in extent. Notwithstanding this, there are species that are primarily abyssal and others that are characteristic of intermediate strata. Murray (1914) places the change to benthos at 400 to 500 fathoms.

Food of Bottom Animals.—Many bottom animals eat ooze or catch falling organisms or organic particles that settle down from above. One species of ooze-eating crustacean has a long, coiled intestine—a rare peculiarity among arthropods (Calman, 1911). There is a great feeding ground at the "mud line," just beyond the edge of the continental shelf, where shore currents cease to stir up the sediments. Below depths of 500 (in some cases 1500) meters there are no plants that carry on photosynthesis and organic food must, therefore, have its origin near the surface. Schizomycetes are prevalent at depths of 800 to 1100 meters (Warming, 1909) and change ammonia into nitrates or nitrites, at great depths little lime is available. The bones of fishes and the shells of molluscs and crustaceans are accordingly lacking in calcareous materials. Clemens (1921) described the food of the muttonfish as consisting of molluscs, echinoderms, and crustaceans. In summer this species feed in bays and estuaries, but from October to May forages over the ocean bottom. Blegvad (1916) has made an extensive study of the food relations of various animals in the ocean near Denmark and certain of his findings are presented in Fig. 1. Both he and Petersen (1918) emphasize the importance of organic ooze as

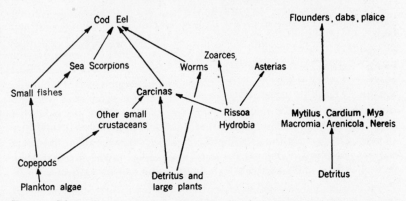

FIG. 1.—Blegvad's arrangement of certain animals on the Danish Coast according to food relations.

a source of food for marine animals. Being interested in the productiveness of the ocean, they also point out that small fishes and other animals that are not eaten by man, or his food fishes, are to be classified as injurious because they occupy space and use materials that might otherwise furnish human food.

Zonation of Bottom Animals.—In her report on certain groups of demersal annelids from the Pacific, Essenberg (1918) says:

The polynoids are divisible into littoral, sublittoral, and abyssal species according to their bathymetrical distribution . . . The facts that certain species are restricted to definite life zones and to definite ranges of temperatures, that the same species occurring in widely separated areas occur in depths of similar temperatures, and that boreal species occur in temperate and subtropical zones as deep-water species seem to point to the conclusion that temperature is the chief factor in determining distribution . . . The greatest number of polynoids are found in the littoral zones where food is more abundant . . . The deep-water species differ considerably from the littoral species, and certain characteristics, such as thin cuticle, the smaller size, the delicate elytra and eyeless condition of many abyssal species point to the conclusion that the latter have undergone a degeneration and physical specialization which make them fit for that particular environment only . . . The great uniformity of littoral species and the great diversity of abyssal genera and species lead to the conclusion that the littoral zone is the center of origin, or the center of dispersal of polynoids, and that species migrate or are driven to abyssal areas where they undergo great specialization and partial degeneration.

Murray and Hjort (1912), Galtsoff (1924), and others have noted a stratification, which is chiefly dependent on temperature, in the arrangement of demersal fishes. Johnstone (1908) points out that "deep-sea" fishing is largely above the 200-meter line, and Meek (1916) notes that the young of demersal, as well as those of pelagic fishes, commonly occur at higher levels than adults. Though most bottom animals are confined to rather definite strata, there are some which have wide ranges. Hickson (1894) mentions a pycnogonid that occurs from low-tide mark to a depth of 2225 fathoms. Shelford (1918) showed that animals brought up from a depth of 2 fathoms were twice or thrice as resistant to lowered salinity and increased temperature as those of the same species from a depth of 75 fathoms, but the latter were more resistant to variations in acidity or alkalinity. On the west coasts of South America and Africa the upwelling of cold currents more or less obliterates stratification, and typically deep-water animals occur at higher levels.

FORMATION 1. BOTTOM ANIMALS ON CONTINENTAL
SHELVES

The Norwegian (Murray and Hjort, 1912) and Danish (Petersen, 1918; Blegvad, 1916) biologists have made comprehensive and detailed studies of the life on the sea bottom along their shores, and their writings present the best account of animals and their relations. The continental shelf, of course, offers a variety of environmental conditions and thus differs from the ocean beyond the action of shore currents and light where the bottom and temperature are very uniform. A variety of strata, consocies, and mores are accordingly present.

ASSOCIATION *a*. ANIMALS ON TERRIGENOUS DEPOSITS

Petersen (1918) lists nine communities that are characteristic of the bottoms on the continental shelf and in littoral regions near Denmark as follows: (1) Macoma or Baltic community, which may be subdivided according to the type of bottom (Mytilus, Mysis, Mya, and Littorina occurring on sand; the plant belt having these types and also an "epifauna" of other species; muddy areas being characterized by eels and polychætes); (2) Abra community in deeper water, consisting largely of clams and sea-urchins that are not eaten by fishes; (3) Venus community on open sandy coasts in depths of 8 to 38 meters; (4) Echimocardium-Filiformis community at intermediate depths, 38 to 41 meters; (5) Brissopsis-Chrajei community, in deep parts of the Kattegat up to 700 meters; (6) Brissopsis-Sarsii community, in deep parts of the Skagerak; (7) Amphilepsis-Pecten community, in deepest parts of the Skagerak; (8) Haploops community, on soft clay bottoms where there may be 3500 worm tubes per square meter; (9) deep Venus community. It will be seen that Petersen's groups are chiefly characterized by particular clams and worms which are practically non-motile, and therefore serve as good indicators of particular conditions.

Many littoral animals are distributed over the floor of the ocean far below the strictly littoral strata and these constitute the greater part of the animals on terrigenous deposits.

Stratum 1. Burrowing and Sessile Animals.—The burrowers in this stratum are mostly clams, sea-urchins (particularly the bilateral types), and annelids. The food of these consists chiefly of mud and living or dead plankton. The same is true of the comparatively few animals, such as barnacles and hydroids, that are attached to the hard parts of other animals or to the rather infrequent hard objects, such as sharks' teeth and pebbles, that rest on the bottom.

Stratum 2. Swimming and Crawling Animals.—Over the surface crawl a few snails and crabs; amphipods swim or crawl about. These feed upon ooze or the larger portions of dead plants or animals. Nautiloids and predaceous fishes like the cod and eel swim about and eat the invertebrates. As in the pelagic region, there is a transition in color and pattern among bottom animals. In littoral habitats occur many colors and patterns, but at greater depths monotones of dull hue prevail.

Luminescence also reaches its maximum at a depth of about 300 meters and decreases toward the surface or the abyss.

ASSOCIATION *b*. ANIMALS ON CALCAREOUS OOZES

Pteropod ooze occurs in depths of less than 3000 meters and Globigerina ooze ranges from 3000 to 5000 meters. Just beyond the edge of the continental shelf, where the slope into deep water begins, is the mud line, at a depth of about 500 meters. Here soft ooze replaces the coarser sediments that are characteristic of shallower water. In this stratum large amounts of organic materials from higher levels accumulate on the bottom and many animals feed on them. Clark (1908) points out that the largest crinoids occur at depths between 100 and 600 fathoms, where most dead microscopic food falls. Murray (1895) points out that a greater variety of species occurs on terrigenous deposits, but more individuals per unit area may occur along the mud line. Below the mud line at about 3000 meters the deep-sea deposits begin with Globigerina ooze. Murray states that 2050 species of animals had been captured between depths of 500 and 3000 meters up to the year 1895.

The burrowing and sessile animals (Stratum 1) are similar to those in the zone above, as are their relationships to predaceous species and the scavengers that swim or crawl (Stratum 2).

FORMATION 2. ABYSSAL ANIMALS

The soft oozes in the deeper parts of the ocean support a considerable variety of animals, but the number per unit of area is always small. Though a number of species have wide ranges, there are also many that are apparently restricted to particular localities. In temperate seas arctic types begin to predominate at depths of about 800 to 1000 meters and the abyssal animals are largely cold-water animals. But calcareous deposits do not occur in the coldest seas and though Globigerina ooze extends to considerable depths, it is replaced by deposits that are composed chiefly of silica or clay below 5000 fathoms.

The fauna of this deepest region is still imperfectly known because comparatively few dredge hauls have been made and in collecting with a dredge there is always some doubt as to whether animals that can swim were actually captured near the bottom or at some intermediate point on the long journey from and to the surface. Such types as worms, molluscs, holothurians, and starfishes are undoubtedly demersal but the habitats of fishes or crustaceans is often uncertain. Murray and Hjort (1912), however, list twenty-one species of fishes, collected before their expedition in the "Michael Sars," that apparently came from the bottom at depths of more than 2000 fathoms, but these species were represented by only thirty-five individuals, or an average of somewhat less than two each.

Association *a*. Animals on Calcareous Oozes

Many invertebrates frequent calcareous bottoms in the abyssal plain beyond the continental slopes. Apellöf (Murray and Hjort, 1912) sets the limits of the archibenthal fauna at about 2000 meters. He found that many of the abyssal species that occurred off the coasts of Africa and Europe were not taken off the American coasts and that common species on the west of the ocean were often absent on the east. He therefore concludes that many of the invertebrates do not have wide geographic ranges, and this was particularly true of those that live on Globigerina ooze. Three bilaterally symmetrical holothurians (*Deima fastosum, Peniagone wyvillii, Oneirophanta* sp.), a starfish (*Freyella sexradiata*), and a sea-urchin (*Salenia hastigera*) are, however, cited by Apellöf as examples of true abyssal species.

The abyssal fauna living on calcareous oozes consists of protozoans, sponges, medusæ, anthozoans (the stalked sea pens being characteristic), archaic crinoids and echinoids, peculiar starfishes and holothurians, brachiopods, sipunculids, annelids (some eyeless), molluscs, amphipods, isopods, barnacles, schizopods, decapods, pycnogonids, ascidians, and fishes. The large-eyed, big-mouthed, acuminate-tailed fishes of the genus Macrurus apparently dominate the abyssal plain.

Murray and Hjort say:

If we fix the boundary of the abyssal plain at the 2000-fathom line, we may consider the area between the 2000- and the 1500- fathom lines as an intermediate zone between the abyssal plain and the continental slope . . . The "Michael Sars" made three hauls with the trawl in such depths, which, compared with our results on the abyssal plain, are very interesting, and invite inspection of their details:

Station 35. South of the Canaries, 1424 fathoms (2603 meters). Trawl dragged two hours. Result of haul: many siliceous sponges (including *Hyalonema*), hundreds of holothurians, large prawns (Benthesicymus, n. sp.), 18 bottom fish (9 Macrurids, 1 *Bathysaurus*, 2 *Holosauropsis*, 5 *Alepocephalus*, 1 *Hariotta*).

Station 53. South of the Azores, 1430 to 1570 fathoms (2615 to 2865 meters). Trawl dragged three or four hours. Result of haul: 2 large and many small sponges, 3 mussels, 5 cirripeds (*Scalpellum*), 30 large prawns (*Aristeopsis*), 15 hermit crabs, 5 *Pentacheles*, 1 large white decapod (*Mundopsis*, n. sp.), 500 holothurians, 39 bottom fishes (17 *Macrurus*, 5 *Halosauropsis*, 2 *Benthosaurus*, 2 *Bathysaurus*, 2 *Bathypterosis*, 6 *Alepocephalus*, 5 *Synaphobranchus*).

Station 88. North of the Azores, 1700 fathoms (3120 meters). Result of haul: a great number of holothurians, sea-urchins, starfish, ophiuroids, some crustaceans (*Polycheles*, *Munidopsis*, *Parapagurus*), 21 bottom fishes (17 *Macrurus*, 1 *Bathysaurus*, 3 *Histiobranchus*).

We thus see that *it is not terrigenous deposits alone which harbor an abundant bottom fauna;* in fact, on true pelagic deposits, like Globigerina ooze, we may have the conditions necessary for abundant life.

The suitability of a deposit does not depend on the amount of calcium present, but "the important item is the *organic substance* contained in the deposits, which fertilizes the surface layers."

Associations *b* and *c*. Animals on Siliceous Oozes and Red Clays

These associations are apparently not unlike those that occur on calcareous oozes. They are, of course, characteristic of deep and cold oceans and are not so well known as those in regions that are more densely populated and readily accessible.

CHAPTER VI

FRESHWATER ANIMALS

The total area of freshwater habitats on the earth is very small compared with that of the ocean or land. Animals living in lakes, ponds, streams, pools, or swamps are, accordingly, more isolated and hence often have less chance to avoid unfavorable conditions by migrating. The salt content and the osmotic pressure in freshwater are variable and, of course, much less than those of the ocean. The amount of salts averages about 0.18 per cent. In rain water there are 30 to 40 parts of solutes per million; drainage water contains from 50 to 230; springs, 60 to 350; rivers, 120 to 350; ocean, 33,000 to 37,370. Ocean salt is made up largely of sodium chloride and the salts in freshwater are mostly carbonates. Freshwater is much more variable than the ocean and its inhabitants are, therefore, generally subject to greater fluctuations in temperature, dissolved gases, turbidity, light, and food. Tides are very feeble or absent and currents are, therefore, more important because they tend to overcome thermal stratification and the variation in gases that is associated with it. All bodies of water that are in contact with the atmosphere carry on a respiratory exchange with it and the amount and nature of the gases exchanged vary with annual cycles and other fluctuating conditions. Ground waters are usually favorable for the growth of diatoms because they contain much carbon dioxide. The presence or absence of carbon dioxide also affects the reaction and concentration of ions. The clearness of water determines the depth to which light can penetrate and at which photosynthesis can take place. Conditions for penetration will, of course, be better in a clear lake than in a turbid stream. Water of precipitation is clear and in a sense reasonably pure. It washes minerals and other substances into bodies of freshwater where they are arrested and perhaps appropriated, digested, and assimilated by plants or animals and thus make continual contributions to the life in such situations. The total volume of a body of freshwater and its volume in

183

relation to its area are important. In a general way the size of
animals is related to the extent of the basins they inhabit. The
largest fishes are usually found in the largest streams and lakes.
A deep lake with a very limited surface area will show pronounced thermal stratification, but in a shallow lake such a condition is prevented by continual circulation through the action
of winds.

Origin of Freshwater Animals.—Evidence from fossils indicates that the animals that lived first on the earth were largely or
wholly marine and that land and freshwater habitats have been
populated by repeated invasions from the ocean. This view is
further supported by the fact that the distribution of certain
groups living today is entirely confined to the ocean, and by
the similarity that the composition of the blood of land and
freshwater animals bears to sea water. Hesse (1920) states
that no great groups of animals have arisen except in the ocean,
but Barrell (1916) claimed that fishes originated in freshwater
and thought it possible that insects invaded land from freshwater, although there seems to be no doubt that arthropods arose
first in the ocean. Pelseneer (1906) has reviewed evidence which
indicates that marine animals are at present becoming adjusted
to freshwater, especially along the coast of southeastern Asia,
where heavy rains considerably dilute the ocean. Animals have
apparently taken up life in freshwater by slowly migrating up
rivers, by being marooned in bays that were cut off from the sea
and in which the water gradually became fresh, and by movements from land habitats. Murray (1895) suggests that freshwater animals have been derived from those of the marine
"mud line," because free-swimming larvæ are rare in both situations. It is certain that the glaciated regions in the northern
hemisphere were free from aquatic life and have been repopulated since the ice retreated. The deep-water animals in the
lakes in such regions have apparently been derived from the
local fauna in each case, and there is no general relationship
even between those in various parts of the same continent. The
invasion of freshwater habitats apparently has been through
spreading and adjustment to local conditions.

In going from the ocean to freshwater there is a marked change
in salinity and animals making such a change must be more or less
euryhaline. The living membranes of some animals will not
permit them to invade freshwater, but other animals (certain

species of Fundulus, Sesarma, etc.) can swim directly from the
ocean into rivers without apparent injury.   Animals of the latter
group are able to maintain the liquids within their bodies as they
were in the ocean, or the liquids become diluted without injuring
them.   The body liquids in Fundulus do not change markedly
when the minnow invades freshwater, but the salts in blood of
crabs may vary from 1.5 to 3.5 per cent.   Animals that have
migrated from the land into freshwater may continue to breathe
air and though living "in" water are not really "of" it; others
profoundly modify their methods of respiration.   Aquatic insects
usually breathe through tracheæ like their land ancestors, but
many, particularly during larval stages, have acquired tracheal
or blood gills and respire directly from water.   In freshwater
there is less competition between varied types and, according to
Darwin (1859), new forms are produced and exterminated more
slowly.   Some types of animals have never been able to establish
themselves in freshwater but species that have done so have in
some cases been able to persist when their relatives that remained
in the ocean became extinct.   Hesse (1920) cites the hydra,
certain crabs and ganoids, and dipnoans as primitive representatives of groups that have died out completely, except for those
that have found a refuge in freshwater habitats.

Freshwater faunas are, in general, distinguished by their lack
of variety when compared with those of land or sea.   No phylum
is confined to freshwater; in fact, the only great groups that are
so limited are the Amphibia and Dipnoi.   Semper (1881) lists
many genera, families, and some orders that are restricted to
freshwater.   Heliozoa, ctenophores, echinoderms, and brachiopods are wholly absent; sponges, bryozoans, and cœlenterates
are represented by only a few species.   The immature stages of
certain insects (damsel- and dragon-flies, stone-flies, may-flies,
caddis-flies) are largely or wholly confined to freshwater.   These
show considerable specialization for various habitats and apparently have long been associated with them.   Caddis-fly larvæ
commonly live in cases, which they attach to objects or carry
about according to the swiftness of the currents in the surrounding water.   Odonate nymphs have rectal or caudal gills and show
a high degree of adjustment to particular habitats—burrowing,
clinging to plants, etc.   Such types have perhaps been aquatic
throughout their phylogenetic development.   Water-bugs, on

the other hand, apparently are recent immigrants into aquatic habitats, for they breathe air and are largely carnivorous.

Adaptations of Freshwater Organisms.—Freshwater plants and animals have certain characteristics which adapt them to the habitats in which they live. The roots of freshwater plants, in general, appear to serve more as holdfasts than extractors of nourishment, though Pond (1905) holds that they may play an important rôle in imbibition. Water-carrying tubes, mechanical tissues, and secondary growth in thickness are absent or poorly developed; large air spaces and thin epidermis are characteristic and there is often provision for the excretion of water; stomata are generally absent from submerged parts; chlorophyll is usually near the surface of plants, where it can best receive the comparatively weak light (Warming, 1909). Many freshwater plants are perennials and vegetative propagation by buds, rhizomes, bulbs, and other means is common. Among freshwater animals there is a rather general absence of free-swimming larval stages and a general tendency to the formation of considerable amounts of yolk in eggs. There is also a prevalence among many types of special adaptations that enable animals to survive desiccation, foul water, extreme temperatures, or other unfavorable environmental fluctuations—the ephippia of cladocerans; the "winter" eggs of cladocerans, rotifers, and rhabdocoels; the gemmules and statoblasts of sponges and bryozoans; the cysts of copepods, annelids, and protozoans. There are also membranes that prevent the excessive absorption of water or the undue loss of salts from the body fluids. In many cases there are special structures for the elimination of water—freshwater protozoans possess contractile vacuoles, which are absent in marine representatives of the same phylum. Hesse (1920) states that a Paramæcium at various temperatures may eliminate from 31 to 700 times its own weight each twenty-four hours, and that crabs excrete urine more rapidly in freshwater than in the sea. Animals that have recently invaded freshwater from the land or ocean have become adapted in various ways, but often show little modification in the patterns of physiological processes or in the structures which functioned in their old habitats. Aquatic insects for the most part breathe air and their tracheal systems are quite similar in their general plans to those of related terrestrial species. Needham and Williamson (1907) point out that dytiscids are adapted to life in water by: (1) great bodily rigidity brought about by fusion and compression of parts; (2) diminished resistance to water by rounding of contours, assumption of boat shape, depression of eyes, loss of hair and sculpture, reversal of antennæ, flattening of legs; (3) great swimming efficiency through flattening, developing fringes, the loss of claws, etc.; (4) ability to stay under water by provision for the storage of air or ability to exchange gases with the surrounding water. Leng (1913) states that some beetles are able to remain submerged for weeks. Needham (1902) showed that insects have become associated with freshwater habitats in various ways and to varying degrees. Those that breathe air may run over the surface, rest beneath the surface film and remain attached to it, or remain below the surface and secure air by means of a long breathing tube or from the gaseous stores of aquatic plants. Those that breathe from water may be swimmers, climbers, clingers, crawlers, or burrowers. Barber (1913) ascribes the adjustments of water-inhabiting bugs to specializations in locomotion, respiration, methods of feeding, and ability to endure foul water.

Food of Freshwater Animals.—The food relations of freshwater animals are somewhat different from those that obtain in other realms, but there is, of course, the usual dependence on photosynthesis as the basic process for food production. Freshwaters differ from the ocean in their lesser salinity and in the lability of carbonates, which are readily dissolved as bicarbonates when carbon dioxide is present or assume a more stable form in its absence. Some algæ are able to take carbon dioxide from bicarbonates and thus to carry on photosynthesis. Assimilable nitrogenous compounds are, of course, essential and are supplied by nitrates, nitrites, and ammonium compounds, the activities of bacteria, and organic compounds from other living organisms. The limited size of freshwater habitats and the consequent nearness of all their parts to the seats of photosynthetic activity make it possible for detritus and other organic foods to be distributed readily into their remotest situations. There will ordinarily be more food and more animals on the bottom of the deepest lake than on the barren abyssal floor of the ocean.

Classification of Freshwater Habitats.—Various classifications have been proposed for the groups of organisms living in freshwater. Steuer (1910) and Needham and Lloyd (1916) have stressed the differences encountered by the inhabitants of the shore habitats in relation to those of the open water. Embody

(1922) and Klugh (1923) emphasized the importance of temperature differences. Shelford (1911), Ward and Whipple (1918), and Klugh (1923) contrast moving with quiet water and intermittent with continual flow. The classification outlined on page 16, seems more natural. The three groups—(1) streams, (2) lakes and ponds, and (3) pools and swamps—appear to be natural groupings with many common characteristics. Streams flow, carry considerable suspended matter, and may vary considerably in volume. Swift streams have more or less constant temperatures throughout the year; large, slow streams vary greatly in temperature. Current movements in lakes and ponds are usually slight, but waves may be important in their shallower parts; thermal stratification and its attendant gradient in dissolved gases is frequent. Shallow swamps and pools have little movement, even of waves; height of water and temperature vary greatly at different seasons.

PROVINCE A. ANIMALS OF FLOWING WATER

"A large lake represents stability of environment, but a flowing stream is the fullest expression of a condition of instability" (Purdy, 1923). Streams flow, carry and deposit sediment, and vary greatly in volume. They have been classified as (1) permanent, (2) those that dry up occasionally, and (3) those in which water is present only occasionally (Needham and Lloyd, 1916), but the writer feels that from a biological point of view streams are more naturally distinguished as swift or sluggish. Streams are not inherently very rich in food resources, but compensate for such deficiency by serving as highways for animals which are through them able to gain access to habitats which contain much food. The fauna of any stream is, of course, related to the location of its basin and its past history. In New Zealand there were no stream fishes until they were introduced by men. In general, stream animals are assorted according to the volume of water available, the larger animals usually occurring in the larger streams.

Variation in Amount of Water.—The variation in the amount of water passing down a stream has various relations to the animals present. The Illinois River flows 227 miles. At flood water it passes through the entire course in about five days, but requires twenty-three days for the journey at lowest water. In this river rains have been found to bring in more decomposable matter and decrease the oxygen content of the water. Turbulence and swiftness injure many animals during floods, and some may actually be swept away altogether. The beetles that dwell near the banks of streams go ashore during floods and thus escape. Winds blow rubbish and floating objects against the shore and thus help the insects to reach the land. Beetles of the genus Stenus "skim" during floods by secreting a substance at the posterior end which drives them along the surface by differences in surface tension (Joy, 1910). Abbott (1870) found that fishes soon sorted themselves into their accustomed habitats after a freshet, but Shelford (1911*a*) noted that it required about a year for the river snails, Pleurocera and Campeloma, to move a mile upstream. Droughts cause most fishes to move downstream, but some, like the horned dace, are able to persist in the pools left in intermittent streams.

Food in Streams.—The available food in streams comes from (1) the large, aquatic vegetation, of which there is usually little in the actual channels; (2) plankton; (3) bottom sediments; (4) stream animals; (5) animals and plants from tributary swamps, ponds, and lakes. In small brooks certain animals, like trout, depend largely on organisms that fall from the banks; in great rivers food may be nearly lacking in one place and very abundant in another. Forbes (1919) points out that the productivity of a river in fishes is directly related to the degree to which the river overflows its banks, foods thus being made available. Richardson (1921) found that the amount of nitrogen in the bottom mud in the Illinois River was several thousand times that contained in all the bottom-inhabiting animals. Most of the animals that live in streams are poikilothermal, and hence their consumption of food varies considerably with variations in temperature. This and the fact that much of the food in streams comes from outside sources make it difficult to make accurate estimates of the amounts that are necessary to maintain the animals in different habitats. The writer (1924) has calculated that a freshwater fish consumes about ten times its own bulk of natural foods each year.

Crozier and Harris (1922) studied the animals that lived on a sewage filter, and in each cubic centimeter of material found 100,000 protozoans, 3500 nematodes, 4000 rotifers, and 150 annelids. Turner (1918) investigated a small, sewage-laden stream and found a "sewage carpet," or "false bottom," of organic material. This was densely populated by protozoans, worms, midge larvæ, podurans, etc., and furnished a feeding ground for minnows, turtles, frogs, ducks, and other birds.

Economic Relations of Streams.—The streams in any region are valuable to men as highways, sources of food, and receivers of the wastes from human activities. They are well suited for the latter function because their continual flow and the normal activities of certain of their inhabitants enable them to purify themselves after they have traveled a comparatively short distance. The pouring of wastes into a stream may be a legitimate use or an abuse. If materials are poisonous or in any other way injure the fauna of a stream, they should not be placed in it, but disposed of in some other way. Many products now wasted so as to destroy stream animals may be made of commercial value if they are saved (Shelford, 1918b). Sewage in a river often increases the number of animals present but does not so affect the plants (Purdy, 1923). The warmer branches of the Ohio River that enter from the south have disposed of much more of their organic matter than the colder streams from the north. The "purification" of a river is accomplished through dilution, sedimentation, insolation, oxidation, and the activities of bacteria, plants, and animals. It is usually more rapid in swifter streams. Baker (1920) states that sewage drove snails out of the Genesee River and that when it was reduced the snails returned. Forbes and Richardson (1908) observed that clean-water animals retired downstream when sewage was introduced into the Illinois River; fishes also left the upper part of the river. In an acid stream (pH, 5.8 to 7.2) Jewell (1922) found that clams, certain fishes, and shrimps persisted, but branchiate snails and certain immature insects were absent.

FORMATION 1. ANIMALS OF RAPIDLY FLOWING STREAMS

Speed in the movement of streams is, of course, due to differ. ences in level. Mountain brooks "tumble down" and springs "boil up" because water "tends to seek its level," or to move toward a condition of stability. The greater the difference in level between source and resting place or the steeper the declivity down which water moves, the swifter it goes. Swift-flowing water is usually well aerated; even when containing little plankton it may, by its very speed, bring enough food so that sessile animals may be supplied. As an animal habitat it has the disadvantages that come with the impact of moving water and the objects that it carries along; also those that are due to the great difficulty that attends locomotion or the maintenance of constant spatial relations with the environment.

ASSOCIATION *a*. ANIMALS OF SPRINGS

Springs are characterized by constant temperature, which usually shows little variation throughout the year. Those that support an abundant population are usually cold, and hot springs usually contain few animals. Over the surface move water-striders and whirligig beetles, which feed largely on insects that have fallen on the water from land habitats (Stratum 1). There are few swimming animals, except an occasional minnow or stickleback and amphipods (Stratum 2). Under stones caddis-fly larvæ, stone-fly larvæ, isopods, flatworms, and snails hide during the day but forage about in the open at night. Depending on the swiftness of the water, the cases of caddis-flies may be fastened firmly to the bottom (Stratum 3) or freely carried about. In springs themselves there are usually few plants, but cress and other emergent vegetation may grow at the margins. Such plants give shelter to fishes, air-breathing insects and their larvæ, and to crustaceans, frogs, and other animals. In spring pools (Stratum 5) where water may be rather quiet, considerable vegetation may grow and types that are usually found in swift-flowing water may be replaced by those that are more characteristic of ponds. Along the margins of springs, in sand or mud, burrowing dragon-fly or may-fly nymphs, and oligochætes may be found (Stratum 6).

In winter, springs furnish retreats for hibernating animals. Often the space beneath each stone is crowded with frogs which remain sluggish and inactive but do not freeze. Intermittent springs have a scanty animal population consisting largely of ubiquitous amphipods, isopods, snails, and insect larvæ.

ASSOCIATION *b*. ANIMALS OF BROOKS

Brooks are characterized by swiftness, but the current at the bottom and sides is much less than that in the center near the surface. The spaces beneath stones (Stratum 3) and occasional pools (Stratum 5) furnish regions of comparative quiet and some true brook animals require such habitats. Hankinson (1922) states that pools and shore vegetation are essentials in the habitat of the brook trout. A brook usually consists of alternating rapids (Stratum 3) and pools, and some animals that frequent the one are seldom found in the other. Beavers build dams across brooks and thus secure ponds which give them a more or less constant water level, space for transportation and storage, and a refuge from enemies. Some brook animals live under or among, not on or above, stones. Usually there is little or no submerged vegetation (Stratum 4) except occasional patches of Cladophora. The temperature of brooks is usually more variable than that of springs. Embody (1922) in considering the suitability of brooks for trout divides them into three groups: (1) those that never rise above 21°C., and which support brook trout; (2) those that reach 21 to 24°C., and in which brown and rainbow trout may live; and (3) those that in summer are commonly above 24 to 27°C., and from which trout are absent. There are usually few aquatic larvæ living in exposed situations in brooks in winter. The low temperatures and the consequent decrease in metabolic rate make animals ill adapted to avoid ice and other floating objects. Intermittent brooks are unfavorable for snails and other brook animals, but under accumulations of leaves in the dry, stony bed of a woodland brook Needham and Lloyd (1916) found living crane-fly larvæ, stone-fly nymphs, amphipods, and earthworms; the last washed into the stream from land. Baker (1919) found snails æstivating in cracks in the bed of an intermittent stream during a drought. The chemical reaction of a brook may be of importance for the animals in it; it has been suggested that trout die after forest fires because the usual slightly acid reaction of the stream has been changed by the wood ashes that wash in from the burned areas.

Characteristic Brook Animals.—The animals that are typical of the rapids in brooks are the nymphs and larvæ of caddis-flies, may-flies, stone-flies, beetles, lepidopters, black-flies (Simulidæ), and other Diptera; also flatworms, mites, and snails. In pools and under stones and logs lurk fishes (trout, miller's thumb, dace, certain darters, catfishes), hellbenders, amphipods, isopods, crayfishes, crabs, atyids, Sphæridæ. In mountain torrents in Colombia the writer (1915) found no crustacean fauna, but only a little catfish and a spider. When the brooks reached the foot-hills, however, atyids were commonly found in patches of drift;

crabs, fishes, and the curious lizards of the genus Basiliscus lurked in the pools and a dragon-fly nymph burrowed along their shores. In the lowlands, where the streams lost their momentum, shrimps and prawns were common.

Adaptations of Brook Animals.—Brook animals are adapted in various ways to withstand strong currents. Insect larvæ may have suckers on their gills, legs, or ventral surfaces so that they can hold on; their legs are often provided with hooks; black-fly larvæ have enormous adhesive organs at the posterior end. The mountain brook catfishes mentioned in the last paragraph are provided with spines along their ventral surfaces; some brook fishes, like certain gobies in Hawaii, have ventral suckers; the coronchos in Venezuela (Pearse, 1920) adhere to the under sides of stones by means of their sucking mouths. Some lepidopterous larvæ live under sheets of silk that they spin on rocks. Most of the clinging animals have "stream-line" forms and rest with their larger end upstream, but a few are flattened and one may-fly nymph is described as being shaped somewhat like the blade of a chisel so that the current against its anterior end or legs forces it against the substratum. The animals that move about are strong swimmers (darters, trout, dace), or never release their hold when moving. Black-fly larvæ fasten a thread along the bottom and cling to this while they reattach their posterior sucker. A number of animals seek shelter under objects in the stream and in some cases dig out hollows on the downstream side of stones. The male horned dace constructs a long pile of stones and rests in a depression at the downstream end. Females deposit eggs in the depression; the male covers them with stones and makes a new depression. In this way the eggs are protected from enemies and moving bodies. In the brooks in northern South America there is an insect that deposits patches of eggs on boulders in swift streams and it is remarkable that these are always on the downstream side, where they will not be injured by floating objects if there is a flood. Caddis-fly larvæ escape from floods, silt, and enemies by living in cases which in swift water are firmly attached. Shelford (1914a) studied the behavior of typical animals from rapids and found that there was agreement among them in preference for hard bottom and reactions toward currents, but lack of agreement in behavior toward light. The last was probably correlated with the fact that some of the animals normally live beneath stones and some in the open. However, toward the two most important factors of brook environment (current and hard bottom) there was general agreement. Many brook animals are nocturnal or crepuscular, hiding during the day but coming out to forage at twilight. Insects that live in rapids when emerging from the pupal state commonly rise rapidly to the surface and quickly fly away.

Swift currents make good aeration and brook animals are adapted to water having a high oxygen content. Stone-fly nymphs have very small gills and very little ability to live where oxygen is deficient. Dodds and Hisaw (1924) found that the area of the gills of may-fly nymphs in mountain brooks varied inversely with the amount of oxygen in the surrounding water, but had no very close correlation with the swiftness of currents. There is an Andean frog that never leaves the water. It breathes entirely through its skin and has very small lungs (Allen, 1922).

Food of Brook Animals.—Many of the inhabitants of rapids catch their food in nets. The quantity of plankton in brook water is usually small, but the swiftness of the current enables plankton feeders to strain large quantities and continually stirs up sediment that may serve as food. Certain caddis-flies are expert net spinners. Some of these feed on floating algæ and animal plankton, emerging from their cases and scraping off their nets at intervals; others prey on living food and are ever ready to pounce on anything that may land in their nets. Black-fly and may-fly larvæ fish with the nets that are formed by the bristles on their mouth parts. Atyids' nets are on the claws of their walking legs. Not all dwellers in rapids are net fishers, however. Lepidopterous larvæ feed largely on filamentous or encrusting algæ; may-flies forage for a variety of foods. In crevices and pools predaceous stone-fly nymphs, crayfishes, catfishes, darters, trout, etc. wait for their prey. In Colombia the writer became acquainted with a spider, with an enormous expanse of legs and a ridiculously small body, that rested along the banks of brooks and at intervals ran out over the surface and captured some floating insect (Stratum 1). In other parts of the earth water-striders and whirligig beetles often rest in eddies along brooks and feed on the insects that continually float down on the surface.

Waterfalls.—Waterfalls are extravagantly developed rapids and there is general similarity between the animals that live in the two habitats.   There are some animals, however, that are particularly associated with cataracts.   The water-ousel builds its mossy nest beneath falls.   Leathers (1922) states that he found the larvæ of the midges of the family Orphnephilidæ only

. . . on a series of "giant steps" where a small stream spreads out over broad and nearly horizontal stones in its precipitous descent. Here the larvæ were found more frequently on the vertical than the horizontal surfaces of the ledges.

Waterfalls are barriers to the migrations of most swimming animals but some, like the salmon, are able to leap up considerable distances.   Eigenmann (1912) describes a fish in Guiana that climbs waterfalls.

The method of ascent of vertical walls by members of the genus *Rivulus* . . . is of great interest.   One of these fishes taken in Shrimp Creek jumped against the vertical face of a huge rock and clung by the adhesion of its tail.   *From this point by another flop it made and clung to another point much higher up the face of the rock.*

Abbott (1870) says that lampreys are able to "suck their way up" the vertical facing of dams.   A basin at the foot of a cataract is often an excellent fishing ground because streams serve as highways and animals journeying upstream tend to collect below the fall.

FORMATION 2.   ANIMALS OF SLOWLY FLOWING STREAMS

Creeks and rivers differ from springs and brooks in the rate of flow of their waters.   This means a lower gradient in the channel and a correspondingly finer, softer, muddier bottom, because the slower the current the smaller the bodies it can move.   Slow current and muddy bottoms permit aquatic vegetation to flourish where the water is not so turbid as to cut off sunlight.

ASSOCIATION *a*.   ANIMALS OF CREEKS

A creek is a small stream that does not flow swiftly.   Cowles and Schwitalla (1923) found that the carbon dioxide in a creek varied considerably in different regions and was highest in ponds that occurred in the course of the stream.

In ponds the pH is modified by the aquatic fauna and flora . . . When water flows slowly over decaying vegetable matter the pH is lowered.   When water flows rapidly over a clean bed, most noticeably at falls and rapids, the pH is raised, probably as a result of aeration. These facts may be readily correlated with the carbon dioxide content of the water.   Hence, in this creek, the free carbon dioxide content seemed to be a determining factor in establishing and maintaining pH values . . . Stagnation of the water and low but uniform pH seem to be two of the factors which determine the distribution of Euglena.

Animals of Creeks.—Certain animals are commonly associated with creeks.   Water-striders and toad bugs run over the surface; beavers bring in green branches from the trees near at hand; muskrats and carp grub out roots along the shores; crocodilians, herons, bitterns, ducks, geese, turtles, frogs, eels, dogfishes, bull-heads, mudminnows, beetles, odonate nymphs, water-bugs, leeches, and hydras hunt for living animals; tadpoles, sunfishes, suckers, breams, crayfishes, amphipods, and snails feed on vegetation and mud, or eke out an existence as scavengers; plankton is often present in considerable quantities and certain species of plankton organisms that do not occur in open water may be abundant.

Creeks, like other streams, show variation in the height of water.   During floods many animals resort to the submerged plants in the stream or rest in the emergent vegetation along the banks.   In winter, turtles, frogs, insects, snails, and leeches hibernate in the mud at the bottom or at the stream margins. Amphipods and some other forms remain active throughout cold seasons.   During droughts many creek animals seek pools or remain in the mud under masses of vegetation.   Iguanas use creeks as a refuge from danger.   When threatened, they dive from the trees where they usually forage, swim under water to the opposite bank, sneak out into the underbrush, and are seen no more.

Association *b*.   Animals of Rivers

A river, on account of its large volume, the fluctuation in the amount of water passing over its stream bed, and rate of flow, varies considerably in its area.   Its connection with tributary swamps, lakes, sloughs, and smaller streams gives it important functions as a highway to feeding and breeding grounds, and as a refuge during periods of cold or drought.   Its turbidity prevents light from penetrating very far and there are many more animals near the surface than at greater depths.

Muttkowski (1918) found a scanty population in the turbid main channel of a river studied by him, but an abundance of animals in the clearer water near the banks. Lakes in the courses of rivers serve as settling basins for suspended materials and serve to equalize the flow of water, and rivers with large lakes in their courses are therefore not changed to such an extent by floods as those without. The temperatures of rivers may vary more than those of smaller streams on account of seasonal changes, variation in the amount of water received from tributaries, height of water, amount of insolation, etc. Kofoid (1908) found that, when the temperature of the Illinois River fell in winter to 7°C., the plankton decreased 90 per cent from its summer maximum.

Animals of Rivers.—Though river faunas are largely derived from tributary habitats, and though many of the animals that live in rivers are also found in other habitats or only live in rivers part of the time, there are many true river animals that are seldom or never found elsewhere. For example, in the Mississippi drainage there are four gigantic fishes (mud-cat, rock-sturgeon, alligator-gar, spoonbill), quillbacks, mooneyes, several minnows, gizzard-shads, mussels, soft-shell turtles, and other animals that do not invade small streams. For the most part the typical river animals are: (1) fishes and turtles that are strong swimmers, (2) heavy-bodied mussels and burrowers that can withstand the strong currents, shifting bottoms, and accumulating drift.

Stratum 1. River Bottoms.—River bottoms above the usual stream channel are only inundated at time of high water, but are tributary to the river itself. Forbes (1919) has called attention to the importance of the backwaters of rivers as places for the digestion and assimilation of foods and has expressed his opinion that the production of food fishes in a river is more or less directly related to the area that may be overflowed. Garman (1888) made a careful study of the animals in the Mississippi River bottoms. He found raccoons present at all times, ascending into the trees at times of high water. There were comparatively few birds, snakes, or amphibians, and no tadpoles, but in the ponds and sloughs there were many turtles, insect larvæ and nymphs (midge, caddis-fly, dobson, stone-fly, may-fly, damsel- and dragon-fly), bugs, fishes from sloughs, creeks, and rivers, bryozoans, hydras, protozoans, and a few snails. In the vegetation were spiders (Tetragnatha), mites, grasshoppers, and crickets. In the tropics foxes, lizards, and crabs commonly hunt over river bottoms. In all climates grazing animals also commonly invade the bottoms to feed. Floods enable fishes (Stratum 5) and other aquatic animals to forage in habitats that are usually not available to them. The writer once caught a bullhead that had eaten a nestling of a bird and on another occasion examined a carp which had gorged itself with grass.

Stratum 2. Shore Animals.—Shore animals are abundant, both in and out of the water. Some land animals come to the shore only to drink and are awaited by predaceous crocodiles and piranhas which seek to devour them. There is a drift line which, though not as clearly defined as along lakes, is sought by various scavenger insects, birds, and other animals. The writer has shown (1921) that at one point on the Mississippi in summer there are more fishes, both in variety and numbers, in shallow water than in any stratum at greater depths. This is probably due to the turbidity and currents, which prevent the growth of plants except in very shallow water, and thus fishes that are associated with vegetation are often caught while taking the shortest route from one feeding ground to another. Young fishes commonly seek the shallows alongshore to escape from their enemies.

Stratum 3. Surface Animals.—The animals that rest on the surface are well represented in rivers by loons, ducks, grebes, gulls, and other water birds, but there are comparatively few insects. Though whirligig beetles are perhaps more abundant along rivers than elsewhere, there is, in general, a scarcity of water-striders and other insects that are so characteristic of ponds, swamps, and small streams.

Stratum 4. River Plankton.—The plankton of rivers has already been discussed (p. 189) to some extent. A considerable portion of it is derived from backwaters and tributaries. The continual movement and turbidity kill many plankton organisms, which settle after dying down and enrich the bottom. Kofoid (1908) characterizes river plankton as: (1) polymixic, (2) fluctuating in quantity and constitution, (3) lacking characterization by any particular species but with a large proportion of littoral species. "Channel plankton of the Illinois River, therefore, has its source in a large degree in impounded backwaters, and is maintained to a considerable extent by their run off." Steuer (1910) describes bacteria, diatoms, protococci, desmids, and roti-

fers as typical of river plankton. He divides different types into
(1) eupotamotic, which is largely rotifers; (2) tychopotamotic,
derived from quiet water and containing many crustaceans; (3)
benthopotamotic, bottom organisms (Oscillatoria, diatoms,
Arcella, etc.) swept away by currents; (4) pseudopotamotic,
textile and muscle fibers, and detritus; (5) autopotamotic, organisms that normally live in flowing water (Micrococcus, Sarcina,
Bacillus, etc.). He also states that plankton is influenced by the
source, swiftness, length, tributaries, backwaters, turbidity, and
contamination of a river and by seasonal changes. Kofoid (1903)
found that the plankton of the Illinois River reached its maximum
quantity in April, May, and June and its minimum in January
and February. Allen (1920) observed an autumnal maximum
in the San Joaquin River. Two-hundred thousand tons (wet
weight) of plankton pass Havana in the Illinois River each year.
This amount is 60 to 150 times that of the average weight of
bottom animals. The nitrogen in the water is 92 to 232 times
that contained in its net plankton (Richardson, 1921).

Stratum 5. Swimmers.—The swimmers in rivers are mostly
fishes and, particularly in the tropics, large shrimps and prawns.
Crocodilians, hippopotami, in some places sharks and dolphins,
are also represented.

Stratum 6. Bottom Animals.—On shifting bottoms there are
usually no plants in the river bed. However, Richardson (1921)
in his careful survey of the Illinois River found that bottom
animals were most abundant on mud near aquatic vegetation.
Howard (1919) surveyed the entire bottom on a 3-mile section of
the Mississippi and reported that, in general, animals were
restricted to a 200-foot zone along each shore, and to a narrower
strip around islands. This distribution had no apparent relation
to depth, for the middle of the river was not deeper than the zones
nearer shore. The most productive areas in this case, in which
the survey was primarily directed toward mussels, were strips
near shore that were swept by strong currents. Mussels, according to Allen (1921), feed almost continuously, and largely on
nannoplankton, so they would derive very apparent benefit from
currents. Over a stretch of 59 miles of river, Richardson (1921)
found that bottom animals were most abundant on muddy bottoms where there was least current. Molluscs made up from 31
to 99 per cent of the bottom animals, which (without considering
calcareous shells) weighed from 10.4 to 5196 pounds per acre.

Richardson found, however, that the fauna of aquatic plants of swampy margins and of lakes connected with the river greatly exceeded that on the bottom of the river itself. The weight of the flesh of the animals associated with vegetation averaged 2118 pounds per acre; the weight of those on the bottom 255 pounds. Settled plankton was found to furnish food for snails, caddis-fly larvæ, Sphæridæ, and other bottom animals. Lakes connected with the river were found to be favorite feeding grounds for fishes and the amount of food available on the bottoms of such lakes was found to be five times as great as that on the bottoms of comparable glacial lakes in Illinois. Some animals that are associated with the bottoms of large rivers are also found on the bottoms of certain lakes: sturgeon, mussels; operculate snails; large, burrowing may-fly nymphs. On the bottom of a canal Baker (1918) found 116 mussels in an area measuring 10 by 15 feet.

At river bends bottom animals are usually assorted according to the swiftness of the current. On the outside of the bend are snails and other animals that frequent harder bottoms. In midstream live such animals as burrowing nymphs and clams, that can flourish on shifting bottoms, but require currents for the bringing of their food. On the inside of the bend, where the bottom may be muddy and even support aquatic plants, conditions approach those in swamps and such animals as pond snails, Sphæridæ, and frogs may be present. In deep holes in rivers, particularly if there is little current, conditions may approach those in lakes, but many of the characteristic animals of the depths of lakes are not present because rivers seldom show a great degree of thermal stratification and deep water is not much cooler than that at the surface.

PROVINCE B. ANIMALS OF STANDING WATER

Of course, there is no such thing in the world as absolutely quiet water, but lakes, ponds, pools, and swamps differ from streams in that their waters flow little or not at all. The standing waters of the earth are again readily separable on the basis of their size and depth: lakes and ponds with their greater volumes and exposed areas being more subject to the action of waves and currents, while pools and swamps are generally stagnant. There are many aquatic animals that cannot exist in environments where there is wave motion. A mosquito larva, for example, must live in stagnant water because surface disturbances prevent the protrusion of its breathing siphon and suffocation results. Other animals are limited in their distribution to habitats where there is continual wave motion or to bodies of water where wave motion is possible. Waterpennies live under the pebbles and boulders on wave-beaten shores. Ciscoes flourish in lakes which have sufficient size and depth to furnish cool, deep, oxygenated, water at all seasons.

Subprovince B (a). Lacustrine Animals

Among freshwater habitats lakes have been most studied by biologists.

Characteristics of Lakes.—Lakes resemble oceans in their general features, but, of course, differ from them in their small size, the presence of definite boundaries on all sides, and in their very low salinity. As a habitat for animals they are not as unvarying as the ocean but are the most stable of freshwater habitats. Forbes (1887) fancifully but properly described a lake as an "island" containing older life in the midst of newer land life. Compared with the land, a lake in many respects does support a more primitive fauna. Its animals are also isolated, closely related, and, on the whole, present little variety. Muttkowski (1918) has set forth the conditions and characteristics of lake life as follows: (1) depth and area enough for wave action; (2) lack of emergent and floating vegetation (on account of wave action); (3) absence of plants, except Cladophora, along the shoreline and the presence of peculiar, flattened, clinging, and burrowing animals; (4) a dearth of animals that breathe air at the surface; (5) a plant zone (that varies with the transparency of the water and with seasonal changes) along the shore and a group of animals that varies in numbers with the plants; and (6) striking thermal stratification and a corresponding distribution of organisms.

Types of Lakes.—Birge (1907) in his classical paper on the "respiration of an inland lake" points out that lakes, like organisms, have periods of birth, youth, maturity, old age, and death. Besides such a physiographic cycle, lakes also have individuality —each taking its character from its drainage basin, climate, shape, area, depth, gradient of its slopes, solutes in its water, vegetation, animals, etc. From a biological point of view depth is perhaps more important than contour or shape of basin. In general, the shallower a lake is the more productive of life it is. Depth also functions in another way by allowing thermal stratification in the water and, where it is sufficient to cut off the lower water from contact with the atmosphere during all or part of the year, may lead to regularly recurring periods of stagnation in deep water. There have been various classifications proposed for distinguishing different types of lakes, but perhaps the most comprehensive and successful were those of Forel (1892–1904) and Whipple (1898), who distinguished polar, temperate, and tropical lakes and subdivided each class according to periods of vertical circulation or "overturn" and the relation between bottom and surface temperatures. Birge and Juday (1911) and Thienemann (1922) have made some modifications of Whipple's original scheme. At present lakes may be divided into the following groups:

I. Polar—temperatures never above 4°C.:
   Type 1. Bottom remains at 4°C. throughout the year; one circulation period possible in summer, but usually none.
   Type 2. Bottom temperatures fluctuate but remain near 4°C.; one circulation period in summer.
   Type 3. Bottom temperatures close to surface temperatures; water circulates more or less continuously except when frozen.

II. Temperate—temperatures vary above and below 4°C.:
   Type 1. Bottom temperature remains at 4°C. throughout the year; two circulation periods possible in spring and autumn, but often none.
   Type 2. Bottom temperature fluctuates but remains near 4°C.; two circulation periods in spring and autumn.
   Type 3. Bottom temperatures close to surface temperatures; water circulates throughout the year when the surface is not frozen.

III. Tropical—temperatures always above 4°C.:
   Type 1. Bottom remains near 4°C. throughout the year; may be one circulation period in winter.
   Type 2. Bottom temperature fluctuates but remains near 4°C.; a circulation period in winter.
   Type 3. Bottom temperature close to surface temperatures; water circulates more or less continuously.

Most lakes of type 1 are over 200 feet deep; those of type 2 are usually more than 25 feet deep; and those of type 3 are usually less than 25 feet deep.

Lake Temperatures.—Probably temperature is the chief factor in determining the "climate" of lakes, as it is of land habitats. It also sets a general limit for the rate of metabolism and thus in determining the total amount of life that may develop in a particular lake. Wesenberg-Lund (1905), Shantz (1907), Coker (1911), Dodds (1917), and Haempel (1918) all agree that there is less plankton in alpine lakes than in those of the lowlands. Dodds (1917) classifies lakes in Colorado as alpine, montane, and plains, largely on the basis of temperature differences. Haempel (1918) states that most plankton species in alpine lakes are probably perennial. Altitudinal lines between lakes are not always sharply drawn on account of size differences. A large lake warms and cools more slowly than a small one, and may support a greater variety of life because it is capable of furnishing a wider range of temperatures. In most lakes plants and animals are on the ascendant in spring and summer when available light and heat are increasing. In autumn there is usually a diminution; storms destroy and wash much of the attached vegetation away. In winter many animals are in a state of torpor and of repressed activity. Some insects become active before the ice leaves a lake in the spring (Muttkowski, 1918). As in other formations, the inhabitants of lakes are adjusted to normal climatic seasonal rhythms in each latitude.

Deep and Shallow Lakes.—The depth of a lake determines its character to a considerable degree. A shallow lake warms and cools quickly, may support standing vegetation in all its parts, is easily made to circulate from top to bottom by winds, and hence rarely shows thermal stratification. A deep lake usually has a high degree of stratification with warm water above and cold below. In summer, deep lakes are usually divided into three rather clearly defined strata: (1) an upper *epilimnion*, which is warm and circulates when moved by winds; (2) an intermediate *mesolimnion*, or thermocline, which is often only a meter or two in thickness and in which there is a rapid change in temperature; and (3) a deep, cool *hypolimnion*, in which there is a very gradual decrease in temperature toward the bottom. A shallow plant-choked lake usually supports more fishes and other aquatic animals per unit of area than a deep one, but the latter usually has a greater variety of species. There is apparently some factor that limits the levels at which animals live. For example, in Wisconsin, lakes up to about 100 feet in depth have the bottom dominated by yellow perch, but in lakes that are deeper ciscoes are usually dominant. In Lake Michigan both perch and ciscoes are abundant, but the former are never taken in deep water. Lake Pepin, which is an expansion of the Mississippi River, and Lake Michigan are both rich grounds for commercial fishermen, but the former yields mostly carp, red horses, buffalo, and quillbacks, while the latter supplies trout, ciscoes, and whitefishes (Pearse, 1921).

Transparency of Lakes.—Transparency of the water in various lakes varies greatly. The zone of photosynthesis may thus be limited to a couple of meters near the surface or extend down through 10 or more meters. A stratum of optically pure water 1 meter thick absorbs 60 per cent of the sun's energy (Birge, 1913). His investigations in more than twenty-five Wisconsin lakes showed that less than 20 per cent of the sun's energy penetrates to a depth of a meter; in turbid lakes the amount may be as low as 2.5 per cent. The zone between 1 and 2 meters usually absorbs 40 to 50 per cent of what passes through the upper stratum. The amount of solar energy below 6 meters is usually "too small to be measured," and 1 per cent of the sun's energy rarely reaches 5 meters. In Green Lake, however, which is one of the clearest in Wisconsin, 1 per cent is present at 7 meters. There is not always correlation between transparency and permeability. The depth to which light penetrates, of course, controls the quantity of plant life that can develop in a lake. All animals are more or less dependent on plants for food, and in many cases for shelter, and other essentials. The writer (1921) has shown that in turbid lakes there is a greater variety and quantity of fish life in the first 5 meters below the surface, but in clear lakes there may be more species and greater numbers of fishes between depths of 5 to 10 meters than in the surface stratum.

Gases in Lakes.—Depth and transparency modify other aspects of lake ecology besides photosynthesis and thermal stratification. The dissolved gases are profoundly influenced. Birge (1907) points out that a lake carries on respiratory processes during which gases (chiefly oxygen, carbon dioxide, and nitrogen) are exchanged with the atmosphere. In winter the oxygen usually decreases in lakes of temperate or cold climates, and carbon dioxide increases because such respiration cannot take place on account of ice. In a deep lake the going out of the ice in spring is followed by the vernal overturn; all the water is thoroughly mixed and aerated at all depths. After a few warm, quiet days the upper portion of the lake becomes warmer than that below and an epilimnion is thus established. As the summer progresses the hypolimnion, being cut off from contact with the atmosphere, loses oxygen and acquires carbon dioxide through the respiration of animals and the decay of organic materials. Finally, there may be no oxygen left and many animals die or migrate into the epilimnion where oxygen is present. In autumn the epilimnion gradually cools and when it reaches the temperature close to that of the hypolimnion, the autumnal overturn takes place and the water throughout the lake is again aerated from top to bottom. If a coating of ice cuts off contact with winds, the lake becomes stratified again in winter and its deep water may again lose its oxygen. When the deep waters of a lake become stagnant, the animals living in them must be able to endure considerable periods without oxygen or migrate. Perch move to high levels but swim down into the stagnant zone at times to feed. They can live for as much as two hours in water without oxygen and draw to some extent on oxygen stored in their swim-bladders (Pearse, 1920*a*). Corethra larvæ migrate up into the epilimnion at night and return to the hypolimnion during the day (Juday, 1921). Sphæridæ that live through periods of stagnation apparently do so by remaining wholly inactive, but chironomids, oligochætes, and protozoans are able to remain active for as much as three months in water without oxygen. Plankton distribution is not closely correlated with the quantities of gases present. Plankton animals do not at once leave regions where oxygen is decreasing, but where oxygen is less than 0.1 to 0.2 cubic centimeter per liter there is usually no living zoöplankton. This usually means that in lakes that stagnate there are few or no zoöplanktonts below the mesolimnion, but sometimes in a clear lake after a period without wind, oxygen may extend below that stratum, or in a turbid lake not extend down to it. Corethra larvæ and some apparently anaerobic protozoans are able to swim about in stagnant water without injury. Dr. L. E. Noland, as a result of his recent work, as yet unpublished, says:

A group of species, *Colpidium colpoda, Glaucoma pyriformis, Glaucoma scintillans,* and *Paramecium caudatum,* were observed to occur most abundantly in infusions of high bacterial content where oxygen was almost or entirely absent.

Animals in Lakes.—A characteristic group of animals inhabits lakes. Some of these animals are also found in other habitats but some are found nowhere else. Ciscoes, lake trout, lawyers, and whitefish are familiar examples of the latter group. Necturus has well-developed external gills and breathes from water, while its relative, Cryptobranchus, that lives in streams, comes to the surface for air continually when kept in quiet water (Willey, 1920). This characteristic lake amphibian is ecologically "more a fish than a salamander" (Pearse, 1921b). The peculiar crustaceans, Pontoporeia and Mysis, are not found in freshwater habitats, except in the depths of lakes. Johansen (1922) in his discussion of arctic habitats says:

Perhaps the best criterion for what may be considered a lake and what a pond in this vicinity, there being all grades between them, is the presence of the typical and common freshwater amphipod (*Gammarus limnæus*) which is not found in ponds, but only in lakes and their tributaries . . . Their occurrence is thus an interesting contrast to the other large freshwater crustaceans (Euphyllopoda), which principally occur in ponds, lagoons, or smaller lakes along the Arctic coast.

Quantity of Life in Lakes.—Alm (1922) has classified lakes according to their dominant species and the food resources present. His work will be discussed later in connection with bottom animals (p. 223). In most lakes the maximum quantities of plant and animal life come in the summer. Rickett (1922, 1924) and Juday (1924) have made a careful survey of the shore plants and plankton in two Wisconsin lakes, Green and Mendota. In Green Lake, which is clear and deep (225 feet), the shore plants extended to a depth of 8 to 10 meters and averaged 15,180 kilograms (1780 dry) per hectare; in Mendota, which is rather turbid and of moderate depth (87 feet), the average yield was larger, 17,778 kilograms per hectare. In Green Lake 9 per cent of the plants grew between 0 and 1 meter; 42 per cent, between 1 and 3 meters; and 49 per cent between 3 and 8 meters. Chara constituted 49 per cent of the dry weight of the plants; in Mendota Vallisneria produced about one-third of the total weight. The total plankton in Green Lake weighed (dry) about 818 milligrams per cubic meter of water, or about 27 grams per square meter of surface.

Results obtained in Lake Mendota indicate that about one-third of the organic matter of the net plankton is derived from rotifers and the crustacea, the two forms which are most concerned in the consumption of other organisms . . . The organic matter in the total plankton which might serve as food for the rotifers and crustacea would weigh about fifty times as much as that found in these two forms of plankton organisms.

In Green Lake the total weight of the bottom fauna was about one-tenth that of the total plankton. These figures give some idea of the food resources in a rather rich lake (Mendota) and a deep, cold, and rather barren lake.

Productivity of Lakes.—The ability of a lake to produce organic food, of course, depends on a variety of factors. A lake with much shallow water above the mesolimnion, thus furnishing good opportunity for decomposition in warm water, will produce more plankton than a deep lake with a bottom that descends rapidly from the shoreline (Birge and Juday, 1911). The capacity of a lake for food production depends on both materials and proper conditions. The temperature, turbidity, amount of available carbon dioxide, or other substances may limit the rate at which photosynthesis may take place. Some deep lakes apparently do not have enough carbon dioxide in summer to produce much plankton, even though many types of algæ are able to convert bicarbonates into carbonates in order to obtain it. The factors that contribute to the productivity of a lake are so complex that it is, of course, not possible to say that carbon dioxide is the sole limiting factor in such cases. Atkins (1923a) has shown that phosphates in ponds decrease greatly in April, until they are practically absent; and (1923b) that silica decreases greatly as it is used up by diatoms. In most lakes the greatest amount of plankton is in surface strata. In his study of shore animals in Lake Mendota, Muttkowski (1918) found that insects constituted 60 per cent of the macrofauna. Land insects that fall into lakes also may make material contribution to food resources. The important foods may vary in different types of lakes and the total amount of food may limit the number of animals that can live. The writer (1921a) has compared Lake Mendota, which is rich in fish foods, with Green Lake, which is rather poor, and has shown that the former supports twice as many fishes per unit of area as the latter. In Lake Mendota (1920a) the yellow perch eat about equal quantities of insects and entomostracans, but in Lake Wingra, which is shallow and contains much vegetation, few entomostracans are eaten. In Lake Pepin, which is an expansion of the Mississippi River, the chief fish foods are plankton, mud, and crayfishes; in the inland lakes of Wisconsin, fishes feed mostly on plankton, fishes, insects, and molluscs; in the depths of Lake Michigan, the fishes depend largely on other fishes and crustaceans that swim near the bottom (1921). More species of lake fishes feed alongshore than elsewhere; more feed on bottom organisms than on those of the open water. Considering all types of lakes, the important *fish foods* are plants, small fishes, insects, entomostracans, and bottom sediment (1918).

Fred, Wilson, and Davenport (1924) have studied the seasonal variations of bacteria at various depths in Lake Mendota. Numbers ranged between hundreds and thousands per cubic centimeter on account of fluctuations in rainfall, wind, temperature, the physical and chemical condition of the water, and other factors. High numbers were found to be due not only to the multiplication of lake bacteria, but also to the presence of bacteria that had been washed in from soil and other sources. Variations in temperature had little effect on the multiplication of lake bacteria and sunlight appeared to inhibit their growth very little. As a rule, there were fewer bacteria in the lake than could have existed on the available food. Domogolla, Juday, Peterson, and Fred (1925) have shown that the waters of Lake Mendota contain:

. . . more than nine times as much soluble nitrogen as total plankton nitrogen . . . There is seasonal variation in the different forms of nitrogen found in Lake Mendota . . . Ammonia, nitrites, nitrates, amino-acids, and proteins reach a maximum in winter and fall to a minimum during the summer. A sudden and marked increase in ammonia and nitrates occurs in February. The bottom water always contains more of the different forms of soluble nitrogen than the surface water . . . The seasonal variation in the different forms of soluble nitrogen indicates that these compounds form part of the nutrients of both plant and animal life of these waters.

The quantities of different protein compounds were also determined.

Zonation of Lakes.—The zonal arrangement, so characteristic of the animals that live in lakes, is due primarily to three factors: wave motion, the depth to which light penetrates, and temperature. Wave motion disturbs the water to varying depths (1 to 5 or more meters), which are generally correlated with the area of the lake, and sweeps the shore clean. "Where the interaction of waves and returning undertow is greatest" is the breaker line, or rachion (Muttkowski, 1918). Above this the beach on wave-beaten shores is devoid of plants and below it the vegetation extends in a zone of varying width, which depends on the slope of the bottom and the turbidity of the water. The maximum depth to which vegetation extends in the clearest lakes is about 25 meters. Thermal stratification may separate a deep lake into epilimnion, mesolimnion, and hypolimnion; once such separation is brought about, oxygen may become deficient in deeper strata and thus prevent certain animals from living there. Stratification and zonation in the distribution of animals in lakes are usually striking phenomena. In Green Lake Juday (1924) found the greatest variety and smallest number of bottom animals between depths of 0 and 10 meters; the maximum number, 20 to 40 meters; and the smallest variety, 40 to 67 meters. In the same lake the writer (1921*a*), fishing with gill nets in summer, found all species of fishes in the lake, except the cisco, between 0 and 10 meters; from 10 to 20 meters only pickerel, suckers, and largemouth black bass were caught; between 20 and 40 meters, only ciscoes. In Lake George, Needham (1922) found the maximum number of insect larvæ at 36 meters and of oligochætes at 50 meters. The zoning and stratifying factors usually divide lakes into (1) a littoral region which extends down to a depth of about 10 meters; (2) a deep-water bottom region below 10 meters; and (3) an open-water region in the middle of the lake. The littoral is divided into zones: the beach above water, submerged beach, breaker line, plant zone (which may be subdivided into several strata). It ends where light and wave motion cease to be potent. In the deep, bottom region live animals that are adapted to ooze, and often also to stagnation. The open water in lakes of sufficient depth is separated into two distinct regions by the mesolimnion.

FORMATION 1. LITTORAL ANIMALS

The littoral region of lakes, like that in the ocean, varies greatly according to exposure to wave action, light, character of bottom, extent of shallow water, solutes and suspended matter in water, temperature, vegetation, and other factors. Its depth also varies in different lakes. In Lake Geneva, Switzerland (Forel, 1892), it may reach down in certain situations to more than 25 meters; in Lake Mendota (Muttkowski, 1918) it extends to about 7 or 8 meters; and in very turbid lakes it is even thinner. Muttkowski's classification of bottom zones in Lake Mendota is as follows:

Littoral (phytal):
    Eulittoral (euphytal):
      1. Shoreline: 0 to 1 meters; rocky, stony, or sandy, barren.
         Shoals: 0.5 to 1 meter.
      2. Surf line (rachion): 1 meter; stony, barren.
      3. Vegetation zone: 1.5 to 6 meters.
         Upright vegetation: 1.5 to 5 meters; Potamogeton, Najas, Vallisneria.
         Recumbent vegetation: 4 to 6 meters; Chara, Myriophyllum, Ceratophyllum, Potamogeton.
         Barrens.
         Rock reefs: 3 to 8 meters; plant marl, stones, rocks with encrustations.
    Sublittoral (dysphytal):
      4. Shell zone: 6 to 8 meters; shell, sand, barren, mud and decaying organic matter.
    Aphytal:
      5. Aphytal zone: 7 to 25 meters; mud, etc.

Muttkowski uses "littoral" as synonomous with "phytal," which is very proper in a lake like Mendota, where the depths of the zone of photosynthesis, the region of wave activity, and the epilimnion are practically the same, but in very turbid lakes the phytal zone may be thinner than that of wave action, and in clear, small lakes it may be thicker. At the head of a bay there may be no shoreline zone and the vegetation zone may come to the edge of the water, the conditions becoming like those of swamps. Along Isle Royal, Gleason (1909) observed that snails were confined to bays on account of wave action. In Lake Oneida, Baker (1918) found the greatest development of plants above the 6-foot contour line, and 88 per cent of the molluscs present were also above it. In Winona Lake, Headlee (1906) described the range of the mussels as extending from the shore to the beginning of soft mud. Allen (1922) states that mussels are restricted to the epilimnion chiefly by currents, temperature, dissolved gases, and especially by the character of the bottom. In general, Muttkowski's scheme fits lake shores very well. He does not consider the land immediately above the water line, however, which, as it is kept bare by storms and the pushing up of ice, is included by many writers among lake habitats as a littoral zone or zones. Muttkowski has been a purist in his classification, excluding muddy shorelines because he interprets them as swamps, and omitting what physiographers call the upper and middle beaches because they are not submerged. The "upper beach" is beyond the limit of the action of waves and ice and forms a transitional area to the land habitats above; the "middle beach" may be invaded by ice in winter and waves during summer storms but is above the surface of the lake when the water is quiet; the "lower beach" is covered by water and is subject to strong wave action.

Littoral Animals.—A characteristic but varied group of animals lives in littoral habitats. Depending on the character of the bottom, vegetation, waves, and other factors, there are swimmers, burrowers, clingers, climbers among plants, etc. Many caddisfly larvæ have flattened cases and thus are not readily rolled over by waves; waterpennies escape the impact of moving water by their flatness and the extreme thinness of their edges. Chironomids are able to live in sandy beaches by spinning threads to fasten the shifting grains together, and quickly build new shelters when rendered homeless by storms. The food relations of littoral animals are diverse. There are scavengers, predators, phytophages, etc. The phytophagous species are, of course, largely associated with the shore vegetation. In the zone below the vegetation the majority of the animals are detritus feeders. The physiological adjustments of animals to shore waters are as varied as the habitats. Some animals live in soft mud where there is little oxygen and others spend their lives on wave-swept rocks. There are also many special adaptations for reproduction. Altogether the shore animals constitute a group of great variety with specializations for various modes of life, but often showing considerable unity in special habitats.

Association *a*. Animals of Hard Beaches

Firm bottoms are developed where strong currents or waves continually sweep the shore and prevent the deposition of fine sediment. In such situations a number of animals live and many are adapted in various ways to withstand or take advantage of the conditions associated with moving water, but there is little in freshwater habitats that is comparable to the barnacles, mussels, and other animals that live along the shores of the ocean on the exposed surfaces of rocks where they are subjected to the full force of waves. All the hard-bottom animals along lake shores live in crevices or beneath stones, where they are more or less continually in turbulent water but are not struck directly by waves or by the objects moved by them.   Clay beaches are either rather barren where wave swept, or are soon invaded by aquatic vegetation and converted into muddy-bottom habitats where they are in quiet water.   Rocky shores and the wooden structures made by man are the typical hard-bottom habitats in freshwater. The only plant that is abundant and characteristic is the branching, filamentous alga, Cladophora, which is well suited to live in moving water and often shelters many small animals.   Other algæ (Rivularia, diatoms, etc.) occur and often help in forming calcareous encrustations over the surfaces of rocks.

Stratum 1.   Beaches above Water.—The upper and middle beaches are rather barren regions on rocky shores, particularly if the rock face is vertical or overhangs the water.   Cliffs, however, are favorite resorts for certain birds, such as kingfishers and swallows, which seek their food in or above the water.   A few transient spiders, ants, beetles, and land snails may hunt over the rock surfaces or hide in sheltered crannies.   If the beach slopes up from the lake, it may have a scattered covering of lichens and in the upper part support a considerable variety of flowering plants.   Here logs and other drift lodge and furnish shelter for insects (grasshoppers, ants, flies), land isopods and snails, frogs, toads, lizards, spiders, chipmunks, and mice.   Some of these animals commonly hunt along the shoreline for insects and other stranded organic materials left by the waves.   Gulls, crows, and blackbirds also frequently forage in such places.   Butterflies and dragon-flies fly over open beaches.   Pools above the reach of waves on rock beaches usually vary considerably in temperature, often being warmer than the lake during the day and cooler during the night.   Most of the animals in such pools can migrate if conditions become too unfavorable, or are easily transported by birds or other wandering animals.   The flora usually consists of algæ and is scanty.   Such animals as hydras, amphipods, entomostracans, immature and adult insects (water-boatmen, water-striders, caddis-flies, dragon- and damsel-flies, dytiscid and hydrophilid beetles), snails (Physa, Limnæa, Planorbis), and shore birds may be present.

Stratum 2.   Animals along Shoreline.—Just below the surface of the water there is the most violent wave motion to be found anywhere on lake shores.   On smooth rock surfaces there are no animals that live continuously along the shoreline, but during quiet weather animals from the vegetation zone below commonly migrate up into this stratum, particularly at night.

Stratum 3. Animals of Rachion.—Where there are stones that are large enough to remain unmoved during storms, the shoreline has a flourishing population beneath the stones and among Cladophora growths. Burrowing insects, larvæ, oligochætes, leeches, and fishes like the miller's thumb and fan-tailed darter are also more common where the beach consists of separate stones. The fauna on these shores is characteristic and often strikingly adapted to the conditions; leeches and may-fly nymphs are flattened and cling tightly; the cases of caddis-flies are rhomboidal or flattened, and may even have lateral flanges to prevent rolling (Molanna); the beetle larvæ (Psephenus) are extremely flat; the snails and leeches have large adhering surfaces; the miller's thumb and fan-tailed darter are fishes with big heads and large mouths that lurk in crevices and are able to dart out to capture food. At the breaker line there is little or no accumulation of shells and other heavier materials as on sandy shores, and few animals are present unless there is shelter beneath rocks.

Stratum 4. Animals of Vegetation.—The animals of the vegetation zone are not very different from those above where there are broken rocks on a beach, but on smooth rock surfaces there are often heavier growths of algæ below the breaker line, and among these amphipods, snails, and insect larvæ find shelter and food.

Stratum 5. Sublittoral Zone.—The sublittoral zone usually occurs at greater depths on rocky shores than elsewhere because, being exposed on outstanding points of land, the beaches are subject to more violent wave action. Here the tube-dwelling chironomids and oligochætes, burrowing larvæ and worms, and snails feed on the accumulated organic materials from zones above.

Association *b*. Animals of Sandy Beaches

On superficial examination sandy beaches may appear to be rather barren, but many such situations teem with life.

Stratum 1. Drift Line.—Sand is a shifting substratum, in water or on land. Along sandy lake shores there are often moving dunes and smaller sand waves that are frequently shifted by winds. On the upper beach, grasses continually over- grow moving sand waves, and, when they stop them, are succeeded in the northern hemisphere by poplars, willows, and oaks. On the middle beach there is usually an abundance of drift and this, by furnishing food and shelter, makes conditions favorable for land animals. Spiders, ants, tiger beetles, toads, skunks, and other predators come here to feed. There are also many scavengers that depend on the drift line for food. On the shore of Lake Michigan, Needham (Folsom, 1922) counted 4000 insects in 1 liter of drift. On the same lake Miss Snow (1902) identified 114 species of insects in drift during a month and a half in spring. She found the greatest numbers were washed up when an offshore was followed by an onshore wind. Wheeler (1887) pointed out that the insects washed up along the drift line were largely flyers and often nocturnal. Herms (1907) made a careful study of the constitutent animals of drift along Lake Erie. After a storm there were 538 fishes per mile. Herms gives a list of scavenger insects, among which flies and beetles are important. Along the shores of Saginaw Bay, Lake Huron, Ruthven (1911) found few animals, apparently because logs and other drift were soon covered over by sand.

Stratum 2. **Animals of Shoreline.**—Barren, sandy shoals along the shoreline are favorite resorts for young fishes of various species. There are also some dragon-fly nymphs that burrow along the edge of the water, and podurans live in or on the sand.

Stratum 3. **Rachion.**—The rachion is usually marked by pebbles and shells, and is frequented by such fishes as the Johnny darter, which feeds on burrowing chironomid larvæ and oligochætes. If there is a considerable extent of shallow water, a bar is usually built at some distance from the shoreline. This protects the water on its exposed side from the action of waves and the number of animals is usually greater on account of its presence. Along the outer margins of such bars, fishes (Johnny darter, minnows, bass) often clear off spaces for nests.

Stratum 4. **Submerged Beach below Rachion.**—Below the breaker line the miller's thumb may lurk among gravel and in the sand are oligochætes and chironomids. Caddis-fly larvæ that build cases of sand grains and creep about over the bottom are often common, dragon-fly nymphs and crayfishes also lie half buried in the sand or forage over the bottom. If plants get a foothold in this stratum, they may gradually dominate it and mud accumulates among them. Very often a sandy shoreline and rachion are succeeded in deeper water by a vegetation zone which has the characteristics of the next association to be described. Mussels flourish on sandy shores, but do not live among dense growths of vegetation. On the other hand, snails are rather rare on clean sand, but increase in numbers when vegetation is present. Animals (hydra, etc.) and plants may be attached to the shells of molluscs or to other solid objects that exist on sandy shores and animals (Hyalella, damsel-fly nymphs, etc.) may live among the plants that grow on such objects. In Lake Oneida, which is shallow, Baker (1918) found animals were twice as numerous on sandy bottoms as on rocks, but Muttkowski (1918) and Gleason (1909) in large, deep lakes found more animals on rocks than on sand.

Stratum 5. Sublittoral Zone.—The sublittoral zone on sandy beaches is often made up largely of the shells of molluscs. It is populated by many of the burrowers that live in the zone above. Chironomid larvæ and oligochætes form the greater part of the population, but such animals as snails, leeches, amphipods, caddis-fly and may-fly larvæ may be present.

Stratum 6. Shorewater.—The shorewater on sandy beaches is continually contributing plankton to shore habitats; much of this when dead settles into the sublittoral region and serves as food for the animals there.

ASSOCIATION *c*. ANIMALS OF MUDDY BEACHES

Muddy beaches occur only where there is little wave movement. They are usually overgrown with vegetation and thickly populated with animal life. The bottom sediments, the large and small plants and animals that grow on them, and the shorewater all furnish food resources that are rich in organic compounds. Aeration is not always good, however, especially where there is much decaying material on the bottom or where photosynthesis is cut off below the surface by coatings of floating plants. Animals on mud beaches have abundant food and are in little danger of injury by waves, but may easily suffocate if they are not especially equipped for respiration in poorly aerated water. In the accumulations of organic bottom materials there may be oscillatorias, beggiatoas, and fungi.

Number of Animals on Muddy Bottoms.—In Lake Oneida, Baker (1918) estimated the number of animals over muddy bottoms, giving his figures as the average number on 16 square inches. Between 1 and 6 feet there were 36.66; 6 to 12 feet,

2.30; 14 to 18 feet, 1.52. In Lake Winnebago (Wisconsin), which is 45 kilometers (28 miles) long and has a maximum depth of 6.38 meters (20.75 feet), Baker (1924) found animals on the bottom in the following numbers per square meter: boulders 331, gravel 1578, sand 1325, mud 1449, vegetation 4400, average 1626. Muttkowski (1918) does not include muddy bottoms in his excellent discussion of the littoral region of Lake Mendota, apparently because he feels that muddy shores are to be looked upon as tributaries but not parts of the lake proper.

Strata on Muddy Beaches.—The shores above the water (Stratum 1) are frequented by foraging birds, rodents, insects, and spiders, and are favorite resorts for basking turtles. The quietness of the water along muddy shores permits the existence of an abundance of surface animals (Stratum 2), such as toad bugs, water-striders, and gyrinid beetles. Ducks, grebes, and other birds also resort to them to feed. The shoreline and rachion (Strata 3 and 4) are often poorly developed or absent. The vegetation zone (Stratum 5) may extend up to the edge of the water and in many cases grades into emergent vegetation, which is characteristic of swamps and may shelter such animals as red-winged blackbirds, swamp sparrows, and rails. The amphibious snails wander in and out of the water; among the plants live snails, insects (bugs, beetles, odonate nymphs, etc.), sunfishes, breams, bullheads, mudminnows, frogs, and turtles. Many of the animals are facultative or obligate air breathers and come to the surface at intervals for respiration. Certain animals (oligochætes, chironomid larvæ, nematodes, bryozoans), however, live attached to or resting upon submerged plants. The sublittoral zone (Stratum 6) on a muddy shore supports the usual group of detritus feeders (snails, sphæridæ, chironomids, etc.). In the shorewater (Stratum 7) over muddy bottoms there is usually quite a distinctive group of organisms, many of which are not found in other parts of lakes. There are plankton animals that seldom occur in open waters and species, such as certain rotifers, copepods, and ostracods, which usually creep about on plants. There may be leeches and insect larvæ which are usually attached or buried in the bottom. On the whole, the shore plankton animals are less transparent than those of open water.

ASSOCIATION d. ANIMALS OF LAGOONS

Lagoons are cut off from the molar activity of the open lake by bars which support emergent vegetation. They are often more like swamps than muddy shores. The lack of wave motion is associated with an abundance of surface animals (Stratum 2). Hall (1924) has described a lagoon where floating plants covered the water so completely that they prevented photosynthesis below the surface; putrefaction and other activities used up practically all the oxygen. Doubtless, similar conditions obtain in many lagoons. There is usually an abundance of plant and animal food, but the water is often poorly aerated.

Animals in Lagoons.—The animals in lagoons are largely associated with the aquatic vegetation, using it for food or shelter. Turtles and frogs may remain submerged for considerable periods, but the vegetation is thick enough so that it gives them support when they wish to rest at the surface. Jacanas, rails, and other birds commonly run over the floating plants. Insects and snails crawl on the surface or lurk among the plants. Certain plants, like the water lily and cat-tail, support interesting and characteristic societies. The plankton, as on muddy beaches, differs from that in open water in the species present and in the greater degree of pigmentation.

Association *e*. Animals of Estuaries

Estuaries usually resemble lagoons in having a soft bottom composed of sediment that contains much organic material, but they differ in containing flowing water. The latter peculiarity has marked effect on the animal life. Gyrinid beetles and water-striders are usually abundant about eddies where jetsam gathers. The water, on account of its movement, is rather well aerated and contains many plankton organisms that have come from stream habitats. The bottom is often thickly carpeted with mussels. River snails and burrowing oligochætes, chironomid larvæ, and may-fly nymphs may be abundant. The vegetation often teems with sponges, hydras, planarians, bryozoans, and insects that depend more or less on flowing water for food and that are not common in lagoons. Certain fishes (breams, tadpole cats, etc.) have favorite resorts at the mouths of streams. Estuaries with sandy bottoms and few or no aquatic plants may be barren.

Formation 2. Limnetic Animals

The animals that live in the open water of lakes are largely minute mites, crustaceans, rotifers, and protozoans, which, with countless floating plants, constitute the plankton. There are also some nekton animals, such as trout and herring gulls, that frequent open waters. In general, there are few limnetic species in a lake, but there are often enormous numbers of individuals. There seems to be general agreement that there is, as a rule, more plankton per unit of area in freshwater than in the ocean (Johnstone, 1908; Lohmann, 1911). Probably this is due largely to the lesser extent of bodies of freshwater. In shallow lakes there are undoubtedly more plankton animals per unit of volume than in those of greater depth. Warming (1909) states that the plants of the limnoplankton constitute one of the most cosmopolitan of formations. In deep lakes there are relatively more plankton animals and fewer plants. Steuer (1910) points out that in the lakes of temperate regions diatoms are usually the dominant plants from December to July and that schizophytes lead from August to November. Rotifers reach their maximum number in summer; crustaceans often have maxima in spring and autumn. The maximum for all plankton plants and animals together usually comes in May in the northern hemisphere. In a lake, seasonal conditions in a particular year may make a certain species dominant, but in another year another species may lead. In alpine lakes crustacea often constitute the major portion of the plankton (Juday, 1907). Steuer (1910) classifies limnetic plankton as (1) true limnetic; (2) passive limnetic (Heliozoa, etc.); (3) tycholimnetic (brought into open water by winds and currents); (4) merolimnetic (*e.g.*, Corethra larvæ, which spend much time in bottom mud); and (5) pseudolimnetic (detritus, bodies of insects, etc.).

Adaptations of Plankton Animals.—The limnetic plankton animals are generally transparent, and when pigment is present, it occurs as small specks. They often have thin shells and means for flotation (oil, surface film attachments) or for impeding sinking (helmets, crests, spines, etc.). Many of them swim well and without much effort, but progress slowly and cannot make headway against strong currents. They are generally adapted to be near but not actually at the surface. Wilson (1917), however, describes larval parasitic copepods which

. . . have the ability possessed by many of the free swimmers, of holding themselves suspended from the surface film of the water by means of their antennæ, their bodies hanging in a vertical position, and they often come to rest in this manner and remain for some minutes.

Wesenberg-Lund (1908) has pointed out that flotation devices wax and wane as the viscosity of the water changes with the seasons. In winter they are least apparent and begin to increase as the water warms and becomes less viscous in the spring. Wesenberg-Lund believes that plankton organisms each year recapitulate their history since glacial times as they change from winter to summer forms.

Limnetic Zones.—The limnetic region of a lake that has a depth of more than about 8 meters shows a rather definite stratification. The thickness of the epilimnion varies with the progress of the seasonal cycle and according to the shape, direction, and area of the surface and the consequent effects of winds. The effects of waves seldom are felt below a depth of about 2 meters, the extent of their influence varying with their height, which, in turn, depends on the size of a lake and the force of the wind that causes them. The zone of photosynthesis varies with the turbidity of the water and the roughness of its surface. The mesolimnion varies in depth and thickness. When a lake is more than 40 meters deep the hypolimnion, even when plenty of oxygen is present, has an upper zone in which there is little life because there is a lack of food. If the deeper water of a lake stagnates and loses its oxygen, many animals migrate into the epilimnion. When the depth is over 70 meters, the whole lake usually is poor in plankton. Many instances of stratification of limnetic organisms have been recorded. Whipple (1896) described the distribution of diatoms. Needham and Lloyd (1916, p. 308) give excellent diagrams that show the distribution of various algæ and protozoans. Juday (1912) refers to an interesting observation by Parker in Lake Cocituate: Synura was not found above depths of 4.5 or below 12 meters. The limiting factor in this case was believed to be temperature, the range for the organism being 6.4 to 19.2°C. and the optimum, 9.2 to 10.4°C. In an alpine lake, Haempel (1918) found three strata: (1) 0 to 3 meters, dominated by mastigophorans; (2) 3 to 10 meters, populated largely by cladocerans; (3) 10 to 40 meters, mostly copepods. In Lake Mendota, Birge (1897) found that plankton was rather uniformly distributed in winter, though one species of Daphnia and young Cyclops were more abundant in upper strata. In summer, 44 to 45 per cent of the crustaceans were in the upper three meters. The young of nearly all species of crustaceans lived at higher levels than adults. There were most crustaceans of all ages at a depth of about half a meter. Food, temperature, and gases all exerted important influences in distribution; light, wind, and gravity were apparently less potent. Stagnation below the thermocline drove out most of the limnetic animals. Light was only important in the upper meter or two. During the day young crustaceans remained near the surface, thus avoiding competition with older individuals. It was noticed that the latter swam upward with greater difficulty. The young of Cyclops were most abundant near the thermocline. In Green Lake, Marsh (1901) observed that Limnocalanus was characteristic of an intermediate region, but occurred above and below in smaller numbers. The depth of the maximum amount of plankton varies widely in different types of lakes, and there is usually little below depths of 35 to 85 meters (Steuer, 1910). Steuer states that stratification usually depends primarily on temperature. In the Bodensee in summer he found Diaptomus and Cylops at all depths; rotifers, Daphnia, and Bosmina were confined to the warm upper stratum (0 to 15 meters); Leptodora was distributed largely between 7 and 18 meters; in the deep, cold water (15 to 28 meters) were Heterocope and *Cyclops strenuus*.

Food in Limnetic Region.—The food resources in the limnetic region depend on photosynthesis. Deep lakes are usually plankton-poor lakes and the depth of the maximum of food resources varies in different types of lakes. Steuer (1910) gives the figures in Table V, which show comparable catches of plank-

TABLE V.—PLANKTON AT VARIOUS DEPTHS IN THREE EUROPEAN LAKES
Expressed in Cubic Centimeters per Unit of Area

Depth, meters	Plöner See	Luntzer See	Neuenburger See
0–2	76.0	6.1	1
2–5	15.2	44.1	2.8
5–10	15.2	56.2	9.9

ton in three European lakes. In the alpine lake listed at the right of the table, the greatest quantity of plankton is at depths of 5 to 10 meters and near the surface there is nothing; in the plains lake (left) there is most near the surface. In lakes the average quantity of available food in each unit of volume generally decreases as the sizes of lakes increase. The quantity of the net plankton is often far below that of the nannoplankton. In Wisconsin lakes the latter varies from slightly less to fifteen or twenty times as great. "Large amount of plankton is usually associated with much CO_2, little oxygen, and a large amount of dissolved carbonate" (Ward and Whipple, 1918). In Green Lake, Juday (1924) found that the dry organic matter from the net plankton varied from 73 to 1135 milligrams per cubic meter and that of the nannoplankton from 795 to 3151. In the former, 53 per cent was crude protein and 12 per cent was extractable by ether; in the latter, crude protein was 43 per cent and ether extract 6.5 per cent. As in other habitats, the quantity of life that may exist depends on the quantity of green plants and the zone of photosynthesis produces these. Rotifers and crustaceans, which are largely confined to the epilimnion in summer, feed directly on plants. Crustaceans, not plants, are the chief food of fishes, like the ciscoes and perch, that feed on plankton. Gulls, terns, fish ducks, trout, and lawyers in turn feed on fishes. In summer, food may be more abundant near the surface and certain animals may migrate there, but in winter the region near the bottom supports most of them. Plankton continually settles down and mingles with the bottom ooze, which supports a group of animals (chironomids, crustaceans, etc.) that furnishes food for many limnetic animals.

Limnetic Plankton Migrations.—Many plankton animals migrate up and down each day, especially during the summer. In an alpine lake Juday (1907) found no periodic diurnal movements and Steuer (1910) notes that such movements decrease or cease in winter. In some cases the extent of migrations is proportional to the amount of light. Young plankton animals move less than adults. Steuer states that peridinians may move downward as much as 2 meters on cold nights. Crustaceans may move 40 meters. Most migrants come to the surface at night and descend into deeper water during the day. Not all species, however, reach the surface at the same time. In bright sunlight even young crustaceans desert the upper half meter. Juday (1921) has described the migrations of the phantom larva (*Corethra punctipennis*) in Lake Mendota. This insect comes to the surface about 1.25 hours after sunset and at 10 p.m. as many as 4730 per square meter were found at the surface. At 4 a.m. all had left the surface and by half an hour after sunrise the majority were buried in the bottom mud, 23 meters below the scene of their midnight foray. Leptodora is a crustacean that makes extensive

vertical migrations.   In summer most migrants in the epilimnion
do not descend below the mesolimnion, and many move only a
meter or two.

ASSOCIATION *a*.   ANIMALS OF EPILIMNION

The stratum of photosynthesis and summer warmth supports
more life per unit of area than any below it, but large surface
invertebrates, like the pteropods, cephalopods, ctenophores, and
medusæ of the pelagic province of the ocean, are completely lacking.   Neither are there any specialized nekton animals that are
comparable to the flying fishes and whales of the open ocean.
Crustacea, rotifers, and flagellates make up the bulk of the animal
plankton; the nekton fishes are largely salmonoids which not only
frequent the open lake, but at certain seasons invade littoral or
deep-water habitats to feed, breed, or pass the winter.   In
temperate regions the epilimnion is clearly defined by distinctive
temperatures only during summer; in winter many of its plankton
animals are rather evenly distributed in a lake from top to bottom.
Daphnia and Bosmina in summer migrate up and down in the
epilimnion but in winter migrate little and are scattered throughout lakes (Steuer, 1910, p. 347).   During summer in Lake
Mendota the black crappie, white bass, and yellow perch feed on
plankton and insects throughout the epilimnion, but in winter are
found only near shore or in deep water.

ASSOCIATION *b*.   ANIMALS OF HYPOLIMNION

In freshwater there is nothing comparable to the fauna of the
"twilight zone" of the ocean.   Throughout the year there is a
stratum where light decreases to little or nothing.   In summer
there is a well-established mesolimnion where temperature
changes rapidly and where oxygen may decrease and carbon
dioxide increase.   The writer's observations (1920*a*) indicate
that fishes do not migrate along the line between warm and cold
water or between water that is with or without oxygen, but have
relations primarily with the surface, bottom, or shore.   The
mesolimnion serves as a barrier in the vertical migrations of many
animals and is invaded at times by animals that normally live
above or below it, but has no proper fauna of its own.

The hypolimnion, however, has certain characteristic animals.
Juday (1919) has described a ciliate that appears in Lake Men-

dota each summer when oxygen is used up in the hypolimnion and remains in abundance until the fall overturn.

There did not seem to be any correlation between the vertical distribution of this ciliate and the temperature of the water or the amount of free carbon dioxide, but there was a definite correlation with lack of dissolved oxygen.

The phantom larva also is found in the hypolimnion in summer. It goes near the surface and by secretion (Akehurst, 1922; Damant, 1924) fills its air sacs with enough oxygen to allow it to remain for a day or more in the oxygen-free bottom mud. During the summer stagnation season perch appear to invade the hypolimnion for brief periods in order to feed on bottom organisms (Pearse, 1920a). There are few or no lake fishes that live in deep, open water without relations with the bottom; no fauna like the bathypelagic of the ocean is present. In lakes that do not stagnate, but have a clearly defined hypolimnion, a number of organisms, like *Leptodora, Heterocope, Cyclops strenuus*, etc., live characteristically below the mesolimnion.

FORMATION 3. BOTTOM ANIMALS OF DEEP WATER

At a depth of 8 to 10 meters the bottom of a lake changes from the sublittoral to the soft ooze that is characteristic of deep water. The ooze may vary, but it always contains more or less of both mineral and organic sediments. The oozes in deep water are usually not so productive of animal life as muddy bottoms in littoral habitats, largely due to the absence of light for photosynthesis and the consequent dearth of organic food, but in many lakes stagnation is also a factor in keeping certain animals out of deep water. Shallow lakes in which water circulates freely at all depths and in which light penetrates to the bottom, or is an important factor in producing growths that have contact with the bottom, have no truly deep-water habitats and, though their bottoms may consist of oozy mud, are to be classified with littoral habitats. Deep-water deposits are usually not developed in depths of less than about 10 meters, and when they are in depths below 50 meters usually have a different fauna from that which is characteristic between 10 and 50 meters. Wesenberg-Lund (1905) has described a diatom ooze as being characteristic of cold lakes of moderate depth, but lacking in very deep lakes, apparently because it is dissolved. He also describes a black, fetid ooze that forms in shallow lakes from Cyanophyceæ and other materials. In small lakes without Cyanophyceæ there may be a chitinous ooze, formed from the shells of Daphnia and other organisms. Alm (1922) names various types of bottoms from the dominant animals that are usually found in them—chironomids, oligochætes, amphipods, turbellarians, etc. Ekman (1915) in discussing the bottom animals of the Vättern distinguishes those on mineral bottoms from those on chitinous ooze. To the writer the important factors that differentiate different types of bottom habitats appear to be: (1) presence or absence of organic food, (2) variable or low constant temperature, and (3) aeration of water. The less there is of organic food the fewer the animals present. On deep, cool bottoms where there is oxygen, ciscoes, Pontoporeia, and Mysis are characteristic; at moderate depths, even where the water is stagnant, dipterous larvæ are typical. Oligochætes, Pisidiums, and some other animals may occur in both situations.

Animals on Deep-lake Bottoms.—Lakes do not have a highly adapted abyssal fauna like that in the ocean, probably because they are geologically too evanescent, but below depths of 10 to 20 meters certain Sphæridæ, midge larvæ, oligochætes, nematodes, and protozoans are usually the dominant animals. Hydras, bryozoans, snails, and mites may also occur. In Lake Erie, Clemens (1922) found millions of hydras (*H. oligactis* Pallas) below the limits of wave action. In deep lakes there are often relicts from glacial times and some of these have marine affinities—Mysis, Pontoporeia, Chiridotea, etc. Calman (1915) believes that some deep-water animals (Asellus) show relationships to those occurring in ground waters. The smaller bottom animals support predatory fishes like the eel, ling, cottids, and yellow perch.

Vertical Ranges of Deep-water Animals.—In Lake Cayuga (depth, 133 meters) Baker (1918) found that molluscs were very scarce below 8 meters, and in Lake Nipigon (123 meters) Adamstone and Harkness (1923) also found that most of the molluscs were restricted to shallow bays, but in Lake Mendota (23 meters) Juday (1922) found an abundance of animals living in the bottom mud. Baker (1918) states that several species of molluscs occur in Georgian Bay at a depth of 37 meters and Ekman (1915) found no significant decrease at greater depths in the Vättern.

In Lake Nipigon the numbers of macroscopic bottom animals per square meter were as follows: molluscs, 178; oligochætes, 87; amphipods, 324; ephemerids, 25; trichopterans, 12; chironomids, 351; total, 1057 (Adamstone, 1924). For Lake Mendota, Juday (1922) gives the following average numbers per square meter in the deep water: oligochætes, 3500; Pisidium, 557; Chironomus, 593; Corethra, 10,830; Protenthes, 185. The dry weights in kilograms per hectare were: oligochætes, 4.6; Pisidium, 2.7; Sialis, 1.8; Chironomus, 22.8; Corethra, 16.0; Tanypus, 1.3; total, 48.2. Nipigon and Mendota may serve as examples of deep and intermediate lakes that are reasonably productive. Zschokke (1901) has given figures relating to the bottom animals in the alpine lakes in Europe; Ekman (1915) has done the same for Swedish lakes.

Depth apparently influences the distribution of certain bottom animals directly and that of others by its influence on other factors. The only molluscs that extend below 25 meters in Lake Michigan are Sphæridæ (Shelford, 1915). In Europe, however, there are snails at great depths (Forel, 1869). In Lake Michigan, yellow perch and common suckers never descend into deep water, while the long-nosed sucker and blackfin live only in deep water (Pearse, 1921). In Lake Nipigon, Clemens (1923) found that the northern sucker lived at lower levels than the common sucker and the "round" above the "common" whitefish. Some animals (Pontoporeia, Mysis) are never found in shallow water, but are most abundant in or near the soft ooze at the bottom of deep lakes. Juday (1924) in Green Lake found the greatest variety of species (thirty-nine) in the stratum between 1 and 10 meters and the least (fourteen) between 44 and 66 meters; the greatest number of individuals occurred between 20 and 40 meters, where there were fewest fishes, at least in summer (Pearse, 1921). Below a depth of 20 meters there were no Hyalellas, may-fly nymphs, Sialis nymphs, caddis-fly and Orthocladius larvæ, or snails. Zschokke (1906) in an alpine lake found that certain animals occurred at greater depths than in those in the lowlands, chironomid larvæ being common at 200 meters. Birge and Juday (1921) in the Finger Lakes in New York found chironomid larvæ at various depths up to 172 meters; at 113 meters in Lake Cayuga there were 3863 per square meter, far exceeding all other animals in numbers. In these lakes the amphipod, Pontoporeia,

was also abundant, and oligochætes in half the hauls furnished
more than half of the organic material.

In speaking of the bottom organisms of Lake Nipigon, Adamstone (1924) says:

There are two distinct groups of animals, the one inhabiting largely
the shallower water 0 to 30 feet deep, and the other forming the characteristic population of all areas of more than 180 feet deep.   The zone
between these depths, that is, 30 to 180 feet, is relatively unproductive.

He divides bottom animals into two groups as follows:

Shallow-water Fauna:
  Mollusca:
    Gastropoda
    Lamellibranchiata
  Chironomidæ
  Ephemerida
  Trichoptera
  Amphipoda
  Nematoda

Deep-water Fauna:
  Amphipoda
  Oligochæta
  Chironomidæ
  Ostracoda
  Mollusca:
    Lamellibranchiata

In Lake Ontario, Adamstone found that there was a higher
percentage of lime in the shallower water, which was, therefore,
favorable for the growth of molluscs, but that the percentage of
organic matter increased with depth, which was believed to
account in large measure for the increase in the number of certain
bottom animals at greater depths.

Migrations of Deep-water Animals.—In lakes where the deep
water becomes stagnant for a period between the spring and
autumn overturns, some bottom animals migrate into the
epilimnion (Limnesia, Sialis, Perca, Leuchthys) and remain, but
others (Corethra) swim up each day and secure a supply of oxygen.
Corethra larvæ escape from predaceous fishes by remaining buried
in the bottom mud during the day.   In Lake Mendota sixteen
genera of protozoans, many oligochætes, nematodes, gastrotrichs,
rotifers, an ostracod, a Cyclops, midge larvæ, and a Pisidium each
year remain for three months on or in the bottom mud in water
that contains no oxygen.   The Cyclops is enclosed in a cocoon;
the ostracod and the clam remain with the valves tightly closed;
the oligochætes, chironomid larvæ, and protozoans remain more
or less active (Birge and Juday, (1911).

Food of Deep-water Animals.—The food of bottom-dwelling
Sphæridæ, amphipods, oligochætes, and midge larvæ consists
largely of organic ooze.   The protozoans consume bacteria and

other minute organic particles. The bottom fishes for the most part feed on plankton as well as bottom organisms and ooze. The yellow perch may feed at times at the surface or among water plants and at times grub about in the ooze. The ciscoes eat mostly Mysis, Pontoporeia, entomostracans, and small fishes. The whitefishes prefer insect larvæ, molluscs, and fishes. The cottids prey on amphipods and schizopods. The ling and trout catch insects and fishes. Suckers are the only fishes that consume ostracods and mud in considerable amounts. Juday (1924) says of Green Lake:

> Considering the entire lake, the dry organic matter in the average standing crop of total plankton was ten times as large as the dry weight of the total bottom population [littoral and deep water], but the organic matter of the average crop of plankton, rotifers, and Crustacea amounted to only one-fifth of the dry weight of the bottom population.

Moore (1922) in speaking of the plants of Lake George stresses the importance of algæ that grow at depths of from 6 to 15 meters as food and shelter for young trout and other fishes.

With the exception of Corethra larvæ, bottom-dwelling invertebrates are small, weak, and, though they usually burrow, in some cases swim feebly. Food settles continually from above and hiding is easy on account of the absence of light and the presence of the soft mud. At times lack of oxygen or unusual amounts of sediment may suffocate bottom animals, but they are generally able to escape such dangers. Except for Corethra larvæ, none of the animals requires contact with the atmosphere and many are able to spend long periods without oxygen. Most of the bottom animals are dull in color and a few have degenerate eyes. Most of the fishes that frequent the bottoms in deep water are also found at higher levels, but there are a few (ling, cottids, etc.) that are not.

ASSOCIATION *a*.   BOTTOM ANIMALS OF MODERATELY DEEP LAKES
HAVING VARIABLE BOTTOM TEMPERATURES

Midge larvæ, chironomids, Sphæridæ ostracods, and protozoans are typical animals on or in the bottoms of lakes (Stratum 1) having depths up to 25 meters. Above the bottom (Stratum 2) swim such fishes as yellow perch and suckers, which feed more or less on the mud-dwelling invertebrates. There are also certain pelagic animals (Leptodora, Limnocalanus) that rest near the bottom, especially during the day.

Association *b*. Bottom Animals of Deep, Cool Lakes

Below 25 meters, lakes with increasing depth contain more of the relicts, Pontoporeia and Mysis, and fewer midge larvæ. Ostracods and clams may be abundant and in some European lakes there are snails, isopods, and mites. Typical fishes are lings, cottids, ciscoes, and eels.

Subprovince B(b). Animals of Ponds

There is, of course, a gradual transition from lakes to ponds and a small lake has general characteristics and an animal population more or less like those of a pond. The shallowness and the limited area make the effects of wave action slight, and floating or emergent vegetation reduces such motion still more. In ponds there are no limnetic or deep-water formations. Svec (1897) studied the infusorians in ponds and found seven pelagic, sixty-nine littoral, and few individuals of six bottom species. The littoral region of a lake shows a great variety of habitats, but a pond is usually rather monotonous. Ponds may differ greatly from one another, however. Scott (1910) has made it clear that inland ponds are colonized accidentally by plants and animals that enter soon after the ponds are formed. The first immigrants to arrive, having no competition, soon spread, and dominate the pond and give it its particular "character." Shelford (1913) has pointed out that aquatic vegetation is characteristic of older ponds and that bare, sandy bottom is usually found only in young ponds. Reed (1901) found the following vegetation zones in Michigan ponds: (1) Characeæ, (2) Potamogeton, (3) Nymphæa, (4) Carex and Sphagnum, (5) Salix and Populus, (6) Gramineæ and Compositæ. In general, the types of plants mentioned are arranged in the order of their succession in ponds. In youth, a pond may support patches of stoneworts on its clean bottom; as sediments accumulate and adolescence approaches, submerged and floating plants increase; at maturity sedges and other emergent plants begin to invade the pond from its margins; in old age, land plants gain a foothold and gradually the pond is converted into a terrestrial habitat. The usual succession of ponds is from bare bottom, to vegetation-covered bottom, to swamp, to land. As a pond grows older its animal life increases in quantity and, with poorer aeration and more putrefaction, there is an increase in the proportion of types that depend more on the atmosphere than on the water for respiration.

Fischer (1924) has made careful studies of the amounts of phosphorus, potassium, and nitrogen compounds in fishponds in Europe. He finds that nitrogenous compounds are usually not removed, but are deposited in ponds, and that nitrogen-fixing organisms are usually present in considerable numbers. In general, fishes increase or decrease as phosphorus increases and decreases. Fischer concludes that phosphorus compounds and nitrogen-fixing bacteria are the chief limiting factors in the production of animal life, particularly fishes, in ponds.

FORMATION 1. LITTORAL ANIMALS

All animals in ponds occur in habitats that resemble the littoral regions of lakes and most of the plants and animals are the same in the two situations. Ponds differ from lakes, however, in the absence of limnetic species which at times invade littoral lake habitats.

ASSOCIATION *a*. ANIMALS OF PONDS WITH BARE BOTTOMS

Young ponds are populated by species of mussels, snails, immature insects, and fishes that may also occur in lakes and rivers. The fishes are those that require well-aerated water for respiration or bare bottom for breeding (Shelford, 1911c). The shores have the usual animals associated with the margins of bodies water. The water itself contains some plankton organisms. The population, however, is usually, on the whole, rather scanty.

ASSOCIATION *b*. ANIMALS OF PONDS CONTAINING VEGETATION

Old ponds usually support an abundant plant and animal population. On the beaches above the water (Stratum 1), spiders, toads, frogs, and many terrestrial animals are to be found. On the surface of the water (Stratum 2), bugs and beetles seek food, and many from below (mosquito larvæ, back swimmers, Scapholeberis, etc.) commonly hang from the surface film. Ducks, grebes, and other birds are also attracted to ponds by vegetation and the animals associated with it. Along the shoreline (Stratum 3) many insects and other animals resort. Adams (1909) noted that aquatic beetles were more abundant near the margins than toward the center; Needham and Williamson (1907) showed that the size of beetles is graded according to the distance from shore, the larger species being farther out in the water. The vegetation (Stratum 4) in ponds supports a large animal population. Immature and adult insects, snails, clams (Sphæridæ), leeches, rotifers, entomostracans, amphipods, oligochætes, nematodes, and protozoans climb about on plants. Among the stems and leaves lurk shrimps, crayfishes, bullheads, mudminnows, breams, and crappies. Attached to the aquatic plants are midge larvæ, bryozoans, hydras, worms, rotifers, and protozoans. Among the plants, turtles, muskrats, and fishes move about, seeking food and shelter. There are also many microscopic animals (entomostracans, mites, rotifers, protozoans) that swim about in the water of ponds (Stratum 5). Not many animals are associated with the bottom (Stratum 6) and some of those that are (rat-tailed larva) have special adaptations for securing air from the surface.

Subprovince B(c). Swamp, Bog, and Pool Animals

In swamps, bogs, and pools the amount of water varies greatly, and at certain seasons water above the soil may be absent altogether. There is often a general relation between the sizes of animals and the volume of the water in which they live; some species grow larger in large bodies of water and some large animals are not present in small bodies. The season of failing water may also directly influence the life cycles of animals. Metamorphoses may be shortened by lack of water; encystment or æstivation may be brought about by changes in the level or content of water.

FORMATION 1. SWAMP AND BOG ANIMALS

Swamps and bogs are usually surrounded by zones of vegetation, which grow more mesophytic and less hydrophytic at higher levels. Swamps are shallow and especially characterized by the presence of emergent vegetation with submerged roots. There is shelter above the surface of the water. Bogs have vegetation, like Sphagnum, which covers part of the surface of the water and the surrounding soil. Sphagnum has remarkable ability to hold water and in some cases makes "climbing bogs" by growing up inclines. The floating plants in bogs and swamps are not the same as the plankton plants of lakes, but largely megaphytes, like Lemna, Ceratophyllum, etc. Even the algæ are not those species characteristic of lakes. Swamp plants are largely perennials, but where a whole area dries up, there may be a preponderance of annuals. Adventitious roots and runners are common and many plants migrate by vegetative propagation. Some plants have two forms which appear above or below the water.

The animal population of bogs and swamps may be dense, but usually presents little variety. There is a more or less definite zonation of certain animals in relation to the shore and stratification with reference to submerged and emergent vegetation. The extreme and sudden variations in temperature and the shallowness keep out limnetic species.

Association *a*. Animals of Swamps

The animal population of swamps may vary greatly at different seasons on account of fluctuations in the height of the water.

Stratum 1. Emergent Vegetation.—The emergent vegetation of swamps is a favorite resort for many birds—rails, bitterns, herons, coots, grebes, swamp sparrows, marsh wrens, blackbirds, bearded titmouse, etc. Most of these find food among the aquatic vegetation. There are also predaceous birds (marsh hawk, short-eared owl) that live about the margins of swamps and hunt among the plants. In winter, meadow voles come in from surrounding terrestrial habitats and live on the ice among the matted vegetation. Muskrats at all seasons find food and shelter in swamps. Most of the invertebrates live on or below the surface of the water throughout most of the year, but in summer there are often many adult insects and emerging nymphs above the water. Amphibious snails also crawl about. Certain spiders (Tetragnatha, etc.) are commonly found. At the margins of swamps there are a number of hangers-on that may live on land or spread out into the swamps on the emergent vegetation. Certain grasshoppers, slugs, frogs, and snakes commonly frequent such situations.

Stratum 2. Surface of Water.—On the surface of the water are water-striders, whirligig beetles, bugs, and spiders. With these are associated frogs and other small animals that hop over the surface of the floating vegetation.

Stratum 3. Submerged Vegetation.—In the submerged vegetation are protozoans, rotifers, nematodes, water-bugs and beetles, insect larvæ and nymphs (dragon-flies, mosquitoes), ostracods, amphipods, isopods, snails, Sphæridæ, mudminnows, bullheads, and turtles. Needham and Williamson (1907) found that dytiscids were largely confined to the cat-tail zone; also that the largest and strongest swimmers ranged furthest from shore. Some animals (Hydra, entomostracans, etc.) that live among the vegetation frequently hang from the surface film (Scourfield, 1911).

Stratum 4. Swamp Water.—The standing water in swamps supports little life that is peculiar. Many of the small animals that swim about are associated primarily with vegetation.

Stratum 5. Bottom Animals.—The bottom animals are few in swamps at time of high water, but in time of drought the bottom muck may serve as a refuge for æstivating insects, snails, and other animals. The vegetation becoming matted over the bottom also helps to conserve moisture and animals may survive dry periods beneath it.

Desiccation of Swamp Animals.—Desiccation is a common experience for most swamp animals and many of them are able to become encysted or assume other resting states. Rotifers, tardigrades, and nematodes can readily survive drying (Baumann, 1922). Mrázek (1913) reported an oligochæte that multiplied within a cyst wall when dried. Frierson (1899) states that a clam, *Unio declivis* Lea, can live for nine months in dry mud without free water. Mudminnows can remain buried in mud for some time and when a swamp dries up completely may migrate to water by wiggling over the land (Gill, 1903). Lepidosiren, when a swamp dries up, burrows into the deepest part, shoves a clay plug up to close itself in, curls its tail over its nose, and remains alive in a slime and mud "cocoon" for months. The eggs of snails, like Limnæa and Aplexa (Baker, 1914), remain alive in dry mud at the bottoms of swamp pools. The winter eggs of swamp cladocerans stand drying (Morgan, 1907).

Effects of Stagnation and Decay of Organic Materials.—Swamps on account of their shallowness, great amount of organic matter, and lack of water circulation are often quite foul and may at times have little oxygen in their aquatic habitats. Under such conditions some chloryphyll-bearing organisms, such as Euglena and certain infusorians, may flourish. The lack of well-aerated water, however, is doubtless associated with the fact that the majority of swamp animals are air breathers. Lack of oxygen may also hasten the metamorphosis of swamp animals (Morgan, 1907). Where large amounts of carbon dioxide and other substances are present, acidity may be an important factor. Warming (1909) states that reed swamps are characteristic of stagnant or acid water. Jewell (1923) found no Cyprinidæ or molluscs in a swampy lake having a pH of 4.4 with abundant oxygen, but certain fishes (perch, bullhead, pickerel) were abundant. In many swamps decay is largely inhibited by acidity and peat accumulates.

Reproduction in Swamps.—The conditions in swamps in many ways influence the reproductive activities of swamp animals. The decay of rubbish may maintain a high temperature even during cold seasons, and animals that resort to swamps may be able to breed earlier or for longer periods than those in other habitats. Morgan (1907) points out that certain swamp clado-cerans have two periods of sexual activity—in July and October. The "winter" eggs of these crustaceans can stand drying and may be produced more than once a year. Kennedy (1907) says the swamp species of odonates in the genera Lestes and Sympetrum are adapted in various ways. There is only one brood produced each year; eggs winter over and hatch with the beginning of spring rains. In temperate regions swamps often afford the earliest open water and in spring furnish more or less warm, protected situations. Amphibians use them for the deposition of their eggs. When the hot stagnation of midsummer comes, most of the tadpoles have turned largely to air breathing and some have become wholly terrestrial. The exact situations where frogs' eggs are deposited are nicely adjusted to various conditions, according to Wright (1921). Some eggs are deposited singly, other in great masses; eggs may float, adhere to sticks, sink to the bottom, etc. Turner and Bahr (1907) have given an interesting account of the breeding of birds in swamps. Decaying plants keep the grebe's eggs warm and the male continually dives for dead rushes which he heaps up over the nest. The rail draws the tips of rushes together over its nest. During rains the male snipe assists his mate with the brooding.

Annual Succession in Swamps.—Peterson (1924) has studied seasonal succession in a swamp near Chicago.

The succession in the pond, in general order of appearance, in spring · was Crustacea, gilled snails, pulmonate snails, insect nymphs, larvæ, and adults . . . The data indicate that the general seasonal succession of animals is caused by temperature-water level conditions, and that pH and oxygen tension are accompanying rather than causal factors.

In winter, swamps are a refuge for many hibernating frogs, turtles, aquatic insects, and other animals. Some of these spread into terrestrial habitats during warmer seasons. In the bottom mud they may be very cold during the winter, but an animal with some salts in its body to lower its freezing point below that of water will not actually solidify, and hence generally survives. While in a torpid condition, hibernators are concealed from predaceous enemies by mud.

ASSOCIATION *b*. ANIMALS OF BOGS

Bogs resemble swamps, but are generally shallower. Their surface vegetation may float on water, but usually rests on a substratum of soft, quaking mud. Sphagnum bogs often enclose pools and about the margins of these sphagnum moss, assisted by other plants, forms mats that extend out some distance over the water. Bog plants have been much studied by botanists, but the fauna has been little investigated, except in connection with other problems. Dachnowski (1912) has perhaps given the most extensive survey of the bog plant societies. Leaf decay is commonly suspended in bogs on account of acidity, lack of oxygen, and low temperature, and peat deposits are therefore characteristic. Bog deposits are often deficient in potassium and available nitrogen (Transeau, 1905). Some of the emergent vegetation (pitcher plant, etc.) has special means for securing nitrogen through animal food. Animal life is, as a rule, rather scanty in bogs, and Dachnowski (1905) has shown that bog water is toxic for a number of species. It has been commonly supposed that bogs are characteristic of cool climates (Transeau, 1903), but Bird (1923) maintains that bog plants depend on acidity more than temperature, and that the insects present are largely associated with particular plants. Needham and Lloyd (1916) state that, in their opinion, plants are eaten less by animals in bogs than in other situations.

Certain insects and snails that frequent the margins of swamps are also found along bogs among the sedges and other emergent vegetation. There are also some, like those that live in pitcher plants, that are not found elsewhere. Frogs, birds (heron, bittern, etc.), and muskrats hunt about over the surface vegetation. On the surface of the pools there may be a few podurans and water-striders. The water contains few animals, except Sphæridæ, certain beetles, and a few microscopic species.

FORMATION 2. POOL ANIMALS

Pools are like swamps in being shallow and of small size, so that the water varies greatly in amount and usually dries up completely at certain seasons, but are unlike them in lacking characteristic vegetation. They are either without plants or possess a vegetation that belongs properly to land. Animals living in pools are usually subjected to wide variations in temperature and must be hardy. Steuer (1910) states that pool plankton is primarily animal and that it consists largely of crustaceans. Pools are formed after periods of rain and for a time serve as refuges, feeding grounds, or breeding places for various animals. Some of the animals die when a pool dries up, some migrate to other aquatic habitats, and some enter into a resting condition.

ASSOCIATION *a*. ANIMALS OF POOLS WITH HARD BOTTOMS

Animals that live in pools in smooth rocky basins, in tanks, water troughs, and similar situations usually have good powers of migration, but, if there is a little sediment present, animals may be able to survive dry periods. Zacharias (1906) gave a list of algæ, protozoa, rotifers, and nematodes that he found in a large stone urn. In pools there may be such insects as water bugs and beetles that remain for a time and then fly elsewhere. Because of the dearth of organic food there will rarely be an abundant growth of plankton, but algæ may flourish and support such organisms as isopods, amphipods, and entomostracans. These may be introduced on the bodies of wandering animals like ducks and snipe.

ASSOCIATION *b*. ANIMALS OF POOLS WITH MUDDY BOTTOMS

In pools where there is an accumulation of sediment over the bottom many animals are able to exist that are not present in pools with smooth, hard bottoms. Scott (1910) studied a pool in a limestone basin in Indiana and gives lists of the plants and animals. There was little plankton in January and February, but in summer considerable numbers of active protozoans, rotifers, cyclopia, and cladocerans occurred. Ostracods and difflugias were common. The former were important agents in comminuting the dead plants, and beetles also helped by knocking the plants to pieces. The annual range of temperature was from 0 to 27.8°C., and animals were generally active when it was above 4°C. On Oct. 12 there was a change of 10° in twenty-four hours. In a meadow pool in Europe, Sekera (1907) found cosmopolitan animals that included rhizopods, infusorians, planarians, and crustaceans. In Bohemia, Mrázek (1913) found an oligochæte that was associated with Apus and Branchipus in pools that dried up. Perhaps phyllopod crustaceans and certain rotifers are as characteristic of pools as any animals. Shelford (1918) studied the succession of animals in a pool in Illinois. About Mar. 15 Ambystomas were depositing eggs; a month later Eubranchipus was common; May 1, *Planaria velata* and *Diaptomus stagnalis* were the dominant species.

Adjustments to Desiccation in Pool Animals.—The animals of pools are usually adjusted to drought and wide variations in temperature. When a pool dries up, many of them become encysted, burrow, or migrate. Some have a brief life cycle and are able to multiply rapidly. There are some that get into pools by chance from other aquatic habitats, but there is also a group that is characteristic. G. O. Sars has described many new species of crustaceans that he has hatched out of dry mud sent from far countries. The eggs of a number of phyllopods are known to be unable to hatch unless they are dried for a time (Herrot, 1917). Shelford (1918) states that the salamander, *Ambystoma tigrinum*, "deposits its eggs and then burrows into the mud and remains ten months in estivation and hibernation." The writer has taken living mermithids, snails, and Sphæridæ from the sediment in the dry bottoms of pool basins. The eggs of Estheria will develop after being dried for nine years (Calman, 1911).

PROVINCES C AND D. AQUATIC ANIMALS OF CAVES

The population of caves is always scanty and most of the animals found there are also epigean. There is always less life in the water and less of breeding activities than in comparable habitats in the world above. Certain species of salamanders, fishes, crayfishes, isopods, and insects are wholly confined to caves. The animals of any particular habitat usually show relationships to the local epigean fauna. In general, there is an unusual development of tactile sense organs and more or less degeneration of pigment and visual organs in long-established cave species. Many transient or accidental visitors to caves are well suited to cave life by their habits. The marine relatives of blind cave fishes have very small eyes and commonly live in holes among rocks. The young of certain cave animals are more sensitive to light than adults. Most of the leeches, rotifers, turbellarians, nematodes, hydras, sponges, and protozoans that have been reported as occurring in caves do not differ from species that are epigean. Scott (1909) studied the plankton of a cave and concluded that it was all epigean. Kofoid (1900) made similar studies, noting a dearth of algæ and preponderance of copepods.

The food of cave animals must all come ultimately from the outside, as photosynthesis requires light. It is derived from organic remains washed in by water, the excreta and other materials brought in by visitors, the fungi and other organisms that develop in darkness. Racovitza (1907) states that inanition is the usual state of many cave animals on account of the general scarcity of food. Banta (1907) also stresses the scantiness and irregularity of food resources. The temperature of caves is usually extremely constant at all seasons, and aquatic cave animals usually do not show marked hibernating periods. Habitual rhythms of rest and activity may persist in animals that invaded caves rather recently. In general, there are the most animals where there are the most loose stones or other materials which give shelter and opportunity for the accumulation of food. Eigenmann (1909) points out that smaller caves usually have richer faunas because the animals are closer to the food resources outside.

PROVINCE E. ANIMALS OF GROUND WATERS

In subterranean reservoirs and streams there are a few animals. These sometimes appear in caves, wells, and even in the depths of lakes. Calman (1911) says:

A very remarkable feature of the subterranean fauna is that a number of animals appear to be more closely allied to marine species than to any known from freshwaters aboveground.

This is said to be especially true of certain isopods.

In subterranean habitats, as in caves, light is absent, temperature is uniform at all seasons, and food must come down from near the surface. Animals are commonly like those in caverns—pigmentless, blind, and unusually sensitive to touch stimuli. Salisbury (1919) estimates the average annual rainfall over the whole earth as about 40 inches, and rivers carry only about half of this away. The remainder disappears through sinks, pools, soil, evaporation, etc. The surface of the earth is the source of ground water, which probably does not descend more than 1000 feet, and is more or less continually moving on account of the unequal distribution of rainfall and losses from wells, springs, etc.

CHAPTER VII

TERRESTRIAL ANIMALS

Land animals that live on or above the surface of the soil are usually subjected to more or less sudden and extreme variations in water and temperature. They also experience periodic fluctuations in light and other environmental factors that change with day and night. Subterranean animals live in conditions that approach those in aquatic habitats, for they are seldom exposed to sudden changes in temperature and are in little danger of desiccation. On land, food resources are, on the whole, more limited and precarious than in water. Plants are often supplied with nourishment slowly or intermittently, in some cases only after rains, and growth is often arrested by drought or cold. The atmosphere, being a medium of low density and high oxygen content, is favorable for locomotion and rapid metabolism.

Zones in Relation to Climate.—Different areas may differ markedly in climate on account of characteristic differences in temperature (maximum, minimum, average of coldest or warmest season, length and temperature of cold or warm season, etc.), available water (rainfall, humidity, evaporation rate, soil, moisture, etc.), winds, intensity and duration of light, soil, topography, altitude, prevailing types of vegetation, and other factors. Most large areas of land are divided into climatic zones, which are related more or less to latitude, altitude, or contiguity to areas of water. Merriam (1898) divided North America into the following zones:

Boreal:
  1. Arctic-alpine—snow bunting, musk ox, lemming, etc.
  2. Hudsonian—wolverine, moose, mountain goat, etc.
  3. Canadian—lynx, marten, porcupine, etc.
  4. Transition—fauna varying with humidity.

Austral:
  5. Upper Austral—opossum, cardinal, burrowing owl, etc.
  6. Lower Austral—mocking bird, road runner, etc.

Tropical:
  7. Tropical—jaguar, armadillo, etc.

239

Dice (1923, 1923*a*, 1923*b*) has attempted a somewhat more intensive classification and points out that:

The life zones of Merriam are founded on the belief that there are zones of life extending transversely across the continent of North America, in the south as well as in the north . . . I have previously pointed out that, although belts of life do occur in the northern part of North America and on mountains, yet the recognition of transcontinental zones of life in the southern part of the United States seems contrary to the facts of distribution . . . The greatest usefulness of the life zones proposed by Merriam should lie, not in their use for the statement or classification of animal and plant distribution, but in the explanation which they may give as to the factors limiting distribution.

Dice (1922) suggests the use of the term, "biotic area," to describe the regions where a group of plants or animals has a more or less common geographic range and shows a general agreement in ranges of toleration to variations in environmental factors. Dahl (1921) has also stressed the fact that the distribution of many terrestrial animals in Europe and Asia is not zonal, but often depends largely on local variations in environment, and is therefore quite discontinuous. He classifies the mammals of each continent primarily by their food habits (p. 64*a*) and shows that when so assorted they fall into rather definite groups which occur in particular areas.

Vertical Zones.—The relations of animals in their vertical distribution with reference to the surface of the earth is somewhat more definite than their horizontal distribution in particular geographic areas. Flattely and Walton (1922) divide animals into two great groups: (1) phanerozoic, above the soil; and (2) cryptozoic, subterranean or living in more or less complete darkness. Shelford (1912, 1913) also makes a primary division of animals into (1) those exposed to the atmosphere, and (2) those out of direct contact with the atmosphere in soil, wood, tissues of living plants or animals, etc. Above the ground, animals may (1) be associated with surface, (2) frequent the vegetation above, or (3) use the atmosphere itself as a highway. A field cricket is usually active on the surface of the ground, a tree cricket lives in the vegetation above, and a condor spends most of its working hours high in the air. In this book, land animals are considered in relation to the following habitats: subterranean, cave, surfaces of soils of various water contents and slopes, grass, herb, shrub, tree, and aerial. Thompson (1922) points out that the air has been the last non-aquatic habitat to be invaded by animals; that those that live in it are independent of contact with solid objects and are able to avoid dangers and unfavorable environmental changes by migrating across areas that are impassable for other animals.

Land Plants as Sources of Food.—Land plants constitute the fundamental food resources for animal life. They differ from those in aquatic habitats in possessing special mechanisms to control the loss of and to increase the intake of water. They also commonly have special means for storing water. Many land plants attain great size and are thus able better to withstand cold, heat, and drought.

Water Loss by Land Animals.—Land animals are commonly adapted to retain water or to be able to renew their supply continually. Their coverings are often such as to retard or prevent desiccation and are rigid enough to prevent injury from falls and moving objects. Living in a gaseous medium, land animals can move with less effort than their aquatic relatives and are, on the whole, swifter. Certain of their sense organs (eyes) are also commonly more acute. Respiration in all animals takes place through moist membranes; land animals must breathe and at the same time maintain their water content at a high enough level so that they will not die. Probably on this account there is a general tendency to carry on respiration in internal cavities where there is little loss.

Density of Terrestrial Animal Population.—On the whole, the animal population of the land is scantier than that in the ocean or freshwater. Aboveground there are no long stretches that teem with life, like the pelagic and limnetic regions of seas and lakes, and there are many barren deserts. Yet McAttee (1907) estimated that a forest floor contained about 1,216,880 living and dead animals per acre, and a meadow about 13,654,710. In a vacant city lot in Illinois Wolcott (1918) found an average of 4,500,000 animals per acre, the commonest types being earthworms, sowbugs, beetles, and ants. Darwin (1881) estimated that there were 26,886 earthworms per acre in his pasture. Forbes and Gross (1922) found summer birds in various habitats in Illinois in the following numbers per square mile: stubble, 324; waste and fallow fields, 716; orchards, 1987. When placed in the order of the number of birds present, various habitats ranked as follows: orchards, yards and gardens, swamps, woods, pastures, shrubs, meadows, waste and fallow lands, cereal crops, plowed fields, corn fields, oat fields, stubble fields.   More than five times as many birds occurred in areas covered by trees and shrubs as in those which bore cereal crops.

Origin of Land Animals.—Palæontological evidence indicates that marine animals existed long before there were any on land, and that land animals have been derived from those that lived in the ocean and freshwater.   At the present time certain fishes, crustaceans, snails, and worms are in the midst of transition from aquatic to terrestrial life.   There are various views held as to the causes for the migration of animals to land habitats.   Hesse (1913) has emphasized the fact that there is an average of only 7.0 cubic centimeters of dissolved oxygen per liter in water, while the atmostphere contains 207 cubic centimeters.   He believes that the lure of oxygen has attracted animals to land habitats in moist climates where there is little danger of desiccation.   Semper (1881) believed that animals invaded the land for food and shelter.   He pointed out that a respiratory organ suited to water breathing would generally function in air if kept moist and prevented from collapsing.   Heilprin (1887) and Flattely (1921) attached much importance to tidal action in the origin of land life, supporting the view that animals that were intermittently exposed to the desiccating action of the atmosphere in the intertidal zone gradually became adjusted to life on land.   Woodworth (1894) and Barrell (1916) maintained that land vertebrates arose on account of periodic aridity which forced them to become adjusted to respiration in air.

Routes of Migration to Land.—Some land animals have apparently been derived directly from the ocean, without first being adjusted to life in freshwater.   The ghost crab (Ocypoda) goes to the ocean at intervals to moisten its gills, and can live only twenty-four hours without water (Cowles, 1908.)   It lives only two hours in freshwater (Gardiner, 1903).   The sand hopper (Orchestia) lives on land near the ocean, but cannot endure freshwater (King, 1914).   Certain crabs (Birgus, Geacarcinus) live most of their lives far from water but return to the ocean for a few days each year to allow their young to hatch.   On the other hand, many animals probably first migrated from the ocean into freshwater and later became adjusted to land life.   Though amphibians were probably derived remotely from marine, fish-like ancestors, they now show little affinity for the ocean (in fact, most species cannot endure salt water), yet many of them have become true terrestrial animals and a few never visit the water, even depositing their eggs on land. Thompson (1922) states that, though preceded by plants, animals have made three great land invasions: (1) the worms, which largely remained within the soil, (2) the air-breathing arthropods, which generally developed tracheæ for breathing, and (3) the vertebrates, which developed internal lungs and toes at the distal ends of their limbs. The snails are also moving to the land at the present time and some have become completely terrestrial. Their slimy coatings and shells protect them from desiccation and make such migration comparatively easy. Tadpoles that start their development in water and later take up life on land are recapitulating their phylogeny. They first breathe through gills and later turn to buccopharyngeal, dermal, and pulmonary respiration. The land animals came from aquatic ancestors and certain aquatic animals now make brief journeys on land to escape unfavorable conditions or to acquire some desideratum. They are apparently able to do this without much trouble as long as their respiratory membranes can function in the atmosphere.

PROVINCE A. SUBTERRANEAN ANIMALS

Animals that live underground, either in soil or in caves, are in little danger from desiccation and are less exposed to rapid and extreme temperature changes than those that live above. They may be at times insufficiently supplied with oxygen and may be obliged to come in contact with injurious substances that are present as gases, liquids, or solids.

FORMATION 1. ANIMALS LIVING IN SOIL

Animals that live in soil are dependent on various factors for existence. Clay, humus, sand, or rock each has its characteristic animals which are influenced more or less by temperature, moisture, aeration, soil reactions, and the presence or absence of particular chemical substances and organisms.

Insolation is apparently more important than air temperatures in warming soil and its effectiveness decreases with altitude (Shreve, 1924). Maximum soil temperatures are generally more variable than minimum. The spring and autumn "overturns" in temperature are very important for soil animals. McCulloch and Hayes (1923) found that the white grub came nearer the surface after the spring overturn and descended after that in the autumn. The ranges of temperature variations decrease with increases in depth. McCulloch and Hayes give the following average annual ranges for the soil in Kansas: at a depth of 1 foot, 28°C.; 3 feet, 21.4°C.; 6 feet, 15.7°C. They say: "The soil responds to great outside temperature changes slowly. The temperature at 1 foot responds the same day, at 2 feet about one day later." At the beginning of March the lowest temperature was found at a depth of about 1 foot; during warm periods in winter the temperatures were about the same at all depths up to 6 feet; in summer the surface had a higher temperature than greater depths, in winter the opposite was true. Soil insects are generally able to endure wide variations in temperature and the same is known to be true of earthworms, isopods, and many other subterranean animals (Cameron, 1913). Koch (1915) states that soil protozoans develop best between temperatures of 8 to 30°C. Some animals are able to endure cold periods because they associate themselves with decaying organic matter that keeps them from freezing. Temperatures may affect soil animals through their influence on moisture. Cold air can hold less water vapor than warm. Earthworms most often make excursions over the surface of the ground when humidity is high and temperature is low (Heimburger, 1924).

Water in Soil.—The amount and the form of water in soil are important factors for soil animals. Shade and protection from the action of wind generally permit greater numbers to exist. Soil insects may be drowned by an excess of gravitational water. On the other hand, soil protozoa are usually encysted except for short periods after rains. Certain tiger beetle larvæ plug their burrows with pellets of clay when the soil is dry (Shelford, 1912). Ants usually excavate most actively just after rains.

Wet soil is often poorly aerated. Porous soils are usually best for larval insects because they contain plenty of oxygen, but some soil-inhabiting fly larvæ can survive for long periods without oxygen (Cameron, 1913).

Soil Reaction.—The reaction of soil often limits the distribution of subterranean animals. Wherry (1922) has found that the greatest number of plants, both species and individuals, usually grow in soil that is slightly acid. Minerals like lime may serve two functions, furnishing material that is necessary for metabolism and making soil reactions alkaline. Coville (1914) found that more fungi and animals that promote decay (bacteria, earthworms, etc.) were to be found in an alkaline soil. Waksman

(1924), however, has shown that fungi increase with fertilizers that tend to increase soil acidity. A dogma has long been current that earthworms cannot live in soils that have an acid reaction. For example, Arrhenius (1921) states that earthworms were found only in soils where the pH values ranged between 6 and 7, which is barely on the acid side of neutrality. Phillips (1923) states that, though earthworms are scarce in markedly acid soil, he has observed one species living where there was acidity that was represented by pH 5, and Wherry (1924) has noted a species, *Helodrilus lonnebergi* Michaelson, that lived in peat where the pH was 4.7 to 5.1. Various species of protozoans are also known to have a wide range of toleration in relation to soil reactions.

Characteristic Soil Animals.—Characteristic inhabitants of the soil are various protozoa, earthworms, tardigrades, insects (especially larval stages), millipedes, isopods, termites, ants, amphibians, reptiles, rodents, and moles. Many other animals may invade the soil temporarily, digging burrows of their own or inhabiting those made by other species. Where conditions are favorable, enormous numbers of soil animals may be present. Earthworms have been estimated at hundreds of thousands per acre (Darwin, 1881; Thomson, 1911; Branner, 1914). There may be thousands of millions of nematodes (Cobb, 1914). Protozoa may range from 30,000 to 150,000 per cubic centimeter, and bacteria from 220,000 to 2,460,000 (France, 1911). McColloch and Hayes (1922) have given an excellent review of the literature relating to the number of soil insects that may occur and report such numbers as 3,586,088 per acre, 84 to 300 per square foot, etc.

There is no doubt that in areas where ants or termites occur the number of individuals present is enormous. It might also be said that soils rich in organic matter usually contain thousands of Thysanura, Collembola, and immature stages of Diptera . . . Insects may be said to utilize the soil for shelter, protection, materials for abode, food, moisture, air, heat, and as an avenue for travel.

Depth of Animals in Soil.—Usually, soil animals are quite close to the surface. Cameron (1913) found few insects below a depth of 3 inches, but noted that larvæ usually burrowed deeper before pupating. In the Belgian Congo, Steel (1913) found the burrows of termites 5 feet below the surface. The pocket gopher seldom goes below a depth of 2 feet. Darwin (1881) observed that earthworms descended to a depth of about 6 feet, and burrows somewhat deeper than this have since been reported.   Earthworms may be arranged more or less in strata, some species regularly being found at greater depths than others (Bretschler, 1901).   The burrows of the prairie ant may be 9 feet deep (Hungerford and Williams, 1912).   Those of the prairie dog sometimes extend to a depth of 14 feet.

Adaptations of Subterranean Animals.—Burrowing animals are, in general, cylindrical in form, stocky, and robust.   McCulloch and Hayes (1922) say in regard to insects:

Certain general modifications might be mentioned as associated with subterranean life.   Usually the body is more elongate, the sense organs more highly developed, the eyes and wings reduced or wanting, and metamorphosis simple.   While all these modifications do not apply to all soil insects, it may be stated that they are often present in direct proportion to the amount of time the insect lives in the soil.

Subterranean representatives of groups that have limbs in other habitats are often apodal (amphisbænians, cœcilians, etc.). Other burrowing animals (mole, cicada nymph, etc.) have enormous digging limbs developed near the anterior end.   Some small animals burrow by packing the dirt toward the sides of their burrows.   The earthworm progresses by eating soil as it burrows.   Hancock (1911) described a burrowing spider that makes its tunnels by repeatedly spinning a disc which adheres to the sand and is then removed.   Soule (1900) observed three species of burrowing caterpillars which did not spin, but packed the soil firmly to form a cocoon before they pupated.   The digger wasps excavate with their legs or mandibles and may use clay or leaves to make their nest cells strong.   Ants often place stones or leaves above their nests to protect them from wind and rain. Burrowing rodents that dig largely with the front feet may have small hind limbs and the pelvic girdle is often more or less modified in order to permit them to turn about in their burrows and at the same time be able to bear young.   Burrowing mammals with narrow pelves (mole) commonly push the dirt to either side and crowd their way through the soil; those with broad pelves (pocket gopher) throw loose dirt back with the hind legs and at intervals push it up to the surface (Chapman, 1919).   Many burrowers use special means to keep the soil from caving into their burrows.   The earthworm lines its galleries with slime; spiders and insect larvæ often spin a lining for their burrows; some tiger beetle larvæ cement sand grains together with saliva.

The eye of the hedgehog is retracted into the skull underground, but protrudes when the animal is above the surface; that of the mole is degenerate. Baumgartner (1905) has pointed out that mole crickets are unusual among orthopterous insects because both sexes stridulate. He believes that the notes of these insects serve both for giving notice that a burrow is occupied and for finding mates. He also calls attention to the fact the the soft abdomen of the mole cricket permits the animal to turn readily in its burrow and is protected from attack by repugnatorial glands. The loss or degenerate condition of visual organs in certain burrowing animals is often compensated for by the greater acuity of chemical or tactile senses.

Food of Animals in Soil.—Subterranean animals are directly or indirectly dependent on vegetation for food. Some feed largely on the underground parts of plants (white grub) or draw plants into their burrows without emerging (pocket gopher); others come out on the surface and drag down leaves, fruits, and other parts of plants (earthworm, ground squirrel); some raise fungi in underground gardens (ants, temites); some depend largely on decaying organic matter; and others are predaceous, seeking food above or below the surface (centipedes, many species of nematodes). Earthworms often allow leaves to decay underground and perhaps depend for food as much on the fungi that develop as on the leaves. Digger wasps are specialists in hunting different kinds of animals and each knows the habits of its prey. Hartman (1915) states that these insects fall into two groups: (1) those which feed their larvæ daily, and (2) those which sting their prey and store it away in nests. The first group are believed to be more primitive. The common mole requires a variety of food, not only devouring insects and earthworms, but also continually consuming some vegetation. One mole ate an amount equal to 66.6 per cent of its body weight in eighteen hours (Hisaw, 1923).

Difficulties of Life in Soil.—Though animals that live in soil are protected from most dangers, they are particularly subject to others. The white grub escapes from desiccation, rapid changes in temperature, and predaceous enemies that work above ground, but is subject to attacks by a fungus and is devoured by moles. Many subterranean animals cannot endure desiccation and many (largely those that come to the surface for food) cannot endure water in unusual amounts. Rains make extra work for ants by filling up their galleries. Ants more commonly burrow in clay than in sand, which caves in easily.   Many ants, wasps, bees, spiders, and rodents build towers or mounds that keep water from flowing into their burrows.   Prairie dogs are probably sensitive to barometric changes, for they begin to bank up dirt about their holes several hours before rains, often even when it is not cloudy.   Prairie dogs build vertical tunnels toward, but not actually reaching, the surface at the intersections of their anastomosing burrows.   When their "towns" are inundated, they are able to live for several hours in the air in the vertical blind passages (Foster, 1924).   Some burrowing animals use their burrows only as refuges from enemies.   The guano birds along the coast of Peru escape the condors and buzzards by their subterranean life and nocturnal flights for food (Coker, 1919).   Harvester ants and prairie dogs cut down the vegetation near the entrances to their burrows, so that the view is unobstructed.

Character of Soil and Animal Life.—The character and the condition of the soil are usually important factors for burrowing animals.   Gleason (1909) found that there was little or no animal life in loose soil that overlay rock unless it had a depth of at least 5 centimeters.   Shelford (1911) showed that several species of tiger beetles, though their larvæ were much alike in structure, chose different types of soils for depositing their eggs.   Cameron (1913) observed certain wasps that burrowed in sandy soil where the sun shone part of each day, the soil being loose and easy to excavate on the surface but moist enough not to cave in easily below.   Turner (1922) described a wasp that made burrows near water and strengthened the walls of its nest by plastering them with moistened clay.   Insect larvæ usually avoid clay soils, but a few frequent them, probably because their firmness compensates for their tendency to hold moisture and maintain a rather low temperature.   Gray sand is more stable and contains more organic matter than white, which is easily blown about (Warming, 1909).   Humus usually supports an abundance of plant and animal life.   Burrowers usually excavate most actively when the soil is in the best condition for digging.   For example, pocket gophers usually work most in the spring.   Good soil for plowing is good soil for the extension of old burrows and the beginning of new excavations.   Some animals are little affected by the nature of the materials in which they burrow.   Certain Australian termites burrow through stone and sheet lead (Stead, 1900); dermestid larvæ make burrows in salt (Blanford, 1899).

Association *a*. Animals in Clay Soils

Many of the animals that frequent clay soils depend on the surface (Stratum 1) for food (tiger beetle larvæ, isopods, prairie dogs) and in a dry climate many are able to go without water except that which occurs in their natural foods. When humus is mixed with clay, earthworms and other animals that live more or less permanently below the surface (Stratum 2) are also present. Insect larvæ like white grubs are usually found in humus soils but may live in clay if roots and other materials are present for food. Prairie dogs apparently prefer clay soils because they do not cave in readily.

Association *b*. Animals in Humus Soils

Humus usually supports vegetation and many animals, but the types of plants and the number of animals present may be limited by such factors as the presence of excessive amounts of acids or alkalies, north exposure and high altitude, so that the temperature is continually low. The animals that depend on the surface (Stratum 1) and those that live more or less permanently underground (Stratum 2) are usually well represented.

Association *c*. Animals in Sandy Soils

Sandy soil is easily moved, and hence burrowing in it is easy, but it caves in readily and does not hold water well. It usually contains few burrowing animals that live more or less permanently underground. Many of the animals that live in sand make burrows beneath plants, where the roots prevent caving.

Association *d*. Animals in Rocks

Animals that frequent holes and cracks in rocks are largely species that may live in similar situations in other habitats. Woodchucks often dwell in rock "slides," but may also dig holes in fields. Ants, spiders, and snails that live in crevices may maintain colonies in the earth, in wood, or in rock. Though animals occasionally burrow in rock, there is no established stratum below the surface.

FORMATION 2. CAVE ANIMALS

In caves there is usually very little annual variation in temperature and humidity. In the deeper parts of Mayfield's Cave,

Banta (1907) found that there was less than 2°C. variation throughout the year. Light is present only near the mouth and animals that live permanently in caves usually exist in total darkness. Food all comes from outside, directly or indirectly, and organic remains are of great importance. Racovitza (1907) says that inanition is the usual state of cave animals. Large animals (including man) leave excreta and bring in objects that are eaten. Streams wash in protozoa, annelids, crustaceans, insects, algæ, seeds, wood, and other things that may serve as food. Fungi are an important source of nourishment for thysanurans, and probably for other animals also.

Adjustment of Animals to Caves.—Banta (1907) states that cave animals are usually most abundant where there are (1) considerable moisture, (2) organic remains, and (3) loose stones or other materials that furnish small crevices for hiding. Some animals show a gradation in their distribution according to their nearness to sources of light; others do not. Most speleologists agree that caves have been populated by animals from surrounding epigean regions. Cave animals are fitted more or less for cave conditions before entering, but some have become further adapted and at present are strikingly adjusted to a stygian existence. Sometimes habits of periodic activity persist among animals that live in the innermost recesses of caves, though the changes that usually accompany day and night do not occur. In general, there are not fixed and limited periods of reproduction at particular seasons. Hibernation and æstivation on account of seasonal variations in temperature and moisture are rare phenomena among permanent residents. The uniformity of humidity and temperature conditions are correlated with the fact that many cave animals are stenothermic and stenohydric. Racovitza (1907) says that the high humidity is favorable to many species because there is little danger of desiccation. In this connection he cites snails that do not form epiphragms to close their shells. Among cave animals organs for receiving tactile stimuli are often large; eyes and pigment are commonly degenerate.

Association a. Transient Cave Animals

Animals may enter caves by accident and remain for a time and others habitually use caves as retreats. Racovitza (1907) classified cave animals in three groups: (1) Trogloxènes, which are facultative inhabitants of caves and have some adaptations which fit them for cave life; (2) Troglophiles, which live more or less continually underground, but have relations with the epigean world; and (3) Troglobies, which are wholly troglodyte. Such animals as raccoons, chipmunks, woodchucks, mice, foxes, weasels, bears, salamanders, frogs, beetles, crickets, spiders, phalangids, mites, myriapods, pseudoscorpions, isopods, and snails (Stratum 1) wander into caves and remain for a longer or shorter time. Some spend the night, others go in and out for months or years, others use the caves for hibernation or æstivation. Flying animals (Stratum 2) often make use of caves. Hahn (1908) states that certain bats spend five-sixths of their lives in caves where temperature varies little and light is absent. They come to the mouth of the cave at irregular intervals, but do not go outside when it is cold or when the sun is shining brightly. Each bat does not roost continually at a particular spot, but favorable situations are usually occupied. Mosquitoes, moths, flies, and other insects hibernate in caves (Banta, 1907).

ASSOCIATION *b*. PERMANENT RESIDENTS IN CAVES

There are a number of air-breathing animals that live permanently in caves. These include salamanders, spiders, mites, and insects, but Banta (1907) states that such animals usually form but a small part of the total population of a cave.

McIndoo (1910) has described the adaptations and habits of two cave spiders—a linyphid and an epeirid. One of these is found only in total darkness, where considerable moisture and places for snares are present, but the other may occur near the mouth of a cave where there is some light. These spiders build webs and catch flies, thysanurans, and myriapods. They also eat each other. The web of one species is so fine that it will shed water. The eyes and eye pigments of cave spiders show various degrees of degeneracy. The epeirid studied by McIndoo was sensitive to light, but the linyphid was not.

Banta (1907) gives an extensive list of cave insects, including psychodid flies that breed in caves, flies and beetles that are adapted to cave life, camel crickets, lepismas, and collembolans. Carpenter (1903) describes three blind beetles from Irish caves. He believes that cave faunas on the whole represent "survivals" of animals that have not been able to continue to live in epigean habitats. The fact that many cave animals show more or less

degeneracy in visual organs has been mentioned. Eigenmann
(1909) and his students have studied the eyes of cave vertebrates
and find various degrees of loss of eye structures and functions.
Banta (1910) showed that an aquatic cave isopod (Cæcidotea)
did not respond to light that had an intensity below 60 candle
meters, but an epigean isopod (Asellus) responded to 1 centimeter.
Banta and McAtee (1906) studied the light reactions of a cave
salamander (*Spelerpes maculicaudatus*) and found that larvæ
were much more responsive than adults. This species deposited
its eggs in January and the young were seen only in the deepest
parts of caves, but the adults were sometimes found under logs a
mile from any cave.

PROVINCE B. ANIMALS ABOVE THE SURFACE OF THE SOIL

Animals that live above the surface of the soil are exposed to
light, temperature variations, and winds. They are more
readily seen by enemies than animals that live underground and
are in more or less danger of being frozen, overheated, or dried up.

FORMATION 1. SURFACE ANIMALS

The animals that are found on the surface of the earth are not
all properly to be classified there. At times, certain burrowing
animals may come from below and animals that commonly live
in strata above may visit the earth's surface through intent or
accident. There are animals, however, that have their primary
habitat on the earth's surface. Many of these are primarily
nocturnal or diurnal and may, during inactive periods, become
part of the thigmotactic fauna that hides under stones, logs,
loose bark, and in other crevices. Animals that stow themselves
away in sheltered nooks are protected from desiccation and
extreme temperatures. Many surface animals have great resistance to low or high temperatures. Moore (1899) observed that
the enchytræid worms that lived on Malaspina Glacier burrowed
into the snow when the direct rays of the sun struck them and
were active chiefly at night. He also kept a Limnodrilus in a glass
of water on his windowsill, where it alternately froze and thawed
all winter but remained alive. On the glacier the temperature
during the day reached 13°C. and at night was about 0°C., yet
the surface was populated by gulls, moths, spiders, flies, thysanurans, and worms. It is said that the agricultural ant of Texas
may work until the temperature of the air reaches 65°C, and that

of the soil 45°C. When conditions are favorable, many surface animals may occupy an area. Their colors may match with great accuracy, the backgrounds on which they usually rest but there are many exceptions, particularly among nocturnal animals, which are often black. Cameron (1917) counted the numbers of insects occurring on soil and low vegetation in summer. On plots 1 foot square he found in a meadow four to thirty-two, and in a pasture three to 122.

Periods of Activity of Surface Animals.—There are many factors that exert influences upon the animals that are intermittently associated with the surface of the soil. Many protozoans that are usually encysted in soil swim about at the surface for a time after rains (Goodey, 1911). Henderson (1905) affirms that land snails become active when the barometer falls, often as much as six or eight hours before rains. Most species are not active during rains, and Henderson therefore concluded that moisture in the air was more potent than that on the ground. Glacier worms are active when there is little or no light (Moore, 1899). Pieron (1908) says that snails and actinians may migrate out of the ocean at night, supposedly because the algæ cease to carry on photosynthesis and there is insufficient oxygen for their needs.

Influence of Soil Variations on Surface Animals.—The most important factors in determining the character of the habitats on soil surfaces are variations in water and soil constituents. Rock and, to a less extent, sand are dry and subject to rapid changes in temperature. Humus is less variable and usually supports more vegetation, hence affording more shelter from sun and wind. Wet soils, though they help surface animals to resist desiccation, are often sour (or acid) and consequently furnish little organic food as a rule.

ASSOCIATION *a*. ANIMALS ON WET GROUND

There are many animals, like certain earthworms and salamanders, that require considerable water and are, therefore, confined to moist situations. There are also animals, like certain ants, that may live both in more or less dry and in moist situations.

Stratum 1. Burrowing Animals.—Burrowing animals may be absent from wet ground on account of excessive amounts of water or of dissolved substances (usually salts or acids), but in many localities earthworms, shrews, crayfishes, crabs, and other subterranean animals come from their retreats, especially at night, and forage over the surface. Some ants that live on wet soils raise their nests above the surface as mounds, but in drier soils the galleries of the same species may be largely subterranean. Termites often frequent wet ground, apparently to escape from their chief enemies, the ants (Branner, 1912).

Stratum 2. Surface Animals.—On wet soil snails, amphibians (frogs, toads, salamanders), centipedes, millipedes, isopods, grasshoppers, spiders, and snakes are characteristic. Many of these animals hide in crevices at times.

Stratum 3. Animals from above Surface.—Species that normally live above surface habitats may temporarily become part of the surface population. During the day, wasps, birds, and other animals seek food or a resting place; at night, such animals as skunks, raccoons, and mice are foraging.

Semiaquatic Animals.—Certain animals that live on wet ground are in a state of transition from aquatic to land habitats. Crabs and crayfishes usully live in burrows, which they leave only at night. Bishop (1920) describes a salamander that lays its eggs in sphagnum moss. The eggs require moisture, but cannot live in moss that is saturated with water.

ASSOCIATION *b*. ANIMALS ON MEDIUM-DRY GROUND

As soil becomes drier it is less favorable for some types of burrowers (Stratum 1) which form part of the surface association at times, and is more favorable for others. Earthworms gradually give place to insects and their larvæ, rodents, tortoises, etc. Soil that contains an intermediate degree of moisture is usually humus and often supports an abundance of earthworms, grubs, ground squirrels, moles, and other burrowers. On the surface of the soil (Stratum 2) are characteristic beetles, ants, grasshoppers, crickets, myriapods, spiders, slugs, voles, rabbits, etc. In a locality there is often a marked difference between the animals that live on exposed soil and those that are found beneath the shade of vegetation. Usually there are fewer surface animals in the latter habitat, probably because many climb upon the plants. Shelford (1912) found that the surface animals among cottonwood trees were largely swift, predaceous, diurnal, and wary. On cloudy days most of them hid underground or in crevices. Mesophytic vegetation harbors many animals (Stratum 3) that at times take part in the activities on the soil surface. Some fall off the vegetation and move about; insect larvæ descend to the ground to pupate; squirrels come down to bury nuts, etc.

Association c. Animals on Dry Sand

Sand is loose and readily moved by winds unless it is wet or is held together by plants. Animals that live on it can easily cover themselves to escape extremes of temperature or to avoid drying out, but many of them are able to endure considerable desiccation. Wasps, spiders, mice, and other animals dig burrows (Stratum 1) and at times run over the surface of the soil with spiders, insects (grasshoppers, crickets, beetles, etc.), snakes, lizards, sand grouse, plovers, antelopes, and rodents that do not make excavations (Stratum 2). Buzzards, dragon-flies, and other predaceous animals (Stratum 3) often hunt over sandy areas, where the scantiness of vegetation makes it easy to observe small animals that may serve as food.

Association d. Animals on Rock

Exposed rock surfaces are dry because they cannot retain much water and are subject to great daily changes in temperature, for they become very hot when the sun shines and cool rapidly when it does not. Rock rarely contains a burrowing fauna, but, when it is broken into pebbles, or contains caves, the number of animals that it may support is greatly increased. The vegetation cover of rocks is usually scanty and consists largely of lichens and mosses.

Notwithstanding the severity of conditions of life on rock surfaces, there is usually a scanty animal population. Snails, ants, spiders, and rodents live in crevices (Stratum 1) and come out at favorable times to feed. Rabbits and other animals that frequent the surface of the ground often rest in rocky situations, where the lack of vegetation leaves an unobstructed view and thus prevents the unheralded approach of predaceous enemies. The open spaces also bring foraging animals like owls, swallows, robber-flies, and dragon-flies, and those that come to play about or mate, like butterflies and midges (Stratum 3). Many of the animals found on rocks are transients from other habitats.

Where rock surfaces slope so abruptly as to form cliffs, they are often frequented by sea birds, swallows, eagles, hawks, wasps, and other animals that thus secure safe nesting sites and seek food elsewhere. They may also be used for the observation of the lowlands by predaceous animals like the eagle.

FORMATION 2.　ANIMALS ASSOCIATED WITH TERRESTRIAL PLANTS

Every naturalist knows that land animals are arranged in associations that are primarily related to plants. The number of individuals and the character of species are usually natural results of what different types of plant associations are able to furnish in the way of food, shelter from enemies and the drying action of air, protection from temperature changes, and other desiderata.

The terms forest, grassland, and desert are a subconscious classification of the principal climatic formations and are only another way of expressing the water content of soils (Waller, 1918).

On the sand dunes near Chicago, Sanders and Shelford (1922) found species of animals distributed as follows: surface, 10; herbs, 34; shrubs, 38; trees, 11. Such numerical differences between the animals in habitats as represented by various types of vegetation are more or less typical of all localities where animals live on land.

ASSOCIATION *a*.　ANIMALS OF FORESTS

Compared to open-ground habitats like prairies, forests are more stable. Their humidity and temperature vary less and more slowly. Barrell (1917) believed that the dangers of life are less in trees than on plains, and stressed this fact in connection with the characteristic animals in the two formations. There are three principal types of forests: (1) coniferous, (2) deciduous dicotyledonous, (3) evergreen dicotyledonous. Forests usually progress to their climax more rapidly on clay soils than on sand, and in temperate and tropical regions conifers may persist in sandy regions because they have less available water. Animals that live in forests made up of pine trees are, on the whole, more exposed to light and variations in temperature and humidity than those that live in broad-leaved forests. Animals that live in forests have the food resources that result from photosynthesis, and a certain degree of shelter. The trees stand above the ground and on account of this fact and also, through their absorptive, transpiratory, and other activities related to water, maintain a certain humidity balance in the atmosphere, which is thus usually prevented from becoming extremely wet or dry. For similar reasons the temperature remains more uniform. Shelter is furnished by trees in another sense: Their broken contours furnish many safe resting and hiding places for animals. As litter from trees accumulates on the ground, insulation and shelter are present there also. Logs and fallen leaves furnish refuges for amphibians, insects, mammals, etc. Some animals use forests as hiding places and find food elsewhere. Deer crouch in the shade of forests, but commonly feed upon the grass on open ground. A lizard in New Zealand spends most of its active life in water but climbs up 12 to 20 feet into trees to bask and sleep (Symonds, 1912). Dense forests are unfavorable for many animals because there is little light and food near the ground; most of the inhabitants are arboreal and live in or near the tree tops. Bates and Zon (1922) in their discussion of research methods in forestry take up many matters of general interest and give tables that relate to the determination of the state of various factors, such as barometric and osmotic pressures, freezing points, alkalinities, and salinities.

Adaptations of Forest Animals.—Animals that live more or less permanently in or among trees show various adaptations to forest life. Hesse (1921) asserts that animals in forests have a tendency to be large, strong, and muscular compared to those in the open country. For an arboreal animal speed is on the whole less desirable than ability to cling firmly and to hide from other animals. Arboreal animals are generally good climbers and such specialized structures as the feet of monkeys, squirrels, sloths, and tree frogs are admirably suited for locomotion among branches. Many have balancing organs that keep them from falling from smooth branches (tails of squirrels, monkeys, and certain birds). Some forest animals (tree frog) are excellent jumpers and commonly leap to seize their prey or to escape from enemies. Many arboreal animals are able to sail or fly. Morse (1904) found that the wings of forest orthopterans were unusually long, and he believed this was to facilitate passages across open spaces. A number of typical forest animals sail or fly (flying foxes, flying squirrels, bats, Draco, and the Javan tree frog). Clark (1925) has contrasted the animals of the South American and Malayan forests. In the continuous leafy canopy of the former, prehen-

sile tails are a great advantage and fireflies find ideal conditions.
In the more open forests of the east, gliding is more advantageous
and gliders are correspondingly common.   Some caterpillars that
feed on the leaves of forest trees spin threads and descend on
them to the ground for pupation.   Rodents with their gnawing
teeth, and woodpeckers, with their peculiar beaks, are specially
equipped to make and inhabit holes in trees.   They are protected
from many enemies by the small sizes of the entrances into
their dwellings.   The holes made by such animals are often
inhabited by others.   Many small boring animals are absolutely
dependent on the wood in forests for food and shelter.   Hingston
(1920) calls attention to the way in which the abdomens of certain
ants that climb up and down tree trunks are attached.   In the
case he cites the abdomen stands at right angles to the thorax,
which is the position it would tend to assume on account of its
weight and slender pedicel when an ant was moving downward
and is thus no greater impediment when the ant moves upward.
Both Hingston (1920) and MacGregor (1920) have noted that
forest birds are commonly gregarious.   The former believes that
insectivorous species are thus able to capture prey more easily
because there are more beaters to raise the insects and more
watchful predators to prevent escape.   MacGregor believes that
birds of different species often consort together in order to keep a
better watch against enemies.   The colors of forest animals often
resemble the backgrounds against which they are seen with great
accuracy.   There are simulators of bark, light and shade shining
through foliage, leaves, twigs, etc.   The chameleon and the tree
frog are examples of arboreal animals that possess remarkable
ability to change their colors.   Collins (1922) has given a very
interesting account of certain adaptations of primates to arboreal
life.   The eyes of men and monkeys differ from other mammals
in having a small lens and cornea which are associated with the
presence of a highly centralized retinular area of sharp vision.
They are unique among mammals in having parallel optic axes.
The recession of the snout in primates has been associated with
(1) the substitution of the hand for it as the chief tactile organ, (2)
the decrease in the use of the jaws for tearing and seizing, and (3)
the decreased importance of the sense of smell.   In the tree tops
there is little value in being able to follow odor trails, but it is of
great importance to be able to see clearly, particularly in judging
distances.

Food in the Forest.—There is no dearth of food in a forest. Many animals that depend directly on its plants are specialists and require particular species or parts. For example, many species of insects attack the basswood. In the foliage there are 4 bugs, 6 beetles, 52 lepidopters, and 1 gall-fly; on the bark, 7 scale insects; 15 beetles and 1 lepidopter bore about in the wood (Gibson, 1904). In his report on insects associated with trees Felt (1905–1906) states that bark borers, twig borers, ambrosia beetles, and leaf feeders are characteristic among pines; borers, fungous beetles, injurious and beneficial leaf frequenters (phytophagous and predaceous), and gall insects are typical among deciduous trees. The important insects feeding upon trees are said to be: saw-flies, cynipids, cecidiomyids, boring beetles, chrysomelids, curculionids, scotylids, lepidopters, aphids, and scales. Weiss and West (1922) found that insects in moist woods usually injured the vegetation very little. Some fed on foliage, but others ate rotten wood, fungi, or other substances. These investigators give the following percentages of insects having various food habits: phytophagous, 37; saprophagous, 35; predaceous, 20; parasitic, 5. In a thicket the percentages were: phytophagous, 63; saprophagous, 9; predaceous, 19. The same writers later (1924) found that there were more species of saprophagous insects in woods and more flowers and pollenizing insects in open fields. It goes without saying that in forests as in other habitats there are fewer predaceous than phytophagous animals.

Reproduction of Forest Animals.—The reproductive habits of many forest animals are adapted to life in trees. Some tree frogs carry their eggs on their backs; others deposit them in the water contained in epiphytes; others roll their eggs up in leaves and the hatching tadpoles fall into water below; the Javan tree frog encloses its eggs in nests within rolled leaves which contain water and the tadpoles complete their metamorphosis in the tree tops. Many animals build nests or utilize holes in trees for breeding purposes. Galls furnish food and shelter to the larvæ of various insects. Girdlers deposit eggs in girdled twigs; the larvæ live on the dying wood for a time, and the twig may fall off and carry its guests to the ground.

Borers in Wood.—The many insects and the few other animals that live in wood constitute an interesting part of the forest population. These animals have means for boring and are usually limited in their ranges of food, temperature, and moisture toleration. Graham (1922) has classified the insects that live in logs into five groups: (1) those that require fresh cambium for food and usually have a brief metamorphosis; (2) those that require fresh cambium for their early development but later are able to feed on outer sap wood; (3) those that feed first on cambium, later on sap and heart wood; (4) those that pass their entire period of metamorphosis in heart wood; and (5) those that do not depend on wood directly, but feed on other organisms that live in it. Graham found that the subcortical temperature of logs that were exposed to the sun might reach as high as 60°C., and that 48°C. was fatal to all boring insects. The bark of some species of trees furnishes efficient thermal insulation, however, and temperatures inside it never reach 48°C. Insects to some extent were found to be assorted in logs according to their degree of exposure to the action of the sun. The food value of a tree is, of course, determined largely by its chemical composition, but its availability may be markedly influenced by its temperature and water content. A Xylographus beetle feeds on ambrosia fungi in wood (Hopkins, 1898). In this case the females winter over in old brood chambers and in spring go to sick or dead trees and cooperate in making a home. One female excavates while another shoves out the chips. A tunnel is thus made and each female constructs side galleries into the heart wood where she deposits her eggs. The entrance to the colony is closed to prevent the entrance of enemies. Many of the large animals, such as rodents and woodpeckers, that live in trees usually work largely in dead wood that has been softened by decay.

Subassociation a(1). Animals of Coniferous Forests

Conifers are xerophytic, in that they are adapted to a low rate of transpiration, but they need an abundance of light. Coniferous forests occur in various climates, but are largely confined to the cold temperate regions where the soil is physically or physiologically dry and the shortness of the warm season prevents deciduous trees from becoming dominant. The ground cover consists largely of perennial plants.

Living among the foliage (Stratum 1) in pine forests are chickadees, jays, crossbills, and other characteristic animals. Mites, beetles, ants, spiders, and porcupines climb about among the branches (Stratum 2); the red squirrel is pursued throughout its range by its chief enemy, the pine marten. Pine trees support many boring beetles that work in bark or wood (Stratum 3). Woodpeckers, in turn, hunt these insects.

Subassociation *a*(2). Animals of Deciduous Dicotyledonous Forests

Deciduous dicotyledonous forests are largely in temperate regions where there is a resting period during cold weather. Foliage may be present on the trees for from five to eight months, but during the remainder of the year the limbs are usually bare. The herbs growing on the forest floor are mostly tall, and such epiphytes as occur are mostly mosses and lichens. Fungi commonly grow in the soil or in dead wood. Trees of the same species are often gregarious and there are several types of forests (beech, oak, birch, etc.) that depend on climate, soil, and other factors.

In the broad-leaved forests of temperate regions phytophagous insects are more or less prevalent and are usually distributed according to their food preferences (Stratum 1). These are pursued by predaceous animals: spiders, assassin bugs, ants, warblers, flycatchers, vireos, etc. Among the branches (Stratum 2) crows, herons, and other birds find safe nesting sites. Scale insects and aphids attach themselves to the trunks or branches of the trees. Spiders, beetles, and predaceous insects feed on these and, in turn, furnish food for such birds as warblers and creepers. The red squirrel of coniferous forests is replaced in broad-leaved forests by the gray and fox squirrels. In bark and wood (Stratum 3) are to be found boring insects, woodpeckers, mice, raccoons, and other characteristic animals. During the resting season many of the invertebrates (except those that bore in wood) are hibernating, or æstivating, and the same is true of certain mammals. The birds, mammals, and invertebrates that remain active through the resting season subsist largely on stores of nuts, wood, buds, animals, or other foods.

Subassociation *a*(3). Animals of Evergreen Dicotyledonous Forests

The necessary conditions for an evergreen dicotyledonous forest are moisture (60 to 80 inches of rainfall per annum) and high temperature. Such forests are characteristic of the moist parts of the tropics and certain temperate portions of the southern hemisphere. The edge of the tropical forest is overgrown with a tangle of lianas, epiphytes, ferns, arums, cannas, etc., but the interior may be rather bare and dark on account of the density of the foliage and the height of the trees.   Epiphytes often cover the branches.   Though many species are intermingled, the interior of the forest is often monotonous and gloomy.   Palm forests, on the other hand, give comparatively little shade and are usually properly to be classified as savannahs.   Allee (1924) has made careful observations of barometric pressure, evaporation, air movement, temperature, and light in the Panamanian forest.   "The series of measurements shows that the lower tropical rain forest presents remarkably constant environmental conditions."

Most of the animals in a tropical forest live in the tree tops (Stratum 1) and are highly adapted to life in such situations. Beetles, butterflies, parrots, toucans, sun birds, humming birds, sloths, etc. feed on leaves, fruits, and flowers.   There are also predaceous species, such as mantids, tree frogs, slender tree snakes, and hawks.

The high humidity in the forest permits many animals that are usually associated with the surface or subterranean strata in other habitats to wander about over the trunks and branches (Stratum 2).   Hence, lizards, snakes, and monkeys are often associated with snails, isopods, and amphipods.   Annandale (1907) has described an earthworm that is abundant in an Indian forest, where it crawls about over the trunks of trees at night. There is the usual society of wood workers in the tropical forest: boring insects (especially termites), woodpeckers, rodents, etc.

Ruthven (1922) divides the forest in Colombia into the following zones, and cites characteristic animals that occur in each:

Below 2200 feet:

Ravine forest—large trees growing up from bottoms of ravines; ground litter developed somewhat; drier than above 2200 feet.

Scrub forest—occurring in clumps on plains and on ridges; little shade, little ground litter; two strata arboreal and ground.

Above 2200 feet:

Tropical rain forest—progressively wetter at higher altitudes; large trees, dense shade, deep ground litter.

Cloud forest—like last, but cooler and more humid; bromeliads more important.

Ruthven points out that above 4500 ft. bromeliads, both epiphytic and ground-dwelling, become more abundant and important as habitats for animals.   Scott (1912) and Picado

(1913) have discussed the relations of forest bromeliads. The former compares the habitats these plants furnish for animals to a swamp, but points out that there are differences in that those in bromeliads are arboreal, have peculiar conditions of lighting, and are restricted in area. Their water reservoirs are supplied by both rain and dew, and contain water when swamps are dried up. Between the leaves of the epiphytes are to be found dragon-fly nymphs; beetle, moth, fly, and mosquito larvæ; frogs' eggs and tadpoles; planarians, earthworms, snails, isopods, amphipods, ants, cockroaches, locustids, earwigs, centipedes, scorpions, spiders, tree frogs, and snakes. Scott (1912) also found dytiscids and many other animals among the bases of palm and pandanus leaves in the Seychelles. Some of the cockroaches and beetles that live between the leaves of such plants are remarkably flat.

ASSOCIATION *b*. ANIMALS OF SHRUBS

Shrubs are usually prevalent in areas where it is too dry or too cold on account of high latitude or altitude to support trees, but where conditions are favorable enough to support larger plants than grasses. Shrubs also often occur in zones of transition, along the margins of swamps or forests. As a habitat for animals they differ from trees in being close to the ground. Morse (1904) has pointed out that the typical orthopterans that live in forests are provided with long, slender wings for flying from tree to tree or across open spaces, but those that live in thickets of shrubs are frequently wingless and specialized for hopping or clinging, prob-ably because flight is difficult. A walking-stick is characteristic of shrubs. When disturbed, it may go into a death feint and remain motionless for a long period, or, if it is knocked to the ground by some passing animal, it may easily climb back among the foliage. Spiders and other animals that visit the ground at intervals are more numerous than those among trees. The lack of large open spaces among shrubs makes it difficult for large predaceous animals to pursue their prey; robber-flies and orb-weaving spiders are more common in such situations than hawks. Certain birds, like the cuckoo, trogon, cardinal, catbird, and brown thrasher, frequent thickets.

Some of the animals (tree frog, katydid) that are found in forests may also live among the foliage (Stratum 1) of thickets. Phytophagous insects, such as chrysomelid beetles, leaf miners, and aphids, are apt to be more abundant and varied than in forests and their enemies, the ichneumons, reduviids, asilids, and aphis-lions, are also prevalent.   Among the branches (Stratum 2) insectivorous birds are characteristic animals.   Forbes and Gross (1922) found more birds in orchards than in any other habitat in Illinois.   Borers (Stratum 3) are not so prevalent as in forests, probably because the small volume of woody structures does not offer as stable habitats.

Association c.   Animals Associated with Low Plants

Plains, prairies, pampas, steppes, meadows, and tundras are alike in supporting low vegetation.   Where there is considerable moisture, composites and other herbs may rival or exceed grasses in numbers, but where it is drier, the opposite is usually true. In Alaska, Dice (1920) has described hummocks of tough grass that occur in low situations where the drainage is poor.   These may be several feet high and are frequented by ptarmigan, shrew, weasel, mink, lemming, vole, moose, and other animals in a country that otherwise affords little shelter.   Waller (1918) in discussing the regions of North America says that the plains begin where evaporation falls below 60 per cent and are characterized by the presence of prong-horn antelope; prairies occur further east where the striped ground squirrel is found.   Ruthven (1908) maintains that few species are wholly confined to the prairies or plains, but that each has certain animals that are distinctive.   On the prairie are the prairie horned lark and nighthawk; on the plains, the pallid horned lark and Sennet nighthawk. The prairie also supports certain animals that properly belong to the eastern forest region, and the plains harbor animals that are perhaps better adapted to life in the prairie.   In localities where there is marked aridity there are often two resting seasons—during a cold winter and a hot summer.   In moister meadows there is usually one period of rest, in winter.

Characteristic Grassland Animals.—The low vegetation in grass and herb association gives little protection from light, heat, and cold.   Hence many animals remain underground part of the time and are often nocturnal or crepuscular.   There are no strata except those on or within plants.   In drier prairies the dominant animals are insects (Vestal, 1913).   On account of lack of available lime there are usually few snails; millipedes and earthworms are rare. Spiders, collembolans, termites, aphids and ant-lions, dragon-flies (many miles from aquatic habitats), locusts, carabæids, and other predaceous beetles, dipterons, and hymenopterans may be more or less common. Snakes and lizards are usually more common than birds. There may be mammals, such as the antelope, bison, buffalo, ground squirrel, vizcacha, skunk, puma, mouse, and rat.

In the tropics dry gass and herb stretches may be interspersed with trees and thus form savannahs. Here such animals as stone curlews and ant eaters are at home. Near the poles the tundra is inhabited by reindeer, foxes, lemmings, and other animals. In temperate regions that have enough moisture to support meadows, thickets, or forests, areas are often converted into pastures, parks, or gardens by man. Sometimes meadows border bodies of water which inundate them at times, but they may also be far from water at high altitudes; or, in any fairly moist region, may occur where continual grazing keeps trees and tall shrubs from gaining a foothold. They are populated chiefly by herbivorous insects, rodents, and other mammals, with the predaceous animals that feed upon them. Mowing and grazing do not kill out certain grasses, but make them form denser growths. Vestal (1913) says that some species of grasshoppers are more characteristic of cultivated than of natural grasslands. Harshberger (1923) has proposed the term "hemerecology," for the ecology of the areas modified by man.

Adaptations of Grassland Animals.—Vestal (1919) has pointed out that many of the insects that live in bunch grass are typically sedentary, but found that the "interstitial" animals, that frequent the spaces between vegetation, are usually swift and predaceous. Many of the larger herbivores (jack rabbit, antelope, mice) are swift, and the same is true of certain of the carnivores (foxes) that pursue them. Morse (1904) stressed the fact that the best flyers among locusts are found in open fields, where wide open areas make dispersal and escape from enemies easy, especially through the aid of winds. Collins (1922) states that the vision of prairie mammals is commonly panoramic and good either in dim or bright light. The olfactory and visual senses are keen and serve to give warning to prey or to notify predators of the presence of food. Jack rabbits and some other animals have very large ears. Predatory animals commonly have a considerable degree of bifocal vision and often see better in dim light than their prey. Animals that depend on speed for escaping usually have the eyes protruding prominently from the head.

Density of Population in Grasslands.—When conditions are favorable there may be many animals present. Wolcott (1918) after studying the Illinois prairie (as represented by city lots) estimated that there were 1,756,932 to 1,009,104 insects per acre and that other animals present in the subterranean, surface, and vegetation strata varied from 3,700,048 to 2,422,760 per acre. In the Illinois sand dunes, Sanders and Shelford (1922) estimated that there were about 84,000 animals per acre. Saunders (1907) gives the following estimates of the average number of acres required by each pair of breeding birds in Montana: grass meadow, 7.5; cinquefoil brush, 7.5; cottonwood grove, 0.53; stream border, 0.45; cat-tail slough, 0.67. These figures indicate that grasses and herbs contain less food for nestling birds than groves or areas near aquatic habitats. Water in the form of lakes, ponds, pools, or streams is not necessary, however, for many herb-inhabiting animals. Some grasshoppers will die of thirst when they have access to a dish of water, but will not do so when drops are sprinkled about that can be sucked off surfaces like dew (Snyder, 1904). Many prairie animals can get along without drinking at all.

Food of Grassland Animals.—Animals that feed on the low vegetation that grows in open places have the advantage of the unobstructed view that enables them to observe enemies, but must be able to endure the lean seasons, when food is greatly decreased or wholly absent on account of cold or drought. The reindeer (Hadwen and Palmer, 1922) is perhaps as well adjusted to life in open places as any large animal. It feeds in the summer on windswept areas near the sea, where it escapes to some extent from mosquitoes and warble flies and is able to obtain salt. In winter it paws through the snow and feeds on a variety of mosses, lichens, and other plants. The lemmings and voles remain active through cold seasons in tunnels beneath the snow. Many prairie animals lay up stores which are often protected by being placed in underground chambers. Pocket gophers and certain other rodents have cheek pouches which they use for transporting food. Ossendowski (1922) gives an interesting account of a rodent which he encountered in Mongolia. This was a gigantic black rat which lived in colonies of one or two hundred. It is said to mow grass with its teeth and dry it. A mound of loose earth about a foot high is then prepared near the mouth of the burrow and the hay is carefully piled on it. About four stakes are pushed through the hay into the loose earth below and the whole mass is then bound together with grass so as to prevent it from blowing away.

Enemies of Grassland Animals.—Enemies that beset the animals of prairies and similar habitats are usually swift and powerful. Many of the rodents are gregarious and commonly give alarm notes that warn of the approach of danger. On the pampas in Argentina the vizcachas are caught by the puma; a fox often usurps one of their burrows and devours their young (Hudson, 1922). The prairie dog of the western plains of the United States is eaten, especially while young, by coyotes, owls, and rattle snakes. Bailey (1893) states that the chief enemies of the ground squirrel are: (1) diurnal hawks and owls, which pursue them above ground; (2) the badger, which digs out their burrows; and (3) the bull snake, which also catches them underground. The reindeer is attacked by the bear, wolf, lynx, wolverine, and eagle. It is peculiar among deer in that horns are present on both sexes.

Burrowing and Non-burrowing Animals of Grasslands.—Though many prairie animals have more or less permanent homes in holes in the ground, there are many that do not do so. Certain rodents (prairie dog, ground squirrel) always live in burrows and are never seen far from them. Hudson (1922) says that bank swallows dig their holes in the sides of the large entrances to vizcacha burrows and are dependent on the rodents for nesting sites. The vizcacha is highly adapted to life in burrows, even having a special claw on the hind foot which serves as a comb for removing parasites. Some prairie animals have permanent holes which serve as dens, but spend more time in them during the breeding season than at other times (coyote, trap-door spiders). Other animals commonly use burrows that they do not dig themselves (snakes, owls). Jack rabbits, many mice, insects, grouse, and other animals do not dig burrows but crouch among vegetation and are well concealed by their coloration.

Strata on Grasslands.—The strata above the ground are not so sharply defined as those among taller vegetation. Animals that are subterranean or perhaps properly to be classified in the surface stratum may have relations with the highest parts of the vegetation. Most of the larger animals, in fact, belong to the surface stratum, yet they are more or less characteristic of situations where low vegetation occurs. Both tree squirrels and prairie dogs are dependent on vegetation and often journey over the surface of the ground, but the former are found in forests and the latter in prairies. About the only type of stratification that applies to the small animals that live among or in low vegetation is that which depends upon whether animals live on the outside of or within plants.

ASSOCIATION *d*. DESERT ANIMALS

Deserts are not wholly due to the extreme condition of any one climatic factor but are primarily brought about by continual lack of water which, though it may be present in considerable amounts during certain seasons or years, is erratic in its distribution, and always meager. The large deserts are mostly just north or south of the equator. Some of these occupy the beds of ancient seas. Some, though they contain more or less water, are physiologically dry on account of the presence of large amounts of salts. These are "alkali" deserts. The low relative humidity in deserts is associated with lack of clouds. The days are bright and sunny, with a correspondingly great action from all the wave lengths of light. Deserts may occur in connection with any type of earth surface, but hard soils are least favorable for animals because they do not, like sand, give an opportunity for burrowers to escape unfavorable conditions. The absence of atmospheric moisture allows heat to radiate quickly from the earth. The nights are usually cold and thus are in sharp contrast to the hot days. There is little or no shade to afford shelter from the intense heat and light. The surface of the soil may reach 75 to 85°C. and at midday is often 20°C. hotter than the atmosphere in the shade. Most animals hide away during the middle of the day and many are crepuscular or nocturnal.

Desert Plants.—In deserts there may be thickets of shrubs, but, as a rule, there is little opportunity for animals to pass directly from plant to plant. Many animals spend much of their time on or below the surface of the soil. The vegetation consists largely of tap-rooted perennials and thick-stemmed plants that have various adaptations for conserving water. For a short period after rains there may be annual plants, which at other seasons are in non-vegetative states (seeds, etc.). The soil of deserts is often rich in plant nutriment on account of the salts left by water that is drawn up from the subsoil and evaporates from the surface, but such food is largely unavailable on account of lack of water to dissolve it. Desert plants, though differing more or less from each other, have a characteristic aspect. Dense woody structures, thorns, bitter or saline saps, dwarfs, rosettes, brief life histories, rolling habits, hygrochasy, enlarged green stems, and absence of leaves are common adaptations. By such peculiarities water is conserved, growth takes place rapidly during the short favorable season, the attacks of vegetarian animals are prevented to some extent, and, in general, the severe conditions of life are better endured.

Adaptations to Lack of Water.—There are many animals that are especially fitted for life in deserts by the presence of particular racial traits. Lizards, kangaroo rats, sand grouse, road runners, gazelles, and camels are typical desert animals. They show adaptation—often to a remarkable degree—to desert life. Perhaps the chief difficulty among desert animals is to obtain and retain water. Some make frequent journeys to sources of water; some drink water but can remain active for considerable periods without it; some can exist without water, except that which they obtain in their food. Desert frogs, and even tadpoles, absorb much water during rains and then remain underground much of the time in order to retain it. The nocturnal habits of animals expose them to evaporation in the atmosphere when it is least effective as a drying agent. Some animals plug up the mouths of their burrows during the day. Lizards conserve water by excreting uric acid instead of urea. Some desert animals are active for brief periods during the year when water and food are available. Buxton (1923) states that fifty species of protozoans were raised from soil after eight months of drought. Not only invertebrates, but amphibians, reptiles, and mammals may thus remain dormant. Buxton (1921) points out that there is concentration in time and space: animals are abundant and active after spring rains, and few insect imagoes are seen in the hottest season; more animals are present among and beneath vegetation and where caves furnish shelter than in open spaces.

Protective Adaptations of Desert Animals.—Most desert animals are colored so that they are not easily seen and commonly show the dull browns and grays that are characteristic of the environment. Many of them are very swift. Lizards that run on sandy areas may have fringes along the toes which aid their progress; the camels also have broad, soft pads on their feet. The rodents tend to have toes that are short, compact, and often reduced in number. Their limbs are generally long and slender and the hind pair are often developed for leaping. A number of desert animals are not only speedy but take an erratic course, which tends to confuse their pursuers. Among rodents such animals often have a long tail which helps in balancing (jerboa, kangaroo rat, etc.). The animals that have long legs and are able to stretch upward are easily able to keep a lookout for enemies. Nocturnal animals especially are often provided with large ears and an acute sense of hearing. Some desert animals are solitary (the kangaroo rat will not tolerate another individual in its burrow), but others are quite gregarious (the huanaco grazes in little herds, with one individual continually serving as a sentinel; Hudson, 1922). Predaceous animals, as on prairies, have unusual adaptations that enable them to capture their prey. The badger digs animals out of their retreats; the swift depends on its speed; the owl approaches swiftly, stealthily, and has very acute vision, especially in light of low intensity. Animals that burrow escape from heat, cold, evaporation, and certain enemies. Some of them have the nostrils protected by special valves and the eyes and ears are likewise often shielded. Some lizards have a transparent disc in the eyelid and are thus able to see when the eye is closed (Gadow, 1913). The dust and alkali in deserts would probably be injurious to certain rodents if it were not for the oily secretions on the fur (Vorhies and Taylor, 1922).

Adaptations to High Temperatures and Strong Light.— Some desert animals are able to endure very high temperatures, but others avoid the light and heat of the meridional sun. Buxton (1923) cites beetles and lizards that sit without apparent discomfort on rocks that are too hot for the human hand. The harvester ant in Texas always builds its nests in open places without shade and does not work on cloudy days. Wheeler (1911) says that it works through the middle of the day when the temperature of the soil is below 60°C. The eggs of the ostrich may be left in the sun without injury, but some birds cover their eggs with sand. Certain desert leaf-hoppers are orbicular, flat, and short winged. They have long slender legs which hold them high above the hot soil as they move about (Hartzell, 1921). Lizards burrow at night to avoid low temperatures and are inactive throughout cold seasons (Gilver, 1922). Some nocturnal animals (bats, owls) seek refuge in caves during the day. Vorhies and Taylor (1922) note the fact that the kangaroo rat escapes the attacks of warble-flies by its strictly nocturnal habits.

Reproduction in the Desert.—Desert animals on the whole produce few offspring. They are well adjusted to environmental conditions and tend to live long lives rather than multiply rapidly. This, of course, is not true of some animals, such as certain insects and mice, that multiply rapidly with the increase of vegetation after rains.

Food of Desert Animals.—The food of desert animals is related to the scarcity of water and the short growing season for vegetation. Wasps, bats, many birds, and some other desert animals visit bodies of water and drink at frequent intervals. The sand grouse not only leaves its nest to obtain water, but carries a supply on its breast feathers for its young (Buxton, 1923). The ostrich, giraffe, eland, pocket gopher, and grasshopper mouse get along without water, but drink when it is available. Pocket mice eat dew and snow but probably do not drink (Bailey, 1923). Some desert beetles also eat dew off plants. A camel can do without water for eight to ten days while subsisting on dry food and, if supplied with green vegetation, for a couple of months. The mule deer and mountain goat get water from vegetation and never go near water to drink. The prong-horn antelope and jack rabbit eat cactus pulp (78 per cent water) and other succulent plants. The jerboa, certain ground squirrels, addax, oryx, and gazelle always go without water and are able to subsist for long periods on dry vegetation. Some carnivorous animals depend largely on insects and vertebrate prey for their water supply.

Several animals that frequent deserts store food during seasons of plenty. The banner-tailed kangaroo rat collects vegetable food, principally the seeds of grasses, from April to November, and larders examined by Vorhies and Taylor (1922) contained from 5 to 5750 grams. The desert kangaroo rat does not store food, but steals from its more provident relative, which kills the thief whenever it finds it in its burrows.   The Texas harvest ant carefully selects seeds off the ground and stores them in underground chambers; the Florida harvester climbs up on plants and picks off seeds.   Both species husk their crops within the nest and carry out the refuse to midden piles above ground.   It is doubtful if either of these ants plants seeds and raises crops; they are foragers and storers (McCook, 1879).   Mann (1913) says:

The harvesting ants are descended from insectivorous forms, which have taken up the grain-storing habit as an adaptation to life in the desert, in steppes, etc., where, during parts of the year, insect food is scarce.   Seeds can be stored and kept, which is not true of insect food.

Honey ants collect honey from aphids (Buxton, 1923) and galls (McCook, 1882) and keep it in peculiar workers which serve as living bottles.

FORMATION 3.   AERIAL ANIMALS

Historically, the air was the last of the non-aquatic habitats to be invaded by animals.   Lull (1906) states that volant evolution has occurred seventeen times among different groups of vertebrates—ten times for gliding and seven for flying. He also affirms that the ability to glide, and probably also to fly, has commonly been associated with ancestral adaptation to arboreal life.   The ability to sail or fly through the air makes greater speed possible than can be attained by cursorial animals.   It is useful for reaching inaccessible situations, escaping from enemies, seeking food, distributing species, migrating from unfavorable to favorable localities, etc.   Of course, there is no animal that lives permanently in the air without contact with solid objects, but there are many animals that spend most of their active lives there.   The swifts even pick off twigs and in part build their nests while fluttering on the wing; a buzzard may soar for hours without flapping its wings.

Types of Adjustment to Aerial Life.—All animals that move through the air are heavier than the medium that surrounds them and hence lack the help of the buoyancy that keeps many aquatic animals near the surface.   The ability of animals to remain in the air depends largely (1) on the ratio of horizontal surface exposed to weight, and (2) the rate of movement.   Ballooning spiders have no active means of progression, and therefore depend on winds. The Javan tree frog, Draco, and flying squirrels volplane down from elevations, and after attaining a certain velocity may even rise somewhat at the end of a journey. The flapping of wings is a much more laborious process than soaring.

Adaptations for Flight.—The types which are most at home in the air are the soarers. Aerial animals are adapted more or less to the life they live. They are usually light, active, keen of vision, have smooth and slender contours, rigid but at the same time flexible bodies, and wide surfaces. Hankin (1920) has described the adaptations of flying animals in great detail. Morgan (1913) says that may-fly nymphs when they are ready to shed their skins go to the surface of the water and gulp air into the alimentary canal in order to inflate the body. He also affirms that adult may-flies carry on similar activities as an aid to flight.

There has been considerable dispute as to how aerial animals maintain themselves in the air. It is easy to see how a wind carries, and even elevates, a mass of web like the balloon of a migrating spider. Gliding downward from elevations is readily understandable. It is also easy to see how a bat, bird, or insect can hold itself in the air by flapping its wings. But how birds and insects are able to soar in the air for considerable periods of time without beating the air with their wings is not clearly understood. Hankin (1920) does not claim that he understands soaring fully, but affirms that the air when exposed to sunlight becomes "soarable." Nocturnal flying animals all flap their wings, but some diurnal birds can soar in the air, even when there is no wind. Hankin uses the word "glide" to mean progression through the air with the aid of elevation or wind. Soaring he believes is made possible by some form of energy that is released from the air by sunlight. Hankin also claims that soaring birds usually avoid upward currents, but Idrac (1920, 1921) stoutly maintains that birds are able to soar solely on account of vertical and horizontal irregularities in the air, especially upward currents. Idrac admits, however, that he does not undertsand how the albatross is able to soar over areas that are apparently uniform and how birds soar in cold regions. He believes that birds make considerable use as highways of zones where there are small whirling currents, and move up and down with them. Hankin has pointed out that the best soarers (vultures, dragon-flies) have longitudinal ridges on the under surface of their wings and that animals that fly by flapping (owls, bats) lack these. Townsend (1909), Beetham (1912), and Hankin (1920) have given extensive descriptions of different types of flight in various animals, describing methods of starting, stopping, steering, balancing, etc. Some birds are not able to take off unless they can gain momentum by swimming or running; many birds are not very expert at what is perhaps the hardest task for all flyers—stopping. Long-legged, short-tailed birds use their legs as rudders while flying; birds with small feet fold them up while flying and steer with their tails. Long-winged birds and bats commonly move up and down by moving the tips of their wings.

Feeding in the Air.—Many animals feed largely or wholly in the air. Bats catch food with their sharp teeth, and Lucas (1897) states that struggling animals are covered over with a sticky oral secretion which prevents them from escaping. Goatsuckers and swifts feed on the wing and have a wide gape with bristles at the corners of the mouth that help in the capture of insects. Hawks and owls have spreading talons for the grasping of food on the wing; dragon- and robber-flies attain the same ends with their leg baskets.

Senses of Aerial Animals.—The high speed at which sailing and flying animals move makes good sense organs necessary. Vision is usually acute; touch and hearing are often developed to a high degree. Quickness of movement and excellent muscular coordination are characteristic. Bats are able to avoid obstacles without using their eyes. Blinded bats can fly about among wires without touching them. The hairs on their bodies are richly supplied with nerve endings and serve sensory functions. Hahn (1908) believes that bats perceive obstacles while flying by making high chirping sounds which are reflected back to their ears from objects in their paths. Birds have large, protruding eyes that enable them to see and avoid obstacles. Bifocal vision is developed to a considerable degree in predaceous birds. The enormous eyes of a dragon-fly cover most of the head, which is loosely pivoted on the body so that it can be turned nearly 180 degrees. Many flying animals have pronounced homing instincts and remarkable ability to return to particular spots or move in a certain direction without losing their way. Bats return after each foray to their accustomed retreats and do not emerge unless the weather is favorable. Birds have roosting places to which they return continually, and are thus saved the trouble of seeking a new site each time the sun goes down. Insects that have regular homes may return to them to sleep. A continual and accurate cognizance of the surroundings through the senses and a recognition of directions and relations are essential for animals that use the air as a highway.

Duration and Speed of Flight.—Animals that have heavy loads in proportion to their horizontal sustaining surfaces cannot make long flights, but those that are highly adapted may soar for hours with little effort and cover great stretches of territory. The "flying-dragon," *Draco voltans*, is able to glide for a distance of 40 to 50 meters. A flying fish can rise 5 to 7 meters above the surface of the ocean and usually does not cover more than 100 to 200 meters in a single flight, though in exceptional cases it may fly 500 to 800 meters. A bird may ascend to an altitude of a couple of kilometers and perhaps traverse a tenth of the circumference of the globe without stopping to rest (Coward, 1912). The speed at which animals fly probably rarely, if ever, exceeds 100 miles per hour and Meinertzhagen (1921) has shown that most birds do not exceed 50.

ASSOCIATION *a*. BALLOONING AND GLIDING ANIMALS

Spiders are the only animals that progress through the air with the aid of balloons of cobweb. They are largely confined to the surface of the soil and low vegetation except when they are traveling, and they balloon at infrequent intervals (Stratum 1). Gliders are found among fishes, tree frogs, lizards, and mammals (Stratum 2). They are all arboreal except the fishes, which gain elevation by leaping out of the water.

ASSOCIATION *b*. FLYING ANIMALS

Flying animals may be differentiated into those that spend most of their time closely associated with the surface of the earth (Stratum 1) and those that live most of their active life in the air (Stratum 2). Grouse, ducks, geese, warblers, grasshoppers, and many other animals, though good flyers, use the air only as a highway in passing to and from roosts, feeding grounds, breeding places, etc. Predaceous animals, such as swifts, nighthawks, vultures, and dragon-flies, are more or less continually in the air seeking food. They are not necessarily to be found above any particular terrestrial or aquatic habitat. Many such animals are able to soar.

APPENDIX I. ANIMALS OF ISLANDS

The animals that live on islands, especially oceanic islands, though dwelling in the same types of formations, associations, and strata that are found on continents, are often subjected to unusual conditions, both in the living and non-living environment, on account of the limited area of the land mass they inhabit and its isolation. The numbers of species of plants and animals on isolated islands are usually limited. Stewart (1915) points out there are more species of ferns than of spermatophytes on the Galápagos Islands, probably because their small spores are readily carried by winds. Schimper (1903) states that there are fewer flowers and fewer insects on islands.

Both phenomena are to be attributed to strong winds, which on one hand lessen the number of insects and plants associated with them, and on the other hand favor anemophilous flowers.

MacCaughey (1917a) has emphasized the remarkable endemism of the plants of the Hawaiian Islands. Over 85 per cent of the flowering plants are not found elsewhere. Endemism among the plants in other Pacific islands is as follows: Samoa 34, Tahiti 35, Fiji 53, New Zealand 75 per cent.

Amphibians and mammals are usually absent from oceanic islands (Wallace, 1912). This makes conditions peculiar. Mores that are dominated in most parts of the earth by ubiquitous rodents or ruminants may be characterized by reptiles or other animals. Darwin (1859) said:

The species of all kinds which inhabit oceanic islands are few in number compared with those on equal continental areas . . . Oceanic islands are sometimes deficient in animals of certain whole classes, and their places are occupied by other classes: thus in the Galápagos Islands reptiles, and in New Zealand gigantic wingless birds, take or recently took, the place of mammals.

In some islands frogs, being introduced and not being kept down by natural enemies, have become a nuisance. Bats, certain birds, and insects are, of course, distributed more or less to all islands. There are often endemic and wingless birds and insects, however. These are adapted to insular life by being unable to fly; in fact, the power of flight might be detrimental because they could be swept out into the open sea and lost.

APPENDIX II. ANIMALS FREQUENTING STRUCTURES MADE BY MAN

Many buildings and other structures that are built by man are occupied by animals and some species are largely confined to such situations. Bats, swallows, swifts, owls, woodpeckers, wasps, and bees find shelter and nesting sites in buildings, but forage for food elsewhere. Predators and scavengers, like rats, mice, clothes moths, house lizards, centipedes, spiders, ants, mosquitoes, bed bugs, and fleas, find temporary or permanent homes in dwellings and also find food there. Some of these animals are very desirable companions for men, others are more or less pestiferous. In the Philippines every dwelling supports a few house lizards that scamper about the walls and do much good by destroying vermin. The cockroaches, ants, termites, and other insects that these lizards devour are not pleasant to have about.

Hobson and Mathews (1923) have published a very interesting account of the "Ecology of King's College Chapel." They divide the animals into (1) independent species, that find food outside the chapel; and (2) dependent species, that carry on all activities within the building. Pigeons, bats, and hibernating insects come and go; ticks, fleas, certain mites, and bird lice for the most part lurk in crevices during the day and come out at night to suck blood; Lepismas and the larvæ of the beetles, flies, lepidopters, and fleas feed on fæces or the bodies of dead animals; spiders, beetles, pseudoscorpions, and certain mites catch small animals and devour them.

CHAPTER VIII

RELATIONS OF ANIMALS TO PLANTS

Though the vegetation of the earth was discussed in the last chapter as an important determiner of terrestrial habitats, it is proper to devote some space to the consideration of certain of the many special relations between plants and animals. The vegetation covering the earth exerts an important influence on climate and other features of particular localities. Changes in it often bring about profound alterations. For example, the denudation of forests has in some regions been the cause of frequent floods.

Interdependence of Plants and Animals.—A plant and an animal are more or less interdependent and the activities of one result in waste products that are necessary for the snytheses of the other. Photosynthesis, the process which gives rise to nearly all the organic food of plants and animals, requires carbon dioxide, which is, in turn, commonly liberated by the disintegration of organisms. Decay is usually brought about by bacteria and other fungi. All protoplasm forms carbon dioxide as a product of metabolism. Except for anaerobic organisms, both plant and animal protoplasm require a continual supply of oxygen for metabolism, and oxygen is an end product of photosynthesis. Carbon dioxide in large amounts is injurious to protoplasm, and its presence may make a particular habitat unfit for life. On the other hand, the fact that carbon dioxide is necessary for photosynthesis makes it a continual necessity for green plants. Fulton (1922) claims that chlorophyll is present in, or is the source of, pigment in protozoans, sponges, actinians, flatworms, and echinoderms. He thinks that hæmoglobin is probably derived from chlorophyll—phylogenetically and physiologically. A stagnant swamp that is saturated with carbon dioxide may be oxygenated by the photosynthetic activity of its green plants during the day, but be uninhabitable for many animals at night. Aquatic plants serve three important functions: (1) the aeration of water, (2) the covering of the bottom, and (3), through disintegration, the enrichment of the water, thus making the growth of a greater volume of plankton possible. Plants have another important relation to animals in their ability to synthesize simple organic nitrogenous compounds that are essential for protein metabolism. Animals are not able to carry on nitrification or nitrogen fixation.

Plants not only furnish food for animals, but serve them in many other ways, giving protection from radiant energy, changes in temperature, and enemies, as well as favorable situations for the building of homes and the rearing of offspring. In any region the number of animals is roughly related to the amount of vegetation. Many animals have very specialized relations with particular plants. Some caterpillars will eat the leaves of only one genus, or even one species, of plant; some bees visit only one kind of flower. On the other hand, certain plants support from 200 to 500 species of insects. The caterpillar of the gypsy moth and the migratory locust will feed on almost any plant. The benefits derived from associations between plants and animals often accrue to the former as well as the latter. Plants are pollinated, defended, and distributed by animals. There are a few plants that capture and devour animals, and many microscopic species that cause diseases.

PLANTS AS FOOD FOR ANIMALS

Vestal (1914) in his excellent paper on the internal relations of terrestrial associations says:

The majority of plant-feeders are adapted to eat herbage of nearly any kind: they are not restricted to particular species or particular parts of plants. They are non-selective feeders.

Most of them are only moderately specialized.

Selective feeders belong with the highly specialized animals . . . Highly specialized forms are thus enabled to avail themselves of opportunities denied to animals of generalized type; but while they avoid competition by the adoption of special kinds of food, or by a special habit of some other kind, they lack the versatility of the less specialized animals, being unable to adjust themselves to changed conditions.

They may be abundant at times but never become dominant through large ecological divisions. When a species becomes abundant, it is usually attacked by many predaceous species that have some flexibility in their food habits. "Animals with non-specialized habits, by taking whatever food is easiest of access, act as regulators." They are important in preserving the balance in nature.   Baker, Korstian, and Fetherolf (1921) have given an illustration of man's effect on such a balance in the Wasatch Mountains.   In that region the coyote is gradually being exterminated, and this leads to an unusual increase in its common prey, the snowshoe rabbit.   In winter the rabbit feeds on the tender buds and twigs and has thus changed the aspect of the country by holding back the upward growth of many conifers for years. Dwarf vegetation is now quite characteristic.   Forbes (1880) has discussed a number of similar relations between plants and insects.

Defenses of Plants against Animal Vegetarians.—Plants that are fed upon by animals often have adaptations that keep many animals from using them as food.   Among peculiarities that are more or less effective for such purposes are thorns, saws, urticating hairs, hard or gritty exteriors, irritating crystals, ethereal oils, bitter juices, alkaloids, etc.   A plant that possesses any one of these is not necessarily adapted to ward off all vegetarians. Some expedients are effective against one feeder and some against others.   A donkey or goat readily browses on spiny plants; certain insects favor the milkweeds (which contain sticky, bitter juices) above all other foods.   It cannot be said that any "adaptation" is effective under all circumstances.   However, those that make plants avoided by animals are most prevalent where there is a dearth of plants for food, *i.e.*, in the desert.

Food Stores.—Animals that depend on vegetation for food often lay up stores to be used during seasons when little or no food is available.   As stores have been discussed rather extensively in connection with other topics (pp. 71, 271), they will be touched on very little here.   Beavers transport green branches to the bottoms of ponds and feed upon them during the winter. The California woodpecker makes holes in tree trunks to receive acorns.   Many rodents store small seeds, nuts, grasses, or other vegetation in holes for use in cold or dry seasons.   Perhaps the most interesting among provident animals are the harvesting ants, which hoard seeds in underground chambers.   Wheeler (1910), in speaking of the work of Moggridge, says:

In confirmation of Pliny and Plutarch he maintains that the ants bite off the radicle to prevent the seeds from germinating, a process which is also arrested by bringing them when damp with rain to the surface, spreading them in the sun and then carrying them back to the granaries. Some of the seeds sprout, nevertheless, either in the nests or on the kitchen middens.

On the other hand, the germination of certain seeds before they are eaten is said to obviate the necessity of cracking their coats by ants. Some species of harvester ants chew up seeds into a dough, which is molded into pellets and dried in the sun, and, like the bread of man, may be invaded by fungi which multiply and make the mass more digestible (Wheeler, 1911). According to Heim (1898), a Mediterranean harvester ant lays up stores in underground mud cells that are originally made by a beetle.

Crops.—A step beyond the storing of food is the raising of crops and the keeping of flocks. Outside the human race agriculture is practiced by ants, termites, and beetles. Certain ants feed on secretions, which are derived from animals but consist largely of carbohydrates that come indirectly from plants. Ants feed thus from other ants, aphids, beetles, insect larvæ, and scale insects. These sources of food are tended carefully, some being carried underground, enclosed in manufactured shelters, or placed in favorable situations on plants.

Types of Crops.—In regard to crops there are some variations among different agricultural insects, though probably no insect raises anything but fungi. The ambrosia beetles feed on fungus that grows on sawdust and other materials that accumulate in their galleries in dead wood. Termites use fæces, sawdust, and other materials for culture media. The hairy ants in Africa make gardens from sawdust, fæces from insect larvæ, and other organic materials and raise several species of fungi. Leaf-cutter ants make beds from bits of leaves. The fungi that they cultivate are not found outside their nests and are pruned in order to produce peculiar growths, which are the only parts devoured. A female leaf-cutter when ready to found a new colony carries away a "brick" containing fungus from her parents' nest and plants this on the first little bed of leaves that she makes, thus starting a new line of cultures. The leaf-cutters have had a marked influence on South American vegetation. The rose, orange, coffee, chickory, mango, cabbage, and some other plants cannot be grown successfully as crops where these ants are abundant, but the insects do not molest some plants (eucalyptus, ramie, grasses, bay, magnolia, cucurbits, etc.). Among certain termites in Ceylon only the queen and larvæ eat fungus, the workers and soldiers subsisting on other foods (Doflein, 1906).

Origin of Agricultural Habits.—Wheeler (1907) states his belief that all ants were originally exclusively entomophagous.

Only a few species have become storers or agriculturalists. Attiid ants, certain termites, and ambrosia beetles raise practically pure cultures of various fungi. According to Wheeler, Von Ihering first suggested that such habits arose from eating fungi that developed on stored foods. Wheeler says in regard to the leaf-cutters:

These insects in the fierce struggle for existence, everywhere apparent in the tropics, have developed a complex of instinctive activities which enables them to draw upon an ever-present inexhaustible food supply through utilizing the foliage of plants as a substratum for the culture of edible fungi. No wonder, therefore, that, having emancipated themselves from the precarious diet of other ants, which subsist on insects, the sweet exudations of plants and the excrement of phytophthorous Rhynchota, the Attii have become the dominant invertebrates of tropical America.

GALLS

Galls are abnormal growths produced by mechanical irritation or the presence of chemical substances. Though a few occur on animals (crab galls on corals, glochidial galls on fishes, growths about trichinæ and chigoes, etc.), they are particularly characteristic of plants and usually furnish food and shelter for plants or animals that live within them. They may be produced on plants by the presence of bacteria, slime molds, fungi, rotifers, copepods, nematodes, mites, or insects. Plant galls are divided into two groups: (1) kataplasms, which consist largely of undifferentiated parenchymatous tissue; and (2) prosoplasms, which contain a variety of tissues. Kataplasms are in a sense deformities of parts that are already present and prosoplasms are to a greater extent new growths that are peculiar and highly specific for each species of maker. The former type are produced by parasitic plants, slime molds, rotifers, copepods, nematodes, Orthoptera, Neuroptera, Coleoptera, Lepidoptera, muscid-flies, chalcids, and saw-flies; the latter are probably caused only by arthropods (Cook, 1923). Both kataplasmic and prosoplasmic galls are produced by flies (*Itonididæ, Trypsetidæ*), Hymenoptera (*Cynipidæ, Tenthredinidæ*), bugs (*Aphididæ, Psyllidæ*), beetles, lepidopters, and mites.

Stimuli Causing Galls.—There has been much discussion concerning the specific stimuli which cause galls to develop.

There have been advocates of mechanical stimulation as the sole cause of galls, and those who contended that galls were entirely due to the presence of chemicals. Most of the evidence seems to support the latter view. It was formerly supposed that insect galls were caused by some substance that the female injected or the injury she inflicted when she deposited her eggs, but very few instances are known that are explainable on such a basis. Though there are some exceptions, insect galls usually do not begin to develop until their larvæ hatch from the egg and become active. In many cases the greatest proliferation of tissues may not take place near the larva, but at some distance from it. This indicates that the abnormal growth is due to some chemical substance that stimulates cell proliferation. The larva continually obtains nourishment through its mouth from the tissues surrounding it. Folsom (1922) says:

The larva by accelerating the rate of change from starch to sugar renders available to the plant more food than usual and therefore stimulates the activity of the protoplasm toward greater cell-growth and more rapid cell-reproduction. Thus the gall as well as the larva draws food from the nutritive zone.

Plant physiologists generally make more cautious statements and await further evidence.

Host Relations of Gall-producing Animals.—Gall-producing animals usually show a considerable degree of specificity in the plant hosts that they attack, and some types of plants support great numbers of galls. Felt (1911) listed 1400 species of galls in North America. Galls may occur on any part of a plant (root, stem, bud, leaf, leaf vein, flower, seed, etc.), but the situation and the form of the galls caused by each species are usually quite characteristic. Insects and other animals that do not produce galls may live in them. Folsom (1922) mentions an instance where thirty species of insects were reared from one kind of gall. Heindel (1905) found thirty-two species of insects in the willow cone gall: one gall maker, ten inquilines, sixteen parasites and hyperparasites, and five transient or accidental guests. The oak, hickory, and grape support many gall producers. Felt (1910) states that the genus Caryomyia is restricted to hickory food-galls and Cincticornia is probably confined to oaks. He also lists eighteen species that are found on asters, thirty-five on golden rods, and forty-six on willows.

THE RELATIONS OF ANIMALS TO FLOWERS

The relations between flowers and insects furnish some of the most remarkable instances of adaptation in the whole of nature and have been much discussed by naturalists.   Robertson (1899) believes that flowers were first visited for nectar, and such adaptations as the sticky pollen and convenient landing places were developed later to insure the calls of insect visitors.   At present insects and other animals receive notice of the presence of flowers by particular colors and odors.   They feed upon nectar, pollen, and other substances that the flowers furnish, and in return benefit the flowers by carrying pollen.   Bouvier (1905) says

To summarize: (1) Nectar and the nectaries are certainly intended primarily for the plant itself and do not prove the adaptation of the flower to the insect.   (2) The colors and perfumes of flowers may be perhaps the result of such adaptation, but in any case they strongly attract anthophilian insects, signaling to them the presence of booty.   (3) In many cases, if not all, the complicated forms of the flowers must be attributed to the adaptation of flowers to their insect visitors . . . It is almost unanimously conceded nowadays that the Mellifera, at least insofar as their collecting apparatus is concerned, are beautifully adapted to the flowers, but, despite the fact that practice has shown that plants are in every way more plastic than animals, it is still strangely disputed that flowering plants have adapted themselves to bees.   If there does exist any reciprocal modification between the Mellifera and flowering plants, it is not at all necessary to suppose that one group has been modified for the benefit of the other.   Each has evolved on its own account.   Explained thus, the many objections to reciprocal adaptation are overthrown.   The bee has but one object, the pursuit of food, and all things which aid him in it are welcome.   Usually the plant profits thereby; sometimes it suffers.   On the other hand, the plant seeks only to assure its propagation and all its modifications tend only toward that goal.   It is only indirectly that colors and perfumes are of advantage to insects; the complicated flower, most favorable to the reproduction of the plant, is to the bees an obstacle . . . It is by no means for the benefit of the plant that the collecting apparatus of the bees is modified, but only that the bee may better nourish itself.   On the other hand, it is to the distinct advantage of the plant and its propagation that flowers are modified in shape, color and odor.   The insect has gained by the conformation of the flowers; the flower by the visits of the insect.

Pollination by Animals.—The great benefit that certain plants appear to receive from the visits of insects and other flying animals to their flowers is cross-pollination. Plants, as a whole, may have various means within themselves that help to accomplish this (unisexual flowers, a difference in the time of maturation of the pistils and stamens, differences in the lengths of stamens and pistils, traps for insects, etc.), but some are absolutely dependent upon the visits of particular insects and are adapted to them by possessing certain foods, odors, colors, patterns, and forms. The adaptations of flowers may also be such as to prevent the visits of guests other than the usual pollinators. There are also many adaptations for loading visitors with pollen (dusters, slappers, exploders, pumps, etc.), and elaborate mechanisms for receiving pollen.

Visits to Flowers for Food.—Certain insects, birds, and other animals are specially fitted for feeding on nectar, pollen, and other flower products, and many can subsist on nothing else. Many moths that do not frequent flowers are poor flyers and have degenerate tongues (Ord, 1900). Many orchids with deep corallas are pollinated by moths with long tongues. Pendulous flowers are accessible to few insects but bees. Many bees feed largely on pollen and have special adaptations for collecting and transporting it. Moths, flies, and birds, as a rule, make little use of pollen and usually have less specialized means for carrying it, if they do so at all. Flower visitors may be classified as *polytropic*, visiting many species of flowers, *oligotropic*, visiting few species; *monotropic*, visiting only one species. Oligotropic bees are usually solitary and have a short flying season when their special flowers are in bloom. By visiting few kinds of flowers, they more or less avoid competition. A honey bee is essentially oligotropic, for it usually feeds largely from one species of flower at a time.

Time of Blooming Related to Pollinators.—In general, the time of blooming of entomophilous flowers coincides more or less with the time, both as to time of day and season, when their pollinators are flying. Robertson (1895) pointed out that introduced species generally have a longer blooming season than native plants, he believes because they are subject to less competition. Aquatic plants also bloom longer than comparable terrestrial species, probably for the same reason. In a recent paper Robertson (1924) discusses the times of blooming of various Illinois plants in detail. Plants that mostly bloom before July include: (1) low plants, that are later shaded by trees or other taller vegetation; (2) 90 per cent of the trees and 64 per cent of woody climbers, though many do not begin to bloom before June; (3) 53 per cent of the shrubs; (4) 68 per cent of all woody plants. Fifty-two per cent of woodland herbs begin to bloom in March and April. Social flowers make up 60.4 per cent of plants in bloom in October; non-social flowers compose 75.7 per cent of those in bloom in April. White flowers are dominant in early spring and late fall; yellow and red during the warmer months. The season for maximum blooming for annual and biennial plants is a month later than that for perennials. Taller herbs bloom later than shorter. Annuals compete with each other in their blooming season less than perennials. Anemophilous flowers are most common in spring, before there are many insects. The short-tongued bees, in general, visit the more primitive flowers, and those that frequent the social flowers are obliged to share them with flies and primitive hymenopterans. Flowers that are adapted to receive visits from a variety of insects often show a tendency to be social and bloom late.

The succession of blossoms throughout twenty-four-hour periods is well described by Kerner and Oliver (1895), who give "floral clocks" for various localities. Insects by flying at a particular time of day find their food flowers open, and thus are not associated with species that fly at other times in order to obtain food from other flowers. Winn (1902) was surprised to find milkweed blossoms invaded by a host of moths just after the sunlight had faded away in the evening.

Adjustments of Flowers to Visitors.—Flowers not only furnish nectar and pollen for food but are visited by animals for various other purposes. They serve as sleeping places and refuges. Crab-spiders, mantids, and assassin bugs lurk in flowers and capture little insects that come for food. Many of the animals that visit flowers are of no benefit, and many are injurious. Needham (1900) noted that *Iris versicolor* was pollinated by bees, flies, and beetles, but robbed by butterflies and weevils, and eaten by orthopterans, moths, and flies. Many flowers are protected from creeping marauders by honey exposed below the flowers, isolation by water, sticky secretions, spines, slippery surfaces, wax, etc. Protection devices against undesirable flyers are chiefly in the flower itself. Lowe (1921) noted that in a wet season bumble bees, instead of taking nectar in the usual way from the flowers of the scarlet runner bean, bit through the side of the floral tube and thus robbed the flowers without coming in contact with the anthers. The wounds permitted the short-tongued honey bees to join in the robbery. The next season was drier and the flowers of the scarlet runner were apparently too tough for the bumble bees to bite through. They fed by inserting their tongues in the usual way, and honey bees did not visit the flowers. When conditions are favorable, a particular kind of flower may have a very large number of species of visitors. Kellogg (1905) reports the following numbers for four plants: *Pastinaca sativa*, 275; *Sium cucutœfolium*, 191; *Cicuta maculata*, 238; and *Solidago canadensis*, 146. Robertson (1922) observed 143 species on sunflowers in Illinois. Weiss (1923a) on *Pastinaca sativa* reports during twenty-six days: 173 Hymenoptera, 14 Coleoptera, 9 Lepidoptera, 6 Hemiptera, 1 Neuroptera; and on *Asclepias verticillata:* 52 Hymenoptera, 42 Diptera, 16 Lepidoptera, and 3 Coleoptera. Above timberline, Kenoyer (1917) found that flowers that required pollination were mostly bee flowers.

It seems that the flowers above timberline are as much visited by insects as those of lower altitudes, and I have no reason to suppose that they are any less dependent for pollination upon their insect visitors.

Kenoyer observed no honey bees, but bumble bees were common. The more specialized the flower the fewer will be the species that visit it.

Odors and Colors as Agents for Advertising Flowers.— There has been much discussion concerning the relative potency of colors and odors in giving notice to pollinators of the presence of flowers. Lutz (1924) has properly pointed out that many of the experiments intended to test color discrimination have been performed in an uncritical way, without adequate knowledge of what the physical character of the "colors" used represented and of what stimulating agents were received by the animals under experiment. Von Frisch (1920, 1923) maintains that color is more important for bees in finding food than odor. His tests indicate that bees perceive about the same range of odor sensations as man. He has shown that bees on returning to a hive notify their mates of the presence of food largely through odor stimuli, and that in this connection sounds are of little or no importance. Lutz (1924) and Von Frisch (1923a) discovered that bees perceive ultra-violet flowers in addition to those having colors observed by the human eye. Lutz believes that the so-called bright colors of plants are due to physiological processes, which result in "by-products of plant metabolism," and are little concerned with the recognition of flowers.

Colors of Flowers.—Green flowers, as a rule, are not entomophilous and often are self-fertilizing; the few insects that visit them belong to the less specialized families. Colors in flowers are often those that appear to make good contrasts with green foliage. Flowers appear, in general, to be larger and brighter where insects are rarer, as in alpine meadows. Sometimes in flower clusters there are sterile, bright-colored, "attracting" flowers at the top and comparatively inconspicuous, food-laden flowers below. Knuth (1898) cited extensive evidence that flies see flowers and visit them through visual stimuli. Clements and Long (1923) have shown that if the corollas are removed from flowers, the visits of insects decrease in number. The exposure of nectar increases such visits. Artificial flowers received only one-eighth as many visits as the natural blossoms they simulated; painted flowers received only half as many. Flowers placed under glass to prevent the escape of odors were visited. Clements and Long conclude that for the honey bee color and form are four times as potent as odors in indicating the presence of flowers.

Odors of Flowers.—Kerner and Oliver (1895) classify flower odors as idoloid, aminoid, and benzoloid. Certain flowers that are carrion-scented are visited by flesh-flies and carrion beetles. Night-blooming flowers are often white and strong scented. Ord (1900) believes that night-flying moths generally avoid light-colored flowers, and that white is more of an impediment than a help to flowers that depend on moths for pollination. He believes that odor is the potent factor. Lutz (1924) also stresses the importance of odors in giving notice of flowers to insects. He observed that many insects that went against the wind found flowers directly, while those that flew down wind often passed them.

Relations of Colors and Odors of Flowers.—Lovell (1914) pointed out that color and odor in flowers may be to a certain extent mutually exclusive. A flower that emphasizes one is often lacking or weak in the other. Insects visit flowers for food and use any means they can to find and secure it. The absence of both color and odor does not cause a flower to be wholly neglected if it contains nectar or pollen. Diptera are attracted by a wide variety of fruity odors, some of which are characteristic of flowers. Bees feed on overripe or even decayed fruit, glandular secretions from the vegetative organs of plants, secretions from aphids and from greenish flowers. These facts do not prove, however, that conspicuousness is not an advantage to a flower. Any surface, bright or dull, will be visited if bees find that it contains food, but it will not be discovered as readily if it is dull. Lovell says:

Insects perceive the colors and forms of neglected flowers, and the rarity of their visits is the result of their memory of the absence of food materials, not because the flowers lack an agreeable odor, which is often not the fact. Colors and odors attract the attention of insects, but bees in their visits to flowers, previously examined by them, are guided largely by memory of past experiences; they are able to associate different sense impressions and unconsciously make analogous inferences.

Lovell is undoubtedly right in these statements, but the whole question should be gone over experimentally with more carefully analyzed and better known "color" and "odor" stimuli. Bees can discriminate and form associations with particular patterns (Turner, 1911).

Types of Pollinators.—The most important pollinators of flowers are Hymenoptera, Diptera, and Lepidoptera, but beetles, birds, and even such animals as snails and bats may serve as pollinating agents. Among insects the most specialized types are those which have built up the most intimate associations with flowers. The primitive Hymenoptera prefer exposed nectar; flies and Lepidoptera are not important pollinators for many flowers from which they suck nectar (Robertson, 1923a). Bees get all their food from flowers and are not in the same "ecological class" with other hymenopterous insects. Robertson (1922) among 437 species of entomophilous flowers found bees in 95.4; flies in 60.4; and Hymenoptera other than bees in 43 per cent. Counting the number of visits, bees represented 33.3 to 60.6 per cent and other hymenopterans, 1.6 to 16.9. Polytropic bees may visit flowers of various colors, forms, and odors; oligotropic bees may depend on one family or species to which they are strikingly adapted. Flowers pollinated by birds are usually red in color and have deep corollas. They probably represent flowers that at one time were served by lepidopters and have been more or less taken over by birds. The red clover in New

Zealand was sterile until bumble bees were introduced (Schimper, 1903). In northern forests, trees are generally anemophilous; in tropical forests, entomophilous (Warming, 1909). The geographic distribution of certain plants and insects is identical. Riley (1892) states that each species of yucca has its special species of Pronuba moth that is associated with it, and he described one species in detail that has long served as a classical example of interdependence between insect and flower. In this case the adult moth does not get any food from the flowers of the yucca. It hatches in one flower, flies to another, lays its eggs in the ovary, and then plasters about the pollen it brought inside the stigma. Insect-pollinated flowers are usually monoclinous and their pollen is often moist, sticky, or adhesive. Many flowers, particularly certain of those with deep corollas that are invaded by hard tongues or beaks like those of moths or birds, have mechanisms for attaching pollinia which are shed in another flower. The milkweed attaches pollinia to the claws or hairs of insects, and these are removed by a mechanism in the next flower visited. Many specialized flowers are so constructed that only one type or species of insect can enter. Schimper (1903) says:

Numerous flowers are robbed and pollinated by the most varied visitors, as their pollen and nectar are offered freely to all, or are easily accessible. Other flowers are, in greater or less degree, adapted to certain definite visitors either because their allurements presuppose certain characteristic tastes, or the access to their nectar is only possible to visitors possessed of certain bodily shape or certain faculties.

PLANTS AS SHELTERS FOR ANIMALS

Many animals use plants as refuges and are thus protected from enemies, evaporation, extremes of temperature, and other unfavorable environmental conditions. Certain katydids and spiders commonly rest in flowers or seed pods. As has been mentioned (p. 262), bromeliads support a large number of animals that are in many cases flattened or otherwise adapted to live in the spaces between the leaves. The leaf-rollers and webworms commonly fasten leaves together to make nests. The ants of the genus Oecophylla cooperate in holding large leaves together and, being unable to spin, use their larvæ as living shuttles so that the threads produced bind the leaves into a pear-shaped nest. Many other insects, spiders, myriapods, snails, amphibians, reptiles, birds, and mammals commonly nest in trees or smaller vegetation. The larva of a moth not only invades and feeds upon the pitcher plant, but passes the winter in a carefully constructed hibernaculum in its base. This caterpillar cuts a groove around the inside of the leaf that it inhabits; the top of the leaf then droops over and closes the opening; thus the invader is protected from parasites (Jones, 1907). Mosquito larvæ are protected from predaceous enemies when they live among thick mats of vegetation; even Gambusia does not attack them.

SEED DISPERSAL BY ANIMALS

The seeds of many plants are absolutely dependent on animals for dispersion and others are often transported on animals by accident. Everyone is familiar with the ticks, burrs, and similar fruits that grow along the paths of men and other animals. Kerner and Oliver (1895) state that 10 per cent of the flowering plants have seeds that are distributed by clawed or barbed processes—some by creeping along the ground, others by attachment to animals. Some seeds adhere to animals by means of sticky secretions on hairs or stalked glands. They make take long journeys with their living carriers and are often plucked off and deposited on fertile soil. Forbes (1885) describes the Pisonia tree of the South Seas as having spiny glutinous seeds that are carried to remote oceanic islands by herons and sea birds. The small seeds of many aquatic plants are carried in the mud that adheres to animals that come to shores to drink.

Fruits Eaten by Animals.—Ripe fruits, by being luscious, showy, and odorous, attract the attention of animals and may be carried about. Unripe fruits are often protected by being hard, bitter, covered over by foliage, and in some cases are even poisonous. The seeds of pine and nut trees are commonly planted by squirrels and other animals. Though many are eaten and destroyed, a considerable number are thus placed in favorable conditions for germination. The gooseberry has four means for dissemination: wind, gravity, running water, and animals. Seeds are distributed over long distances largely by water, winds, or animals (Cooper, 1922). Robertson (1897) describes certain seeds that have crests that protrude from their coats. He asserts that such appendages serve as "handles" for the mandibles of ants and that certain of the seeds have no means of dispersal except by ants.   Some seeds that are adapted to such dispersal have an edible portion on the outside and are discarded after this is eaten.

Many fruits that are commonly eaten by animals contain seeds that have hard coats, contain bitter substances, or have other qualities that make them inedible, but other fruits bear seeds that can pass through the alimentary tracts of animals without injury and are deposited with fertilizing materials in the fæces. Kerner and Oliver (1895) carried on extensive experiments concerning the viability of seeds eaten by birds, and also found that a few seeds might occasionally pass through mammals without losing their viability.   A few millet seeds grew after passing through a cow, and lentils survived journeys through the horse and pig, but most seeds were crushed in the mouths of such animals.   Birds fall into the three groups: (1) those that grind up the hardest seeds (pigeon, crossbill, goldfinch, etc.); (2) those that destroy soft seeds but allow hard seeds (cherry, berry) to pass through (raven, jackdaw); and (3) those that deposit many viable seeds that have passed partly or wholly through the alimentary canal.   The blackbird, thrush, and robin cast up from their crops all stony fruit seeds that are more than 3 milli- meters in diameter, but allow small seeds (75 per cent viable) to pass out of the anus.   Some seeds passed through such birds in three-fourths of an hour.   Recent work has shown that barberry seeds are commonly viable after passing through animals.

CERTAIN SYMBIOTIC RELATIONS BETWEEN PLANTS AND ANIMALS

Aside from symbiotic relations between animals and plants in connection with flower pollination and seed dispersal, there are certain intimate relations that deserve to be mentioned.   There are many algæ that grow on the shells of snails (Iltis, 1913) and are carried about.   They probably derive some benefit from such association.   The snails may use portions of their own gardens for food and are camouflaged by them to some extent.   Fulton (1921) reviews the few cases where algæ live in actinians and flatworms.   He concludes that such plants are slaves and merely serve to nourish the animals in which they live without receiving much benefit in return.   If such animals are kept in the dark, they feed on their contained algæ, which finally disappear. Buchner (1921) believes, however, that many plants live in symbiotic relations within animal cells. He describes various algæ and bacteria that dwell in protozoans, actinians, ctenophores turbellarians, annelids, rotifers, bryozoans, echinoderms, molluscs, tunicates, and insects. He also agrees with Brues and Glaser (1921) that certain fungi that live in insects are symbiotic. Particular groups of enlarged cells (mycetostomes) harbor the fungi in the fat bodies of Coleoptera, Hymenoptera, Lepidoptera, Diptera, Hemiptera, Orthoptera, and Corrodentia. Various methods are employed to transfer the fungi from parent to offspring. In beetles, Pyrosomas, Cephalopods, and fishes symbiotic plants may serve for luminescence.

Ant Plants.—Among the most interesting of the symbiotic relations between plants and animals are those of the ant plants. Most of these plants provide shelter and food for their guests, which by their presence defend the plants from browsing animals and phytophagous insects. In America the ant plants are largely acacias and cecropias (Safford, 1922). The former usually have hollow stipular thorns for ant dwellings and glandular secretions near the tips of the leaves which furnish food. Acacia ants drive away leaf-cutters (Folsom, 1922). The cecropias are provided with many small chambers in their stems and food is present on their petioles, but many of their ants feed on the secretions of aphids that are kept inside the stems. The ant plants of the Malayan region have been carefully described by R. W. C. Shelford (1916). The common types have numerous sponge-like, intercommunicating spaces in a succulent tuber and many small openings to the exterior. Schimper (1903) does not believe that these plants developed in association with ants. He looks upon the spaces as adaptations for respiration which have been secondarily used as a dwelling by the ants. Schimper describes many types of ant plants, including some that provide dwellings in leaves and outgrowths from stipules. Wheeler studied an ant plant in British Guiana that had fifty species of organisms associated with it: twenty-eight ants, beetles, coccids, etc. (Cockerell, 1922). Heim (1898) describes groups of ants that live in and defend the tender buds of palms. After describing such more or less accidental, but nevertheless fortunate, associations, Heim discusses various degrees of adaptation in plants and ants for symbiotic relations with each other. Ridley (1910) points out that ants associated with plants may be beneficial, neutral, or injurious.

PLANT ENEMIES OF ANIMALS

There are a number of types of plants that do injury to animals. The spiny seeds of the Pisonia tree often, by becoming entangled in the wings and feathers, cause the death of birds that normally function in their distribution (Forbes, 1885). Animals that are chased or fall among saw-edged or spiny plants may be killed.

Plants That Catch Insects.—The most important of the plant enemies of animals are the insect catchers. These are characteristic of soils where available nitrogen is deficient and animal diet serves to supply this necessary food element. The sundew, Venus' fly trap, and pitcher plant have quite specialized means for capturing insects. The bladderwort entraps crustaceans and other small aquatic animals. It has been admirably described by Needham and Lloyd (1916). Schwartz (1905) and Lochhead (1918) have given good general accounts of insect-catching and insect-eating plants.

Some insects take advantage of the pitcher plant, and what is a dangerous trap for other species becomes for them an especially safe refuge. A mosquito larva habitually lives in the water that stands in this plant (Mitchell, 1905). Hubbard (1896) discusses certain moths that make their homes in pitcher plants and light with impunity on the spiny inner walls. Their larvæ allow the liquid in the pitcher to escape by cutting a hole near the base, which insures a dry interior that gradually becomes partly filled with grass as the larva grows. A wasp also uses pitchers as a place to rear her young, stuffing in grass and plant fibers which float above the liquid at the bottom. On this raft she constructs a few mud cells. A spider is accustomed to spread its webs across the mouths of pitchers and to spin its cocoons inside. The maggots of sarcophagid flies are commonly found at the bottoms of pitchers. They feed on the mass of entrapped animals and thus rob the plant. Jones (1904) extended Hubbard's observations on pitcher plant insects somewhat, and also described the capture of victims in detail.

Fungi That Attack Animals. — Certain bacteria and other fungi commonly attack animals. There is one group (Laboulbeneaceæ) that infects by means of explosive fruits that shoot spores at passing insects. Cordiceps commonly sends its hyphæ through the bodies of white grubs. There are a number of fungi that cause diseases in the skins of animals. These are quite common in dark races of men in the tropics. Bacteria are, of course, causes of disease in all classes of animals.

ANIMALS THAT CARRY PLANT DISEASES

Among phytopathologists there has been steadily increasing interest in, and recognition of the importance of, animals as carriers and inoculators of the diseases of plants. Gardner (1918) states that plant diseases are usually spread by winds, waters, birds, insects, and some other animals. Man has been especially important as a carrier for long distances, through the marketing of his crops and shipment of propagative parts. Domestic animals spread soil-infesting parasites; birds are particularly important in the distribution of tree diseases.

Insects are the chief inoculators of plants with certain diseases. Lochhead (1918) states that flea beetles eat holes in the leaves of potatoes and permit blight to enter; aphids and other insects carry apple and pear blight; the squash bug, cucumber beetle, flea beetle, melon aphis, and ladybird beetle carry cucurbit wilts. The activities of the plum curculio allow brown rot to enter. Tree crickets are said to carry canker and cane blight. Folsom (1922) says that fire blight is carried by bees and other insects to the nectaries of flowers, where it multiplies and from there invades the plant. Some insects are able to carry the organisms causing cucurbit wilt through the winter in their alimentary canals. Rots, cankers, and mosaic diseases may all be found to be connected more or less with insects.

CHAPTER IX

THE RELATIONS OF ANIMALS TO COLOR

Color is a rather unsatisfactory word to use in connection with animals other than man, because colors are psychological products which are largely the result of human equipment for the sensory reception and interpretation of wave movements of different rates of frequency that are known to science as light. An animal that responds to particular rates of vibration, or that discriminates between them, does not necessarily perceive colors as man does. But though the quality of the sensations in man and other animals may be quite different, there is abundant evidence that certain animals are able to perceive what man calls colors and to respond to differences that are due to variations in the quality of light as distinguished from its intensity.

Color Discrimination.—Wallace (1895) stated that animals have probably passed through a progressive series of changes—at first possessing only a general sensitiveness to light, then developing more or less ability to discriminate between different wave lengths, and finally acquiring some power to discriminate and remember combinations of patterns. Many animals are unquestionably able to discriminate and form adaptive associations with what the human eye perceives as surfaces of different colors. Young barnacles attach themselves more readily to dark- than to light-colored objects; mosquitoes and bees are more likely to attack persons dressed in dark clothing than those in light. The skins of flounders can closely simulate the backgrounds on which they rest in both pattern and color, and such simulation cannot be effected except by means of stimulation received through the flounder's eyes (Summer, 1911; Mast, 1916). There has been considerable argument as to whether certain animals possess color vision (Frisch, 1923a) or do not (Hess, 1921), and much of the misunderstanding in this connection has been due to the fact that experimenters studied animals that were adjusted to low or high light intensities (*i.e.*, were dark- or light-adapted), and hence

did not behave as they would if tested in intensities to which their
eyes were at the time adjusted.   Sparrow (1923) has shown that
the spectra of lights reflected from animals do not correspond very
closely with those of backgrounds that the same animals appear
to the human eye to match rather accurately in coloration and
pattern.   He suggests that colors may often be adapted for eyes
that see in a different way from those of man.

Colors of Animals.—From a physical point of view the colors of
animals are due (1) to specific pigments that absorb certain
light vibrations and reflect back others, (2) to structural peculiarities in surfaces that cause them to diffuse or refract rays of light,
or (3) to combinations of absorptive, refractive, reflective, or
diffractive influences.   From the point of view of their usefulness
in the lives of animals, colors, *per se*, may be classified as significant or non-significant (Poulton, 1890).   Many of the internal
organs of animals that are never seen by friends or foes have
characteristic colors which are probably of no adaptive importance,
but are to be looked upon as chance by-products of structure or
physiological activity.   Perhaps all colors were originally of this
type, but some have become adapted so that they enter into
relations which the animal bearing them has with its environment.
The colors of animals in particular regions often have a general
similarity.   The crustaceans in the depths of the ocean are
generally pale and pellucid; those in shallow, well-illuminated
waters are decked out in various hues that more or less match the
backgrounds on which they are usually seen.   The colors of
crustaceans in all three situations doubtless result from metabolism and other physiological processes, but the last type seems to
be adaptive to a greater degree than the first two.   It is undoubtedly true that differences in climate, as represented by variations
in light, water, temperature, and other factors, influence the
coloration of animals; also that different types of foods may lead
to characteristic colorations.   However, the fact that coloration
is more or less a by-product, and not in all cases of adaptive value
in relations with the environment, does not imply that certain
colors may not be of relative or of prime importance in the
adjustments of certain animals.

Adaptiveness of Colors of Animals.—Various views are held in
regard to the adaptive value of colors in animals and in regard to
the types of uses they may serve.   Braun (1914), who studied the
Microlepidoptera of the genus Lithocolletis, believes that the

markings and patterns are due to physiological processes and that they follow orthogenetic trends, "independent of external conditions." She and Folsom (1922) point out that in insects there is a tendency to (1) form a general ground color, which is (2) followed by the deposition of pigment in bands or lines, which (3), in turn, break up into spots or are followed by the deposition of pigment elsewhere. Selous (1908) and Shelford (1912a) appear to doubt the adaptive value of coloration in animals for concealment. The latter says:

Such doubtful protective devices as protective coloration, mimicry, aggressive coloration, etc., cannot be counted as any significant part of ecology until they are first established in fact and are shown to have some regular relation to reactions to environic factors or at least to activity. All the chief typical cases that come under the head of protective coloration, mimicry, etc., are much shattered by such facts as are presented by Selous ('08, Ch. I and II).

Crozier (1921) found that along the shores of Bermuda Stichopus was sometimes conspicuous and sometimes much like the backgrounds on which it rested. He says:

There is no more reason to regard the conspicuous type as a warning agent than there is to consider it the unchecked expression of innate metabolic activities.

Enough has been said to emphasize the fact that all colors are not "adapted" to the environment and that it is not wholly scientific to expect that they should be. Writers on the coloration of animals have expressed diverse views, some of them radical and extreme. Wallace (1912) pointed out that the general uniformity of coloration among members of a species and among many animals in similar habitats indicates that colors have some utilitarian value to the animals possessing them. Thayer (1909) and Longley (1917a, 1917b) support the view that all external coloration tends to render its possessors inconspicuous. Wallace (1912) and Poulton (1890) believe that coloration may serve various uses.

Classification of Colors.—Poulton's classification of the "significant" colors of animals (other than those which have direct physiological value) is as follows:

I. Apatetic colors—resembling the environment or some part of it:
    A. Cryptic colors—concealing resemblances:
        1. Procryptic olors—resemblances for protection.
        2. Anticryptic colors—resemblances for agression.

   B. Pseudosematic colors—false warning and signaling colors:
     1. Pseudaposematic colors—protective mimicry.
     2. Pseudepisematic—aggressive mimicry and alluring coloration.

II. Sematic colors—warning and signaling colors:
     1. Aposematic colors—warning colors.
     2. Episematic colors—recognition markings.

III. Epigamic colors—displayed in courtship.

Epigamic in this scheme might have been considered the same as episematic colors if they had not been believed to be concerned with a type of recognition that involved some degree of appreciation of beauty as distinguished from that of a mere mark of identity. All matters relating to the coloration and uses of colors in animals are not yet on a scientific basis. There is need of more (and more critical) observations on the behavior of animals in relation to colors. In the accurate description of colors the "Code des Coleurs" of Klingksiegk and Valette (1908) will be found useful.

CONCEALING COLORATION

There has been much dispute concerning the functions of coloration in animals. The Thayers (1909) have done much to clarify ideas in this field. They stress the fact that sight is often the important sense in enabling animals to escape from enemies or to find prey, because light travels essentially in straight lines and gives accurate information as to direction and location. They have made it plain that bright colors are not necessarily conspicuous and that animals which are conspicuous in certain environments may not be so in others. A successful disguise may be effective only at certain very short periods of time and at other times be of little or no importance for concealment or may even be conspicuous. Concealing coloration makes animals match the backgrounds on which they are seen and enables them to escape discovery by other animals. For example, iridescence tends to obliterate animals when they are seen on water or in foliage. A bright spot reflected from an elongated, iridescent, moving animal that is seen among leaves may appear to stand still. Streaked bodies and barred tails tend to deceive a watchful eye as to the general form of the body on which they appear, especially when the body is in vegetation. The white tops of nocturnal animals, when seen by animals on the surface of the ground, tend to make the bodies of the animals that possess them blend with the sky line. Animals are generally countershaded and this neutralizes the illuminating effects of light falling upon their bodies from above. The most highly illuminated parts are darkest and the parts of the body that are in shadow are lightest in color; thus animals blend more readily with the surroundings by appearing to lose their appearance as solid objects interposed between the eye of the observer and the background.

Longley's Work on Reef Fishes.—Longley (1916), through his excellent studies of the gaudy fishes that live among and near coral reefs, has given strong support to Thayer's views concerning the importance of concealment as a general explanation for the coloration of animals. After prolonged investigation, much of which was conducted by means of a diving hood among the reefs beneath the surface of the ocean, he concluded that the colors of reef fishes were largely adapted for concealment. Green fishes were usually associated with vegetation; blue fishes were found above the bottom, swimming freely in the open water; gray, as a type of coloration, was three times as common among fishes that swam about considerably as among those that were confined largely to the coral heads; yellow and brown seldom extended over a large portion of a fish's body and were often associated with gray; red fishes were largely nocturnal; banded fishes usually moved about much. Gaudy fishes were not avoided by predaceous animals, but appeared as often as constituents of the foods of predaceous species as those that appeared to the human eye to be somber in hue.

Effectiveness of Concealing Coloration.—There seems to be no doubt that most animals are so colored that they are not readily observed by their enemies or by the animals on which they prey. Desert animals are commonly decked out in dull grays and browns and plankton animals are generally transparent. After a careful study of certain snails (Purpura) along the New England coast, Colton (1922) concluded that size and shape were influenced to a considerable degree by environment, that the shell sculpture and coloration were hereditary, and that the relative proportion of any color variety that might occur in a particular locality was due to selection. On light bottoms there were more light-colored snails and on dark bottoms there were more that had dark colors. Di Cesnola (1904) has demonstrated that coloration has real protective value for mantids. He experimented with green and brown individuals that were picketed by means of threads on green or dead grass. Brown mantids were commonly eaten by birds when left on green grass, but usually escaped notice when on dead grass, and the opposite was true of green individuals. Gerould (1921) observed that grass-green caterpillars remained unnoticed on grass, but mutants of blue-green type were soon devoured by sparrows. Mottram (1914) advanced the view that male birds are often brighter colored than females because they are of less value to the race. They may be destroyed after they have exercised their fertilizing functions without endangering the survival of the young. Mottram believes that their loss through the attacks of predaceous enemies serves to a certain degree to protect the females, because enemies are thus kept more or less in a condition of satisfaction in regard to their food requirements. Schreiner (1897) points out that the male ostrich sits on the eggs at night and the female usually covers them during the day, and says:

It is scarcely possible to conceive a more effective disguise than the sober brownish gray of the hen for day sitting, and the black of the cock for night.

Birds of both sexes, when on the nest, rest the head, neck, and tail on the ground and are very difficult to see.

Many animals show a high degree of adaptation for concealment, not only in general coloration, but in pattern, form, and behavior. Carpenter (1920) gives many such instances among African animals. There are insects that resemble leaves or sticks, mantids and spiders that are able to catch their prey through their resemblance to flowers, etc. A South American fish, both in appearance and movement, resembles a drifting leaf (Eigenmann and Allen, 1921). The resemblance of the animals that live among Sargassum to the fronds that surround them has frequently excited the wonder of observers. Such instances of general and special resemblance in form and color might be multiplied almost indefinitely.

How Animals Resemble Backgrounds.—Apparently, the resemblances that individual animals show to their surroundings have come about by various means. In some cases they appear to be due largely to the effects of food, light, and other factors on metabolic processes; in others they are concerned with complicated adjustments that involve nervous mechanisms. The Thayers (1909) have shown that background picturing without countershading is not effective in rendering animals inconspicuous. The color patterns that occur among animals are generally characteristic of well-lighted environments where there are a variety of color tones and patterns. Shore fishes and crustaceans wear varied coats; those in the deep sea are dressed in solid tones of black or red; those in caves are largely lacking in pigment. Burrowing dragon-fly nymphs are monotone, but those that live on the bottom or among plants show varied patterns (Tillyard, (1917). The background pictures on the bodies of many animals not only depict the backgrounds on which they are usually seen in great detail, but also show perspective. For example, the markings on certain grouse and shore birds represent the lights and shadows that are characteristic of areas of vegetation; the markings on the head and neck are smaller than those on the body, and thus to the eye of an observer the former blend more readily with backgrounds that are a little more distant than those against which the latter are seen. Some animals picture backgrounds in a rather general way, and many are dependent on ruptive patterns, which do not represent average backgrounds in great detail, but serve to break up the outline of an animal so that is not readily recognized as being what it is. A butterfly that has black and white wings is generally less conspicuous than one which has wings that are wholly white or black. Thayer (1909) discusses many examples of such coloration.

Color Changes That Are Related to Environment.—There has been considerable discussion concerning the effects of variations in environmental factors on the coloration of animals in relation to backgrounds. There are a number of species of butterflies in which winter and summer, or wet- and dry-season, forms occur, and in a few instances these are believed to show variations that are correlated with patterns that are better adapted for concealment. Marshall and Poulton (1902) described "wet" and "dry" color phases of *Precis antiope* and affirm that "Adaptation . . . , in the direction of conspicuousness, is characteristic of the under side of the wet phase." They believe that there is more danger from enemies during the dry season and that the butterfly is then better concealed. Poulton (1888) showed that the coloration of certain lepidopterous pupæ was remarkably like that of the backgrounds around the larvæ from which they came, and that the color influence was potent when it affected a larva for only an hour before it transformed into the pupal state. Menzel (1913) has made similar observations. Clark (1921) has shown that a young shrimp (*Hippolyte varians*) is at first colorless, but a week after taking up a sedentary life has come to resemble very closely the particular seaweed to which it is attached. Meinertzhagen (1921) states that crested larks are colored like the soils which they frequent and that they breed true to such colors, without reference to general humidity or rainfall. He says: "This same influence appears to affect nearly all ground birds which live more or less in the open." On the other hand, Summer and Swarth (1924), who have made extensive studies of mice and other rodents, say: "Climatic factors, rather than the optical properties of the background, are responsible for the differences of color," and express the opinion that relative humidity is probably the most important factor in producing various coat colors.

Many animals are able to change their coloration and patterns to match different backgrounds. Some require considerable time to accomplish such changes, but others have them under nervous control and bring them about instantaneously. Tillyard (1917) states that dragon-fly nymphs change colors more or less to match the environment. He believes that such changes are not brought about through the eye, but are due to the "chemical plasticity" of pigment-forming substances just before or during molting. Such animals as tree frogs, chameleons, and lizards change their colors readily through the migration of pigment contained in cells in the skin. Such migration may be effected by stimulating the pigment cells directly (with chemicals, light, or temperature), by indirect effects from stimuli received through the eyes, or by causes which apparently originate within the animal affected and are transmitted by the nervous system. Longley (1917, 1917*b*), Connoly (1925), and Doflein (1910) discuss the color changes of fishes and crabs. In general, they find that changes in shade may occur during short periods of time, but changes in pattern require longer. Mast (1916) has studied flounders, which possess remarkable ability to change their colors and patterns to simulate backgrounds on which they rest, and has shown that adjustment in pattern is dependent on stimuli received through the eyes.

Behavior in Relation to Background.—The behavior of many animals is such as to enable them to take advantage of their coloration by assuming relations that are favorable for concealment.

Longley (1918) has shown that among fishes some types of coloration are suited for continual activity and others for sedentary life. In discussing birds Palmer (1909) says that habits of stillness are generally necessary adjuncts of protective coloration. The stone curlew has a crouching habit, which conceals it from enemies, when it hatches from the egg (Farren, 1907). Annandale (1902) describes a bright-colored beetle which frequents vegetation and is readily mistaken for a flower when quiet. It is active during the middle of the day, when its enemies are least active, and when disturbed at any time quickly drops to the ground and remains quiet. Longstaff (1906) and others have noted that many butterflies alight facing away from the sun, so that they cast very little shadow and, although Shrader (1917) maintains that they do this because they are thus able to see better, such a position doubtless aids in concealment. Longstaff (1906) gives many instances where butterflies when alighting selected the backgrounds which matched their own coloration. Mast (1916) states that flounders select backgrounds that match their own color and shade, but do not show a high degree of discrimination in regard to patterns. Decorator crabs pick objects off the sea bottom and fasten these to recurved hooks on their dorsal surfaces. There seems to be no doubt that this instinct is adapted for concealment, but the crabs do not show color discrimination in the selection of materials for their decorations (Mast, 1911; Pearse, 1911).

Effectiveness of Concealing Coloration for Predator and Prey.—In considering all cases of coloration it must be kept in mind that types of coloration and pattern that are effective for some enemies may not conceal from others. There are varying degrees of discriminative ability among predaceous animals that depend on sight for capturing their prey. Some animals are concealed as long as they are still and will remain immobile even when mutilated. Other animals that are well concealed when quiet disclose their presence by movement. Probably no means for concealment by coloration is effective against all enemies at all times, and such means do not enable predaceous animals that depend on their concealing coloration always to secure prey. There is no doubt, however, that concealment is generally obtained through appropriate coloration by many animals. Such coloration may, therefore, appropriately be termed "protective" or "aggressive."

COLORATION FOR WARNING AND RECOGNITION

Warning coloration is characterized by conspicuous colors or markings that give notice to enemies of distasteful or injurious qualities. Recognition marks are conspicuous features that enable members of a species to recognize each other or that facilitate the distinction of different types of individuals within a species.

Bright and Conspicuous Colors Are Not Necessary for Warning.—Many bright-colored and conspicuously marked animals that have been cited as furnishing examples of warning coloration or recognition marks will have to be reëxamined in natural surroundings and in the presence of natural enemies before their validity as such examples can be admitted. Longley (1916, 1917, 1917a, 1917b), studying communities of gaudily colored coral reef fishes which had long been *assumed* to afford examples of warning or immunity coloration (Reighard, 1908), showed that all the species he observed were colored primarily for concealment. He (1916) says:

It is not demonstrated . . . that any class of markings serves for purposes of recognition, or for signaling between individuals of one species. Neither is it proved that some color combinations warn off possible enemies, nor, indeed, that any type of the pigmentation is functionally conspicuous.

Judd (1899) pointed out that many caterpillars that had been supposed to be warningly colored were not refused by birds on account of their coloration, but because they were covered with hairs. He also called attention to the fact that rose chafers and aphids are seldom eaten by birds, although they are not warningly colored. For birds, color is only one of a number of qualities that may give notice of distasteful or harmful traits, and human standards for brightness of colors, distastefulness, or other qualities that make particular animals avoided may not be the same as those of birds that might molest them. Richardson (1914) has described a California lizard that commonly feeds on bright-colored flowers and warningly colored wasps. Marshall and Poulton (1902) state that spiders and mantids apparently have no appreciation of warning colors and that parasitic insects and robber-flies commonly attack warningly colored insects. "Warning" colors may perhaps even be of advantage to parasites in finding hosts.   Marshall and Poulton believe that all predaceous invertebrates probably have to taste each of their captures in order to determine its palatability. Folsom (1922) states that the use of recognition marks is not known among insects.   Even the staunchest supporters of coloration for warning and recognition (Poulton, 1890; Carpenter, 1920) admit that it is not effective at all times and against all enemies.

Validity of Warning Coloration.—Notwithstanding the doubts that are raised when such evidence as has just been presented is considered, there appear to be many valid cases of warning coloration.   The effectiveness of warning coloration in preventing attacks, of course, depends largely on the enemies concerned, particularly in regard to discriminative powers and ability to remember and to form associations.   Folsom (1922) believes that colors are of less value against insect aggressors than other qualities, such as odors and spines.   Poulton (1890) long ago pointed out that the tastes of all insect eaters are not the same, and also showed that frogs, lizards, and birds refused warningly colored insects, apparently through visual discrimination, after a little experience.   Pocock (1911, 1911a) has called attention to the fact that shrews are protected from many predators by their rank and musky odor; that they squeak continually while running about, and are, therefore, not readily mistaken for mice. In this case "warning" of distasteful qualities is given to enemies through sounds.   Shrews are said to be killed and eaten by owls, and are often killed by cats, which do not eat them.   The Indian musk shrew is quite fearless, squeaks continually, and is conspicuous when running about at night.   The same is true to some extent of the porcupine, hedgehog, and skunk.   Among animals that have undesirable qualities, warning may be given by various means that are perhaps effective against certain enemies but not against others—conspicuous colors, odors, terrifying or startling sounds or appearances, etc.—or there may be no warning.   Clark (1908) has noted that crinoids in their coloration show no apparent relation to environment, though warning coloration would be advantageous to them for they are quite inedible.   Certain animals that are apparently not offensive in any way may have bright colors, but this fact does not prove that warning colors may not be effective for animals that are offensive.   The fact that many animals that have quite effective concealing coloration are also quite offensive does not prove that animals that are offensive and warningly colored do not profit by such a combination. Because certain animals that have adaptations for warning are eaten by certain enemies, warning through coloration is not necessarily a complete failure.

Discriminative Ability of Some Animals Is Adequate to Make Warning Coloration Effective.—Clark (1925) says:

A bird's eye is a wonderfully perfect mechanism. It differs chiefly from mammal's eye in being built about a lens of shorter focus. The image projected by the lens of a bird's eye therefore lies all in one plane, or nearly so, resulting in the equal definition of all objects in the field of vision. This is quite necessary for an insectivorous bird catching its prey upon the wing or for a predaceous bird. Distance means little to them, detection of their victims everything . . . To a predaceous or an insectivorous bird a landscape would consist of a clear-cut patchwork of all colors and of sizes. Each stick and stone would stand out sharply, no matter how distant it might be. Against a background of this kind these objects would be least conspicuous which were most boldly colored in the sharpest contrasts, dark and light, more or less regardless of what the colors were . . . In the relatively long-focus mammal eye and the corresponding lizard eye sharp vision is only possible in a single plane, which is continually shifting back and forth. Beyond this plane the landscape becomes blurred and tends to be reduced to the average color of all its various elements. Thus the creature least conspicuous to a mammal or a lizard would be one most nearly like the *average color* of the background against which it would ordinarily be seen, and not adorned with sharply contrasting colors, dark and light, matching the *details* of that background, as in the case of birds. The difference in the sight of birds compared with that of mammals and of reptiles would easily explain the brilliant colors of most butterflies when on the wing contrasted with their cryptic colors when at rest; the brilliant colors of many flower-, rock-, and fence-frequenting insects; the bright colors of most male tree-top birds and the dull colors of their mates.

There is apparently no doubt that fishes, amphibians, reptiles, birds, and mammals have a sufficient degree of *discriminative ability* to make warning *colors* effective (Frisch, 1923a). Perhaps certain arthropods may possess similar ability. It is not so clear, however, that all cases that have been cited as evidence of warning coloration have their basis in *color* discrimination, yet many of them appear to be reasonably interpreted in such a way. It must be kept in mind always that objects that are distinguished by man solely on the basis of differences in color

may be distinguished by some other sense than sight by another
animal.   Mottram (1918) gives evidence that trout and certain
birds avoid warningly colored insects.

The Observations of Carpenter in Africa.—Such cases as the
following described by Carpenter (1907, p. 209) are difficult to
interpret, except as indicating the effectiveness of warning
coloration.

Just as cryptic insects must behave in accordance with the resemblance to their surroundings, so aposematic species have a behavior in
keeping with their coloring.   It would be of little use for a gaudy, distasteful insect to retreat timidly or endeavor to hide itself on approach
of an enemy which, only partially seeing, might grab at it and damage
it fatally before the mistake was found out.   Everything is to be gained
by flaunting the banner in the face of the enemy, so that there can be no
possibility of a mistake.   Consequently, aposematic insects are of the
boldest demeanor, and are the species most frequently seen by the
casual observer.   If endeavours are made to catch one, for instance a
Planema butterfly, it merely flits out of reach, and returns to the same
spot unalarmed.

A large grásshopper, *Dictyophora laticincta*, family *Acrididæ*, was
frequently met with on the islands fully exposed on pathways: a bloated
creature with heavy body, whose wings are so atrophied that it cannot
possibly fly.   So sluggish is it that it scarcely troubles to move out of
the way, or gives a feeble hop merely carrying it for a distance about
equal to the length of its own body.   In color it is grey-black, and the
short wings are scarlet, and there is some of the same color along the
sides of the fat abdomen.   If persistently annoyed it will raise the wing
covers to show the red wings underneath.   Such an insect, *a priori, must*
be distasteful, and proved to be so when offered to my young monkey
who would eat greedily until he was sick equally large, but procryptic,
grasshoppers.

Since I offered this grasshopper to Wee Man he naturally thought it to
be edible and at once seized it, though he did not straightway bite it as
he would have done had it been the procryptic species he was accustomed to eat.   While he held it in his hand the grasshopper emitted
copious bubbles of strongly smelling yellow froth from the thoracic
spiracles, forcing it out by at first distending and then strongly contracting the abdomen, so that a hissing sound was produced, audible
several yards away.   At the same time the wing covers were raised so
as to display the bright-red, black-bordered wings.

Wee Man was obviously most interested in this very curious and, to
him, novel phenomenon, and tasted the froth, but though he obviously
did not like it, he persisted in trying to eat the insect, pulling it to pieces
and tasting each.   But none of it was actually eaten! . . .

The above observations on the monkey and grasshoppers have exemplified the deliberate use of the aposeme by an insect when hard pressed. This is again brought out very well by an experiment with fowls, the subject being *Phymateus viridipes*, another large grasshopper with a hard green colour, with spiny thorax, and fully developed blue and crimson wings, so that when flying it is extremely conspicuous.

One of these was put on the ground some little distance away from a group of fowls, one of which at once ran up to it. The grasshopper remained where it was, but, when the fowl came dangerously near, raised the wings and wing covers perpendicularly and opened out the former to show their bright-red coloring. The fowl halted, looked at it, turned round and walked away, nor could it be induced to watch the insect. After a similar result had been obtained on another occasion, the grasshopper was killed and laid down near the fowls, the wings being, of course, hidden beneath the covers. A half-grown fowl at once ran up and pecked at it, and being pursued by another, ran off with the grasshopper, put it down and pecked at it again, but certainly did not seem to relish it, finding it very tough. The fowl at length pecked off the legs but made no impression on the body.

Just as it was about to leave it, a second half-grown fowl rushed up, took it away and pecked vigorously at it, pulled off the head but did not eat it, and finally walked away and left it. These observations show, firstly, the value of the aposeme in warning off dangerous enemies, and secondly, the distastefulness of the owner.

It will have been noted that the fowl made no impression on the tough body of the grasshopper, and this brings out another point. Should an aposematic insect have the misfortune to be one of those that are tasted by an inexperienced young foe, it may quite possibly survive the tasting, and be able to propagate its kind if it is of sufficient toughness. Consequently, one finds that aposematic species, in strong contrast to procryptic species, are endowed with astonishing powers of resisting injury, at any rate in the case of Lepidoptera. It is quite impossible to kill a Danaine or Acræine butterfly by the mild pinch on the thorax sufficient for a non-aposematic Pierine or Satyrine, for their tissues are so elastic that but little impression is made on them.

Carpenter's account has much of the enthusiasm that is so characteristic of the Poultonean school, but on the whole is quite convincing. Many other apparently valid instances of warning coloration might be given. Poulton (1890) pointed out that warning colors that have developed in various groups of animals often show a tendency to follow the same general plans. This is, of course, advantageous; different species are thus of help to each other because fewer individuals are sacrificed in teaching predaceous animals that particular color patterns are associated with offensive qualities. Such qualities are often localized on parts of the body where they may be readily presented to enemies—tussocks on caterpillars, nematocysts in the dorsal papillæ of eolids, etc. In some cases conspicuous markings attract attention to some non-vital part, which may stand attack or even be lost without serious injury to the animal as a whole—"eye" spots on the wings of butterflies, antenna-like appendages on the posterior borders of wings, the tails of lizards, etc. Fowler (1918) has described a locust nymph in northern Africa, which is well concealed by its remarkable resemblance to the stones among which it commonly rests. When disturbed, however, it spreads itself out and takes on a form resembling that of a scorpion, at the same time displaying the bright yellow coloration on the inner sides of its femora.

Recognition Marks.—Morse (1907) asserts that bright-colored orthopterans are seen and followed by other members of the same species. He says:

There can be no doubt in the mind of one who has watched these actions repeated over and over again that these colors are a means of signaling, of attracting attention, and thereby maintaining communication between sexes or individuals of a community.

Among orthopterans wing colors are commonly displayed during courtship. The writer (1914a) has shown that male fiddler crabs wave their brightly colored claws when females are in view. Many birds display their colors, in some cases resorting to definite situations in order to dance and make such displays. Among many species the colors shown during courtship are concealed at other times. There appears to be little doubt that such exhibitions as are made by birds do serve to attract attention to particular sexes, but whether they are generally subjects of æsthetic appreciation among animals is questionable. Folsom (1922) states that the sexes of insects are often differently colored and that colorational antigeny is most often seen among butterflies, odonates, and beetles. He believes that sex differences in color have little or no protective value and that, though sex recognition on the basis of color among insects rests largely on assumption, it is plausible. Poulton (1890) asserts that recognition markings serve to keep gregarious birds together during flight. He cites the conspicuous white tails of the rabbit and antelope as examples of recognition marks, but these are classified by Thayer (1916) as "flash" marks, which are believed to be concealing because they confuse a predator during the critical instant when it is attempting to grasp its prey. Poulton (1890) affirms that the markings on the eggs of colonial sea birds enable them to recognize their own eggs. Animals that develop bright colors during the breeding season are often particularly wary at that time.

Conclusion.—All cases of warning coloration and recognition marks that have not been subjected to critical scientific inquiry should be considered as on trial until they have been further investigated.

MIMICRY

Mimicry is the imitation in form, color, or behavior by a comparatively defenseless and edible species (mimic) of another species (model) which has qualities that cause it to be avoided by predatory enemies. The imitation is usually not conscious, but is apparently brought about by natural selection among variations of hereditary patterns. The general idea of mimicry originated with Bates (1892), who stated that insects that had a bad odor or taste were commonly avoided by predators, and that innocuous species were mimicked in appearance by species that did not have bad odors or tastes. Müller (Longstaff, 1912) introduced the idea that two species that are more or less distasteful may both derive benefit by resembling each other. Dixey has extended this idea into his theory of reciprocal mimicry or mimetic attraction. There has been much discussion concerning the origin and evolution of mimicry, and Longley (1917b) gives a rather complete review of the work in this field. Wallace (1905) was the chief advocate of conspicuous (warning) coloration as a necessary accompaniment of mimicry. He laid down the following five conditions for Batesian mimicry:

(1) That imitative species occur in the same area and occupy the same station as the imitated. (2) That imitators are always the more defenseless. (3) That imitators are always less numerous in individuals. (4) That imitators differ from the bulk of their allies. (5) That imitation, however minute, is *external* and *visible* only, never extending to internal characters or to such as do not affect the external appearance.

Longley (1916) says:

Mimicry has arisen through bionomic pressure applied first by indiscriminate feeders, which have forced upon their accustomed prey color combinations which most effectively conceal it in its normal environment. In addition, by chance, in a few of many thousands of cases in which colors appropriate to the surroundings and habits of their possessors have been evolved, patterns have appeared, sufficiently like one another to deceive enemies that exercise discrimination in the choice of food. From this point onward the evolution of resemblance has proceeded according to accepted formulæ, without conspicuousness being involved in the process.

Longley believes that two animals become alike in coloration because they occupy the same habitats and have similar habits; *i.e.*, convergence in coloration follows convergence in habits and habitats. Punnett (1915) has advocated the view that mimicry has arisen through parallel mutations rather than by actual imitation (conscious or unconscious). Carpenter (1920) has presented excellent evidence that natural selection does operate to bring about mimicry.

Characteristics of Models and Mimics.—Models and mimics may be said to have certain general characteristics. The model must have offensive or undesirable qualities that make it avoided by predaceous enemies—chemical substances, spines, hard shell, habits of movement that make capture difficult, etc. There must be a tendency for animals to vary so that certain species or groups may come to resemble each other more or less. Finally, certain animals have apparently come to resemble others which serve as definite models. Semper (1881), Wallace (1905), and even Poulton (1890) to some extent, with other older naturalists gave extensive lists of models and mimics without very definite knowledge of the habits or distribution areas of the species discussed. There has been a more and more critical examination of the evidences for mimicry and there are now a number of agnostics among competent naturalists. Eltringham (1910) states that conspicuous insects are often distasteful. Longstaff (1912) says that models need be only relatively impalatable; they may be eaten by certain species but not by others; they may be taken by extremely hungry animals; they need not necessarily deceive all enemies. Carpenter (1920) points out that a mimic's habits need not necessarily resemble those of a model closely. Farquharson (1922) in speaking of butterflies states that the flight of mimics is usually more rapid than that of models.

Examples of Mimicry.—There are many instances of mimicry that might be cited: hymenopterous models that are mimicked by flies, beetles by orthopterans, tiger beetles by crickets, wasps by crickets, etc.   There are also examples of aggressive mimicry. For example, the resemblance of spiders to the ants with which they consort enables them to approach prey which does not avoid ants.

Criticisms of Theories of Mimicry.—Mimicry has not been accepted by scientists without considerable argument and there are today many critics of current theories.   Packard (1904) long ago argued that Müllerian mimicry had come about through the similar effects of light and moisture conditions on animals living in the same areas, and expressed the view that mimicry as the copying of the coloration of one animal by another had not been demonstrated.   Thayer (1909) doubted that animals had come to resemble other animals, as such, but postulated the parallel development of color patterns to fit into similar environments.   Wheeler (1922) mentions an instance among ants that he apparently feels gives support to the same view.   He says:

> Those who are interested in mimicry will observe that in its form, the dull black of its body and yellow antennal tips, *Gigantopsis* bears such a striking resemblance to *N. apicalis* and *obscuricornis* that the latter might be regarded as its models.   Furthermore, these Ponerines sting very severely, whereas Gigantopsis can be picked up with impunity. In Kartabo, nevertheless, the models are much less frequently seen than the mimic.

Wheeler also points out that similar conditions have been found among butterflies, and that among his ants the behavior of the so-called models is quite different from that of the mimic. Longley (1917a), while accepting mimicry, does not believe that it is concerned with *warning* coloration as a characteristic of the model.   He believes that coloration may be one of a number of qualities that may make an animal recognized as a distasteful one, but he does not believe that it is the factor primarily concerned in mimicry.   He states that the coloration of animals which have geographic ranges that do not coincide at any point may be much alike.   In parts of Japan there are bee-like syrphids, but no bees.   Longley holds the view that, not resemblances in

color, but those in habits and habitats, initiate mimicry. Lutz
(1911), Cockayne (1911), and Punnett (1915) have doubts about
mimicry because birds do not appear to eat butterflies to any
extent and apparently do not exercise a great degree of discrimination in the selection of their food.   Manders (1911) has carried
this argument farther and claims that there are mimics and
models among the butterflies of the islands, Bourbon and Mauri-
tius, where there are no insect-eating birds or other animals which
could exert a selective action.   He also claims that there is no
butterfly-eating bird in Ceylon that can discriminate between
different species of adult butterflies, and that young birds learn
to eat proper foods largely by imitating their parents.   Punnett
(1915) holds that the selective action of predaceous enemies is
not important as a factor in producing mimics.   He says:

> The function of natural selection in respect of a mimetic likeness lies
> not in its formation but in its conservation.   It does not bring about
> the likeness, neither does it accentuate it: it brings about the survival of
> those forms which happen to shew the likeness.

He affirms that there are no pierid mimics in Africa, though
these butterflies are much persecuted by birds.

Support for Mimicry.—Among those who support the view that
coloration is important in the development of mimicry, Swynnerton (1915) has done a great service by accumulating a large
number of instances of attacks on and captures of butterflies by
birds.   This observer states that inedibility is a relative term
which depends upon the degree of hunger in an insectivorous
bird, but cites specific instances where mimetic resemblances
have deceived birds.   Longstaff (1912) observed that birds persistently tried to eat warningly colored insects, but ate other
insects first when they could be had.   After experience, birds
refused distasteful species.   Marshall and Poulton (1902) fed
insects to baboons and felt that they secured evidence of the
effectiveness of mimicry.   Eltringham (1910) affirms that conspicuous insects are usually distasteful.   He found that lizards
refused caterpillars which had been fed on ivy, but ate those of
the same species that had been fed apple leaves.   Though this
indicated discrimination on some other basis than coloration, he
presents other evidence that indicates the operation of mimicry
through coloration.   Eltringham shows that both sexes of one
species may mimic a female model of another, and that females

may mimic male models. Pocock (1911) carried on feeding experiments to test the effectiveness of mimetic resemblance. Poulton in an appendix to Pocock's paper says:

With regard to the experiments on mimicry, it appears to me that they satisfied all that theory, as propounded by Bates, demands. They fully confirm Professor Lloyd Morgan's experiments on birds, with the drone-fly (*Eristalis*) and the honey bee (*Apis mellifica*) as well as with banded and unicolored boxes holding respectively meal adulterated with quinine and meal untampered with. They show that several species of birds, after learning by experimental tasting that *Bombus hortorum* is unpalatable, refused to touch *Volucella bombylans*.

Pocock also showed that black beetles were unpalatable to certain ground-feeding mammals and that other distasteful beetles were commonly mimicked. Conspicuous lepidopters were commonly distasteful to birds. Though the tastes of birds and mammals were found to differ markedly, the species of insects that showed the greatest degree of cryptic coloration appeared to be most palatable.

Mimics That Behave Like Their Models.—Perhaps the best support is given to colorative mimicry by the animals that not only look like their models but also behave like them. Pocock (1910) described the young of several species of mantids that resembled ants in appearance and movement, also young mantids that showed warning coloration and resembled distasteful bugs. Mann (1911), in Brazil,

. . . . observed the Proctutrypid, *Mimopria ectinophila*, with *Ection hamatum*, the host ant. The parasite runs along with the army of workers in an ant-like manner, and is sometimes picked up and carried by the ections.

Longley (1922) described a small fish on the reefs about Tortugas that picks parasites from large fishes, which apparently favor such attention. The small parasite picker is mimicked by a blenny which accompanies its schools in small numbers and resembles it in appearance and in movement.

Carpenter's Work in Africa.—Carpenter (1920) has given the most recent and convincing demonstration of the effectiveness of colorative mimicry through his prolonged observations of African butterflies. He states that mimics are, in general, more easily alarmed and less resistant to injury than their models. He mentions certain spiders and capsid bugs that run about with ants and resemble them in appearance and behavior. He asserts his belief that certain warningly colored insects act as "centers" about which mimics are built up. Mimics may or may not belong to the same genus, family, order, or class as their models. He shows that, while bee eaters are especially fond of bees, these insects are commonly avoided by other species of birds; and their fly mimics profit accordingly. He points out that Longley's (1917*b*) explanation of mimicry by convergence does not satisfactorily explain resemblances in behavior between mimic and model.

Carpenter's (1920) best evidence for the dependence of mimicry on coloration is in his studies of the butterflies of the genus *Pseudacræa*, which commonly mimics several models. Many of the species of *Pseudacræa* (family *Nymphalinæ*) are dimorphic. One species has fifteen forms, certain of which mimic at least eight species or subspecies of the genus Planema (family *Acræinæ*). Where selective agents and a single model were absent, various color varieties of the mimic occurred together. Carpenter bred eggs from some varieties and obtained adults that belonged to other varieties, which usually did not occur where the parents lived. He found that localities where particular models were absent also lacked the mimic for that color pattern, though other varieties which had models present persisted. His observations and breeding experiments appear to demonstrate the effectiveness of mimicry and the validity of selection by predaceous enemies as a factor in eliminating certain color varities and fostering others.

One of the remarkable points in the resemblances is the fidelity with which a single polymorphic species mimics sundry species of models of very different appearances in different localities; and where a model is sexually dimorphic the sexes of the mimic faithfully copy the corresponding sex of the model. Yet in the very locality where this dimorphism of model and mimic exists other species of monomorphic models are closely copied by monomorphic forms of the same species of mimic.

In some instances the models of one species were seen to be courted by the mimics of the opposite sex.

CHAPTER X

INTRASPECIFIC RELATIONS

The relations between animals of the same species are various, ranging from those associated with competition for territory or food to those connected with social life and polymorphism.

Competition.—Among animals the individuals of a single species most nearly occupy the same habitats and show the greatest degree of similarity in requirements for food, protection, and reproduction, even when they are compared with closely related species or mores.   Accordingly, competition is most keen among individuals of the same species.   More young barnacles settle on the rocks along the seashore than can come to maturity. All through nature there is adaptation to loss of individuals through intraspecific competition.   Even within the body of mothers, certain ovarian eggs are sacrificed in order that others may survive or have the advantage of better conditions for development.   It is the usual condition in nature to have more individuals produced than can possibly survive.   Thus is provision made for loss through intraspecific and interspecific competition and from other causes.   The survival of individuals in intraspecific competition is, in part, due to innate ability, but chance fluctuations in environment may operate in such a way as to favor maladapted or comparatively unfit individuals. Every individual struggles to survive—struggles against unfavorable conditions in the environment, against other species of animals that seek to devour it or to keep it from existing, for other reasons, but most of all against other individuals of its own kind.

Cooperation.—On the other hand, there is more or less of a tendency to cooperate all through the animal kingdom.   It finds its inception in the essential adjustments between cell parts and between the cells of metazoans; it reaches its climax in the complex cooperative associations of colonial and social animals.   Huxley (1912) has stressed the fact that the chief characteristic of individuality is independence, which is usually

317

associated with more or less toleration of fluctuations in environment and a certain consequent immunity to elimination through accidents. An individual that sacrifices independence in order to cooperate usually gains a greater degree of ability to survive and becomes a part of a larger social unit. A natural result of cooperation is division of labor, which results in tissues, organs, castes, and other parts of great wholes. Such parts are specialists for particular functions. In order better to preserve its race, an animal may give more or less care to its own reproductive products, which are in a sense an extension of its own individuality. Thus a more or less permanent society may be established and continue by an overlapping through two or more generations of instincts for self-preservation.

Alternation of Generations.—Another peculiar type of adjustment to various conditions in the environment has come about through the more or less regular alternation of different types of individuals through successive generations. During times when (or in situations where) conditions for propagation are favorable, new individuals are often produced rapidly and by simple methods; in environmental conditions that are less favorable, other types of individuals occur which propagate by methods that produce more resistant products or products that are more likely to possess variations that may survive in the conditions that obtain.

Sex Relations and Reproduction.—The relations of individuals of a species in connection with reproduction often attain great complexity among diœcious types. There are often elaborate activities connected with mating. Among polymorphic species there may be a high degree of specialization of the sexes for various functions that are concerned directly or indirectly with reproduction. As so many of the important intraspecific relations of animals are concerned with reproduction, it seems proper to begin this chapter with a discussion of sex relations. After that, colonial and social life, polymorphism, and alternation of generations will be discussed.

SEX RELATIONS

Among many species of animals the sexes are of approximately equal size, but among others there is often great discrepancy between the average size of males and females.

Among certain species of worms, crustaceans, and rotifers, the male is always minute. Some of these tiny males are parasites on their females, and some have no digestive system, but receive enough nourishment from the egg to furnish energy for their short lives. A female seal is a timid creature, only a fifth as heavy as her pugnacious mate; a queen termite may weigh a thousands times as much as a king. Female spiders are usually larger and more pugnacious than males. As a rule, females are larger than males when they chiefly exercise their primary function of nourishing eggs and young; males are small when they devote their sexual activities to seeking out and fertilizing females of their eggs. McCook (1890) states, however, that among the species of running spiders the size of males in relation to females increases in proportion to the amount of moving about the adults do. In some species the males are larger than females, which is quite unusual among spiders. When there is competition for mates or when the individuals of one sex protect those of the other from danger, the sex that takes the aggressive rôle is commonly larger. There are many exceptions to such rules, however. The male dogfish (*Amia calva*), for example, makes a nest, cares for the eggs, watches over the young, and fights enemies, but is smaller than the female.

Numerical Ratio between Sexes.—The numbers of males and females are nearly equal in some species and quite different in others. Among vertebrates males and females commonly occur in about equal numbers. Some phyllopod crustaceans are known only as females and in other species males appear only at certain seasons or during particular years. Many cladocerans, rotifers, and aphids pass through a number of generations without males, reproduction taking place through the parthenogenetic development of eggs. In studying the rotifers in Danish ponds Wesenberg-Lund (1923) found that the life of males was often only a few hours in length and never more than four or five days. Periods of sexual reproduction were commonly preceded by an enormous increase in numbers, and before such periods males were rare or absent. Wheeler (1916) has described the nuptial flight of the bulldog ant in Australia and says:

As soon as a male (and there were apparently hundreds of males to every female) captured a female on a bush, other males surrounded the couple till there was a struggling mass of ants forming a ball as big as one's fist.

Sex ratios are doubtless adapted to particular conditions of reproduction and of environment,but the exact nature of such adaptations has in most cases not been determined.

Sex-determination and Environment.—Environment often plays a rôle in the determination of sex. Animals differ in the degree of control that may be exercised by factors outside their bodies. In rotifers and bees, males are apparently produced by the parthenogenetic development of eggs which will develop into females if fertilized. There is also the possibility in such cases that two types of eggs are present, one of which must be fertilized and the other not. In aphids and cladocerans both males and females may be produced from parthenogenetic eggs. Sumner (1922) gives instances where sex is determined in the sperm or egg, or by external factors. In some instances of apparent control of sex by variation in environmental factors, there has only been a greater mortality of germ cells that would have produced males or females. Geiser (1923) believes that in such cases females are more likely to survive. In many species of animals sex is apparently determined by the combination of Mendelian characters, and is, therefore, determined before a particular individual begins its embryological development. Many investigators believe that the metabolic states of the eggs or sperm cells, or of the parents that produce them, exercise more or less control over the sex of the offspring. Whatever the factors may be that determine sex, and they appear to vary somewhat among different types of animals, there is no doubt that environment may in a number of cases exercise considerable control over sex ratios or the types of sexual individuals that occur. Certain conditions favor the formation of spermaries on hydras, other conditions are more favorable for the formation of eggs. Environment may exercise control of the appearance of male-producing or female-producing eggs in rotifers (Whitney, 1917), cladocerans (Banta, 1916, 1917), and aphids (Morgan, 1907). In some species the sex of an individual may change during its life.

Many instances might be cited to show that environment exercises more or less control over sex, but only a few which illustrate the influence of different types of factors have been selected. Green food when fed to certain species of rotifers causes more males to be produced. Shull (1923) also found that the number of males diminshed during long-continued parthenogenetic reproduction, not, he believes, because parthenogenesis is unfavorable for male production but rather because metabolism continues at an undisturbed and rather uniform rate. Male production is a response to a change in environment. The appearance or non-appearance of male rotifers is doubtless controlled in this case by chemical substances. Wesenberg-Lund (1923) has made observations on the rotifers of Danish ponds that appear to support this view. He found that males appeared after there had been an enormous increase in numbers and that such increase was arrested by heavy rains. The fact that the development of secondary sex characters is influenced by hormones and that the gonads of a freemartin are influenced by hormones from a companion embryo of opposite sex also shows that chemicals may exercise considerable influence over sex and sex characters. Riddle (1920) maintains that sex-determination is perhaps largely concerned with the character and rate of metabolism. Shull (1923) in speaking of rotifers says:

The essential chemical event, as far as sex is concerned, produced by fertilization may turn out to be the same as the event occurring in the maturation of the female-producing parthenogenetic egg.

He affirms nothing is known that makes a metabolic theory of sex-determination untenable. Certain hermaphroditic snails (Crepidula) have been shown to be usually only functionally male or female. If a large and a small male are placed side by side, the larger gradually becomes a functioning female; if the same experiment is performed with females, the smaller becomes a male (Gould, 1917). Such influence of sex through size and proximity is doubtless due to the action of particular chemical substances. Temperature, directly or through its influence on other factors, also has a potent influence on the sexes of many animals.

Seton (1909) and Geddes and Thomson (1914) have discussed the evolution of sex in the animal kingdom. These authors believe that animals were at first sexless, then hermaphroditic, and mated promiscuously; that further development led to polyandry, polygamy, and finally to monogamy. Seton argues that monogamous animals will always surpass others in the struggle for existence.

Secondary Sexual Characters.—Secondary sexual characters have excited much discussion among naturalists and a number of theories have been proposed to account for their origin and development. There have been strong advocates of natural selection and of the effects of use and disuse as factors in the development of secondary sex characters. Recent discussion has centered largely around the actions of hormones and differences in metabolism between males and females. There is no doubt that certain secondary sex characters appear when hormones are secreted (often as gonads mature), and that they can be induced under experimental conditions by the injection of hormones. Some males are known to show characteristic differences in metabolism from females of the same species. Examples of striking differences between males and females among domestic fowls are familiar to everyone. Similar instances might be cited among worms, crustaceans, spiders, insects, fishes, amphibians, reptiles, birds, and mammals. Hudson (1913) points out that moths having semiapterous females and flying males are commonly associated with a widely distributed food and that they usually appear early in the spring, when low temperatures make extensive flights undesirable. Eigenmann (1912) in discussing the fishes of British Guiana says: "The secondary sex differences of the Poeciliidæ are varied and great," and mentions peculiar fins, ocelli, etc. Montgomery (1910), in his consideration of the mating of spiders, lists six types of secondary sex characters: (1) weapons employed by males in their combats with one another; (2) characters used for sexual recognition and sexual stimulation; (3) characters of more immediate value in insuring approximation of sexes and copulation; (4) characters of value in provision for, and for the nurture of, the progeny; (5) characters associated with differences in habits between the sexes; and (6) characters of especial value in protecting a particular sex against other species. Secondary sex characters are usually qualities that are present in both sexes but are developed to a greater degree in one than in the other. Goldschmidt (1923) has made a comprehensive study of "the mechanism and physiology of sex-determination." He states that secondary sex characters may be produced through hormones from a centralized gland (hormonic) or from tissues generally distributed through the body (genetic). In either of these cases sex transformations or sex intergrades may be produced by destruction of glands or inhibition of secretions. In moths, Goldschmidt has been able to produce all degrees of intersexuality experimentally.

Mating Activities of Animals.—The activities associated with reproduction that relate to the environment and to objects outside the bodies of the animals performing them are often manifest long before the fertilization of the egg and may continue for years after the young are able to shift for themselves. Many animals carry on an elaborate courtship as a preliminary to mating. At the breeding season there is a sexual urge, or desire to mate, which in many cases is brought about by the presence of internal secretions. Various special adaptations, both structural and behavioristic, which are apparently related primarily to courtship, have been developed. It is desirable for a male or a female to possess certain apparent characteristics which render sex readily and indubitably apparent to individuals that need mates. In addition to qualities that make the discrimination of sex quick and easy, there are often those which make one sex attractive to the other, so that it is actively sought for, and those which stimulate the performance of acts that are essential for reproduction.

Animals That Depend Largely on Touch for Mating.—There are animals that depend largely on touch stimuli during their mating activities. Chidester (1911) after studying four species of crabs concluded that sex discrimination was largely accomplished through tactual stimuli and that "opportuneness of proximity" was the chief factor in mating. During the breeding season males were restless and moved about continually; females were rather passive and awaited the visits of suitors. McCook (1890) and Montgomery (1910) agree that snare-weaving spiders depend largely on touch during their mating. A male seeks out the web of a female, timidly takes up his position at the margin, and sends signals in to his prospective mate by shaking the threads. If the female is ready to mate, she may permit him to approach, but if she is not, she quickly chases him away or catches and devours him.

Animals That Depend on Odor for Finding Mates.—Moths depend largely on odor for finding their mates. The males usually seek out the females, and usually approach them against the wind (Webster, 1903). Several investigators have shown that a marked male moth is able to find a concealed female, even when it has to travel a mile or more. Green (1919) in speaking of *Simocephalus vetulus* says:

Sexual attraction is limited not only to sexual females in the sexual state, but is confined to a limited period of a few hours before the ephippial egg is laid. It seems to be due to some kind of substance emitted by the female and borne by her exhalent respiratory current, where it is detected through a chemical sense by the male.

The males of solitary carnivores (marten, cougar) commonly distribute "signs" on their hunting grounds during the breeding season, so that visiting females may know that the areas are occupied by males.

Animals That Depend on Sounds during Mating.—Certain insects and vertebrates make considerable use of sounds during mating. This is especially true of nocturnal species and those that are concealed—the call of the whip-poor-will and cricket are familiar to everyone. During the breeding season many birds are accustomed to sing or call from conspicuous perches. Some birds resort to "singing trees" (Mousley, 1921) or other favorite situations for their singing. Hawkins (1920) believes that bird songs serve primarily to arouse sexual excitement, not to win mates by their æsthetic appeal.

Animals That Depend on Visual Stimuli for Mating.—Among animals that depend largely on visual stimuli for finding mates the fireflies are excellent examples. The males fly about flashing their lanterns at a rather rapid rate; the females sit in the shrubbery and glow at intervals. There is no question that the lights serve as signals for finding mates (Mast, 1912a). Certain marine annelids make use of luminescence for mating in much the same way (Galloway and Welch, 1921). Among diurnal vertebrates use is commonly made of colors and peculiar patterns for the discrimination of sex. Male fiddler crabs appear to make use of colors in mating. The males stand at the entrances of their burrows and wave their bright-colored claws to attract the attention of the females (Pearse, 1914a). Folsom (1922) does not believe that insects make use of color discrimination in mating. Some insects, however, undoubtedly depend primarily on vision for finding mates. The males of the flies of the family Dolicopodidæ have little flags on their front legs. They walk about on leaves and wave their signals to attract the attention of females. Among certain species of empid flies a male while flying about before a female spins an ornate capsule, which he offers to her as a present.

Animals That Have Various Means for Courting.—Many animals use various means in attempting to secure mates. Hancock (1905) has described the courtship of a tree cricket. In this instance the male approaches the female with wings upraised and sings loudly. He also has an "alluring" gland on the dorsal surface of his thorax, and the female mouths this over while mating. Huxley (1912) has made careful observations on the behavior of the redshank during the mating season. The cock pursues the hen on the feeding grounds, following her about persistently. When thus attended the female usually runs or flies, but if she stops the male begins his display. He raises his wings and vibrates them rapidly, sings, and steps high with his feet. He also makes "love flights" above the breeding grounds, performing peculiar antics on the wing, and frequently calls from conspicuous situations.

Courting.—The function of courtship is to demonstrate sex and secure a mate by arousing desire. Usually, males are most active, but sometimes the female takes the leading rôle, and sometimes both sexes are equally active. The male of the palmate newt is brightly colored, has a prominent dorsal frill and a filament extending beyond the tail. During the breeding season he places himself in front of a female, bends his tail toward her and vibrates it rapidly. If she turns aside he moves in front of her again, but if she stops he deposits a spermatophore which she often picks up (Cummings, 1910, 1911). The female European cuckoo is often pursued by as many as eight suitors; the males in summer appear to frequent definite areas and call for mates (Woodruffe-Peacock, 1910). Tower (1907) noted that at maturity male tiger beetles were usually more active than females, but in the absence of a mate either sex became more active. He found that prevention of normal reproductive activities increased the death rate. The male horned dace carries stones in his mouth and constructs a crude nest, in which he solicits passing females to lay eggs (Reighard, 1890). The females of the red-necked phalarope reach the breeding grounds before the males and fight over each male as he arrives. The male courts the female and leads her toward a definite nesting site that is in the area she is defending from encroachment by other mating pairs. The male takes a leading part in the care of the eggs and young (Bahr, 1907a). The red-throated diver, according to Huxley (1923), continues its courting behavior after pairs are mated for the season and the displays are similar in both sexes. Huxley holds, however, that among most animals females have a lower level of sexual emotion than males and require special stimulation before coition. He believes that too frequent coition is thus prevented. Many male birds (*e.g.*, house wren, American robin) continue to sing and in other ways pay attention to the female throughout the breeding season, thus apparently stimulating her to continue the usual activities in the reproductive cycle. Continual singing also serves to give notice to other birds that a particular area is already occupied by a nesting pair. Males and females that mate and continue to consort together while rearing young commonly make some division in the necessary labor. This perhaps reaches its climax in the Indian hornbill. The male seals the female up in a hollow tree where she can brood in safety, and wears himself thin seeking food for her and the young.

Contests for Mates.—Among species where there is rivalry for mates, the members of the aggressive sex, which is usually the male, often fight among themselves. Male tree crickets fight in the presence of females. Male running spiders commonly engage in combats during the breeding season. After a swarming flight, a male termite attempts to drive away all others from the female that he is following. Male penguins fight fiercely and the winner then courts the female. Many other instances might be cited (stag, grouse, alligator, salmon, beetle, etc.). Darwin (1859) believed that such combats during the mating season resulted in the selection of the better individuals by the sex being contested for, because it chose the victors, and that the race thus progressed. There are many cases in which males actually fight to hold mates, and these are particularly clear cut among polygamous animals, such as seals and certain ruminants. There are other cases, however, where the winning suitor is not always chosen as a mate, but the loser is often favored. Such combats (grouse) apparently serve only as a part of the activities which bring the more passive sex to a state of sexual excitement.

GREGARIOUS, COLONIAL, AND SOCIAL ANIMALS

Some animals of the same or of different species resort together in circumscribed areas chiefly because they are dependent on habitats which are limited in extent; other groups may be formed by animals that seek to associate with each other.

Colonies are made up of animals that are connected together, often by a common flesh or skeleton. They are generally produced by the budding of a single original individual. Societies consist of animals that are independent as individuals in that they are able to move about separately, but live together with more or less interdependence and cooperation because there is division of labor.

Gregarious Animals.—Some gregarious animals are hostile to each other. Fiddler crabs fight continually, and one is very quick to attack another which invades the preserve about the mouth of its burrow (Pearse, 1914a). Herring gulls on their crowded nesting areas are quite quarrelsome, the adults and larger young often killing the smaller birds. Each parent has a strongly developed instinct to guard its nesting precincts (Strong, 1915). Longley (1918) found that a burrowing fish (Gnathypops) near Tortugas was commonly found in colonies and says the distribution of this species is "probably in part due to the discontinuous occurrence of suitable bottom rather than to the social instincts of the fishes themselves." Nesting ibises of two species occupy a considerable swampy area in Australia, where their nests are closely crowded together and favorable spots are occupied by groups of young and their attendant nurses. In another part of the same swamp spoonbills and little cormorants nest together. Both these breeding grounds are occupied by the same species year after year, though they are apparently not essentially different from other available areas. These birds apparently have a place association, or homing instinct, in relation to a particular area (D'Orbain, 1906). The albatrosses show similar relations to Laysan Island, where a million are estimated to breed. Their young eat 600 tons of squids per day. Each mother appears to recognize her own young and pecks others that solicit food from her. The wood rat in Oregon forms groups that build great nests in trees. Each rodent is separated from other individuals by a partition, but different individuals run about the nest freely and are more or less tolerant of each other (English, 1923). Such animals as have been mentioned are apparently gregarious because they are associated with areas that are particularly favorable, or particularly favored by the species concerned. Some animals show more or less gregariousness of a type that has no particular reference to areas but relates primarily to individuals. In such groups of animals there are bound to be certain disadvantages and certain advantages for individuals. Competition is keenest among members of the same species and a gregarious animal lives in the midst of fellows that are jealous of every success. On the other hand, a group is more likely to receive notice of danger than an isolated individual and some species (prairie dog, flamingo) commonly give warning calls when an intruder approaches. Herds of elk and deer are able to ward off attacks of large carnivores by associating together. If animals are close together it is easy to find a mate, and even the choice of a particular type of mate is possible. Tiger beetles are not gregarious or social but frequent restricted areas and different species have been observed to attempt to mate with each other (Shelford, 1911).

Gregarious Predators.—Many predaceous animals form groups for hunting. The individuals of a group may be more or less jealous and intolerant toward each other, but, having a common desire for food, they are willing to cooperate in securing it. A buzzard dropping down to its meal is observed by its keen-eyed fellows that soar at some distance, and within a few minutes after the death of an animal many of these birds may be feeding on the carcass. Lions may hunt singly, but usually go about in small groups, consisting of a male and two to four females, and Selous (1908) has observed as many as twenty together. Wolves commonly hunt in packs and are thus able to kill animals that are larger and stronger than themselves. Insectivorous birds commonly fly in flocks and are probably thus able to capture agile insects that might be able to escape from a single hunter. Widman (1896) pointed out that birds with long wings are more often gregarious than those with short wings, apparently because they are able more easily to cover long distances for feeding and roosting. He also states that birds of different species often go about together in flocks and that among passerine birds only assassins, like the shrike, are habitually solitary. It is "not safety from enemies which makes birds congregate."

Gregarious Migrators.—Many species of birds commonly congregate into flocks after their breeding season and migrate together. Whittle (1923) has presented some evidence that certain flocks of birds are relatively permanent associations of individuals that have bred in the same general locality and have migrated together. Some young animals are very gregarious. Many young fishes commonly swim together in schools and some continue to do so throughout their lives (Meek, 1916; Snyder, 1922). Gibson (1903) has described the behavior of *Hyperchiria io* caterpillars, which feed together side by side under leaves, and tent caterpillars, which are gregarious when not feeding. Cenethocampa caterpillars build nests in pine trees and migrate in processions. The leader of the procession changes from time to time and all individuals seem to have a strong instinct to follow a temporary leader (Brindley, 1910). The spiny lobster is gregarious (Crawford and Smidt, 1922). Several individuals may crawl about on a rock, the antennæ of one individual touching the body of the one in front of it.

Social Life Not Commonly Derived from Gregariousness.— Though gregarious animals have in many instances a tendency to cooperate to some extent and to make some division of labor among themselves it is proper to say that such associations have rarely if ever led to a high degree of specialization in communal life. The specialized societies have largely grown up out of families. The tenacity with which the members of extensive and crowded groups of animals, such as those found among aphids, fiddler crabs, barnacles, and mussels, cling to their individuality indicates that mere living together does not necessarily lead to social life.

Colonies.—Colonies occur among species of animals that are attached and have, by an extension of natural growth processes, formed a more or less loosely organized group of individuals that is organically connected and often shows a considerable degree of specialization along the line of division of labor and cooperation for the good of the whole group. Sponges form loose colonies that are without much unity. Individuals are hard to segregate and may be fused or separated without greatly interfering with the parts.

Correlation between Members of a Colony.—In cœlenterate colonies individuals are usually connected by a common flesh. There is often more or less polymorphism and alternation of asexual with sexual methods of reproduction. Division of labor among the members of a colony may be carried to a high degree. Brooks (1885) has discussed the origin of metagenesis and polymorphism in cœlenterates in a masterly way, and his ideas will be presented in the next two sections in this chapter. The individuals of the sea-pen (Renilla) in their withdrawals and expansions show no particular coordination or sequence, but the peristaltic waves which pass over the peduncle and the luminescence are unified activities that are characteristic of the colony as a whole. Bryozoans and ascidians show more or less division of labor among the individuals in their colonies. Van Name (1921, 1921a) maintains that simple ascidians probably came from colonial ancestors which were obliged to give up budding habits because they became too large and complex when they took up a free-swimming existence. He thinks it possible that the ancestors of the vertebrates may have been colonial. Williams (Allee, 1919) found that when a bryozoan colony (Pectinatella) was starved it lost one individual after another and the whole colony did not die at once. In all cases of division of labor among colonial animals the segregation of activities is so bound up with polymorphism that it may properly be left for discussion in the next section.

Social Life.—As has been suggested, social life rarely, if ever, arises from the chance association of individuals of a species and a high degree of social specialization always grows out of relations that are primarily those of the family. Social life is dependent on cooperation. Lowie (1920) in speaking of human society says: "Biologically every community must rest on the family," and Wasmann (1913) makes similar statements concerning ants. Kropotkin (1916) has emphasized the fact that food necessities tend to make animals competitive and antagonistic, and that reproduction tends to bring them together. The burdens laid on parents in bringing forth and rearing young have in many cases led to far-reaching results in the way of cooperation, the lengthening of life, the production of food and the maintenance of food resources, and even in intellectual life. In well-organized social life there must be continual compromises between selfish instincts and those that are for the good of the community. Lameere (1922) holds that the social life of ants saves the race from extinction because the worker individuals continually seek for food and continually regurgitate it to their fellows, thus supplying the reproductive individuals. Steiner (1924) has stressed warmth as a factor in the development of social life and claims that animals cannot cooperate effectively unless they are able to maintain a high body temperature over long periods of time.

Social Insects.—Wheeler (1923) has discussed the social life of insects in his incomparable way. He points out that tendencies toward social life were present as far back as the Carboniferous period, and that ants were socially in about their present state at the beginning of the Oligocene, some fifty million years ago. He asserts that social habits have arisen twenty-four times in more or less distantly related families of insects, and in every case through the prolonged association of a mother (or of both parents) with eggs and young. The social habits of insects have their origin largely in the propensity of females to lay their eggs on or near food which is suitable for the hatching larvæ. Some parents further remain with the eggs and young until they are able to shift for themselves; some actively seek and store food for their coming offspring. When the adult stage is lengthened so that parents may have prolonged association with one or more generations of offspring, a high degree of social life becomes possible. The societies of insects differ from those of man in that they lack "time-binding" elements, such as books and inventions, which civilization carries along in a cumulative way in succeeding generations.

In the termites and all the beetle groups the colony consists of a male and a female parent and their offspring of both sexes; in all the Hymenoptera, Dermaptera, and Embidaria the female alone founds the colony, which is developed by her daughters. The former groups are, therefore, gynandrarchic, the latter gynarchic.

Ants, according to Wheeler, are the dominant insects on the earth, probably exceeding all other insects in numbers. Their dominance is due in large measure to their social life. Like the societies of man, theirs have passed, and are passing, through hunting and pastoral stages, but many have now attained a high degree of development. Most ants feed only on liquids and continually practice trophallaxis (mutual feeding), which tends to spread all available food throughout the community. Ant communities vary in numbers "from dozens to millions."

Social Mammals.—Seton (1919) has considered the development of social life of mammals and states that, aside from primates, it reaches its highest level among rodents. The primitive society consists of a mother and a few of her offspring. When the father is also a member of the community, social life is at once on a higher level.

Division of Labor in Societies.—The division of labor among social animals usually tends to develop specialists for reproduction, foraging and feeding, and defense. A community has a certain unity because its individuals are interdependent and

cooperative. Wheeler (1911a) has discussed the ant society
as an organism. He first classifies "persons" of different grades
as: (1) protozoans, (2) simple non-metameric persons, (3)
metameric persons, (4) primitive colonies, (5) families or colonies
of reproductive type, (6) cœnobioses, (7) true or human societies.
He likens an ant community to an organism because it has
individuality, soma (workers and soldiers), and germ (queen).
It may live thirty to forty years and carry on "asexual reproduction." Workers serve primarily for provisioning the community,
but also retain their nursing instincts. Wheeler (1907) says:
"Instincts relating to the nurture of the young bear the aspect of
a dominating obsession." This makes the entrance of guests
and parasites into an ant community comparatively easy.
Some ant queens cannot establish a new colony without the
assistance of workers. In some species minute workers cling
to females that are making their nuptial flight and are thus
at hand to assist her in establishing her new home. Soldiers,
according to Wheeler (1911a), have "fear and rage" instincts
specialized and some perform very special duties. For example,
in the genus Colobopsis, which bores in wood, certain peculiar
individuals stand at the entrances of dwellings and use their
bodies as living stoppers. The heads of these soldiers completely close the entrances. If a member of the colony attempts
to enter, the doorkeeper stands aside, but all other solicitors
are excluded (Wheeler, 1904). In bee hives certain individuals
serve as sentinels and turn back all strangers at the entrance.
Lameere (1922) holds that reproduction is limited in social insects
to prevent overpopulation. The ability to reproduce is limited
to a few individuals and in many cases the brood is destroyed or
devoured by members of the community if there is a scarcity
of food. On the other hand, an ant queen that is deprived of her
first brood will rear another—which is a remarkable instance
of regeneration. Uichano (1919) studied a Philippine termite
which raises fungus for food. The male and the female build the
nest together, and the latter may probably live for as long as
twenty years. Some termite soldiers not only bite but also
throw out from their heads a sticky secretion which entangles
enemies. Hopkins (1898) has shown that female Xylographus
beetles help each other in making excavations in soft wood.
One gnaws away the wood while the other pushes out the shav-
ings. They prepare beds for rearing ambrosia fungus, which is

their chief food. A chamber is set apart for the bodies of dead beetles and other undesirable objects. In some species of these beetles the males are wingless and few in numbers. In such cases the females stand guard at the entrance. Among other species, in which males and females occur in approximately equal numbers, the males act as guards, often spending their lives watching the entrance and dying there. Holmes (1922) has attempted to classify social behavior as chiefly sustentative, protective, and ameliorative, and gives various subdivisions under each of these headings.

Cooperation in Societies.—In social life division of labor must ever be accompanied by cooperation, and often this is carried to remarkable extremes. Robaud (1911) has given an interesting account of the specialization of the maternal instincts of wasps. In primitive species food is collected and sealed up with the eggs. Some wasps remain with the eggs and assist the larvæ in feeding; a step above this condition are wasps that give the larva its entire food from day to day; and at the top of the series are the wasps which give their larvæ specially prepared food from day to day. Robaud believes that maternal instincts represent an equilibrium between hereditary habits and physiological necessities. Wheeler (1923) has made it plain that the social life of insects and their relations with foreign animals that invade their homes depend largely on trophallaxis. The instinct to regurgitate food when solicited by a fellow is so strong that an ant which is practically starving will sacrifice food. Social insects that gather food commonly gorge themselves when they can; they often store and use food with great economy. Mann (1913) quotes Cornetz as denying that ants show any real cooperation in carrying food to their nests; the presence of food is believed to excite the homing impulse in each individual. Other evidence indicates, however, that ants cooperate to such a degree that a returning worker can indicate to its fellows whether few or many workers are needed to carry in a discovered supply of food (Hingston, 1920). Passalid beetles modify wood before feeding it to their larvæ and stridulate to keep their groups together. In wasps there is mutual exchange of food between larva and worker, but bees do not obtain food from the young they attend.

Cooperation is not only concerned with the division of available food, but often reaches a high degree of specialization in other respects. Ants assist each other in many ways—lick and clean their fellows, carry the injured, etc. Uichano (1919) found no guiding or directing individuals in termite societies, but excellent cooperation. Toleration in ants in some cases permits the mixing of different communities (von Natzmer, 1913; Wheeler, 1911). A queen ant is not hostile to young queens in her nest, as queen bees are. Social spiders in India live together in groups of forty to a hundred, repairing their common nest together and feeding amicably together from the bodies of captured animals (Jambunathan, 1905). In a troop of monkeys the patriarch, usually the largest male, "exerts authority, maintains discipline, interferes in quarrels, chastises offenders, settles family disputes" (Hingston, 1920). Gain (1913) gives an excellent picture of social life among penguins. During the breeding season there is great rivalry for nests among adelie penguins. "Quarrels over ownership increase; each works for itself; selfishness is master; everywhere is distrust." Watchful care is continually necessary to prevent the stealing of materials for nests. But after the young appear there is great rivalry among adults to brood and care for them. They are herded and watched over by sentries which keep away the skua gulls. The emperor penguins do not build nests, but hold their eggs between their legs. They fight with each other for chances to incubate eggs, and to brood or feed young. Cooperation is always essential in society.

Advantages of Social Life.—The advantages of social life are many, but there are also inherent disadvantages. Cooperative activity makes the securing and conserving of food and the defense of the community easier. The association of adult œcophyllas with their larvæ permits them to take advantage of the spinning ability of the latter and use them as shuttles for weaving threads to bind the nests together. Close association between individuals gives opportunity for learning. The life of social insects appears to be guided largely by instinct, but among the higher vertebrates there is more or less learning by imitation and training. Communication by the use of language of various types is also a product of, and an asset to, social life. A social system may have a span of life which far exceeds that of the individuals that compose it. Ant societies may exist for thirty or forty years. Branner (1912) estimates the number of individuals in the nests of leaf-cutter ants as varying from 175,000 to 600,000. A queen termite during ten years may lay a hundred million eggs. Wheeler (1923) notes that termites as a result of social life have shown a tendency to deteriorate in their physical prowess, but tend to a higher degree of nervous organization. He also observes a similar, though less pronounced, tendency in ants. Social life makes the keeping of domesticated animals and the pursuit of agriculture easier, thus rendering food resources more stable. It enables animals to maintain a higher temperature, so that activities are less intermittent. Every apiculturist knows that bees remain warm throughout cold seasons. Steiner (1924) has shown that certain ants also maintain a rather high temperature in their nests. Time-binding, by which one generation obtains the benefits of experiences gained by those preceding it, is only possible among social animals. Ants inherit established nests, pastures, and hunting grounds. Man, with his unusual means for intricate expression through language and his great accumulations of learning and invention, has a society that is unique in possessing commercial, industrial, and intellectual aspects that are not found among other animals.

Disadvantages of Social Life.—Against social life there is always the argument that individuality is sacrificed. The specialization essential to cooperative division of labor leads to a certain limitation and loss of power among individuals. There is also an interdependence which may be fatal if all members of a society are not present and doing their parts. The instincts to feed, foster, and defend other individuals make the invasion of a society by parasites and guests easy. In India a moth and a mouse are regularly associated with the nest of social spiders (Jambunathan, 1905). A large number of myrmecophiles and termitophiles have been described; there are many parasites in human society.

POLYMORPHISM

All through the animal kingdom there is more or less tendency toward the development of different types of individuals. Cells tend to differentiate into tissues; colonies into functionally different individuals, etc. Huxley (1912) has discussed heterogeneity among animals with particular reference to individuality and points out that "compound wholes" which consist of many parts often differentiate within the whole into a variety of parts. Form differences among individuals within a species are often correlated with differences in habits or habitats. They find their fullest expression among colonial and social animals as an adaptation for division of labor. Sexual dimorphism is perhaps more common among animals than any other type of individual-istic differentiation, and many species show constant and characteristic differences between males and females. But there are many species, even among animals that are not colonial or social, that show two forms of one sex. For example, the males of certain Hercules beetles are horned or hornless. Colonial cœlenterates, bryozoans, and tunicates furnish some wonderful examples of polymorphism, but this type of specialization for diversity of function is perhaps at its best among social insects, especially ants and termites.

Types of Polymorphism.—Montgomery (1906) has classified the intraspecific form relations among adult animals as follows:

I. Monomorphism.

II. Polymorphism:

    1. Among individuals of the same generation.
       a. Sexual dimorphism.
       b. Reproductive and non-reproductive individuals.
       c. Different types of males or females.

    2. Among individuals of successive generations:
       a. Sexual and asexual individuals.
       b. Sexual and asexual individuals which also show differentiation among corresponding unisexual individuals or among diœcious and monœcious individuals.

In this section only polymorphism among animals of the same generation will be discussed. Montgomery's classification, while valuable in indicating the general types of relations that occur between different intraspecific forms, does not conform to general usage in regard to the term "polymorphism," which to most scientists signifies the concurrent association of different forms of one species that are in essentially the same stages of their life histories.

Polymorphism as Division of Labor.—Polymorphism as an adaptation for division of labor has apparently arisen in various groups by the specialization of qualities already present. Some parts have been developed to a greater degree and others have been more or less suppressed in the formation of particular types. Often the labor performed by a particular individual corresponds with the degree of development it has attained. The nymphs of reproductive forms of termites perform labor in their societies which is much like that performed by the worker caste (Thompson and Snyder, 1919), and, conversely, the worker is in a sense an undeveloped individual that is comparable to a nymph.

Types of Individuals among Polymorphic Animals.—The number of different types of individuals that may occur in a polymorphic species varies greatly. Many hydroid colonies commonly have feeding and reproductive individuals, those of Hydractinia regularly show stinging individuals as well, and some siphonophore colonies possess from five to seven types. Thompson (1922) states that among the termites of the genus Termopsis:

Four stable castes are of common occurrence; the first form, the second form, and the third form are the fertile reproductive castes; among the soldiers the females are sterile and the males are probably also sterile. There is no true sterile worker caste.

Wheeler (1923) says that eight castes are known among termites, but there are seldom more than five or six in one species. The usual castes, which occur in both sexes, are as follows:

1. First form adults—pigmented; eyes, brain, and frontal gland large; wings present (shed after nuptual flight).

2. Second form adults—wing pads present; eyes, brain, and frontal gland intermediate in size; substitute royal forms.

3. Third form adults—wingless; brain small; eyes and frontal gland vestigial; substitute royal forms.

4. Workers—unpigmented; brain small; compound eyes and frontal gland vestigial; head broad.

5. Soldiers—wingless; head large and more or less pigmented; brain small; compound eyes, vestigial; frontal gland often large.

Wheeler (1907) in his scholarly and inspiring discussion of polymorphism in ants describes twenty-seven castes, which are largely among females. All ants, except certain degenerate, parasitic species, have a worker caste. Among primitive ants, workers are monomorphic and have about the same size as sexually mature individuals. Wheeler discusses nine types of specialization: (1) workers are of same size and appearance as sexual forms; (2) some workers differ from sexual forms and others are intermediate, thus forming a more or less graded series; (3) workers are dimorphic and rather constant in size, thus constituting worker and soldier castes; (4) soldiers have become extinct leaving workers monomorphic; (5) workers have disappeared completely; (6) workers have remained stationary and females have increased in size; (7) workers have remained stationary and females have diminished in size; (8) female has disappeared and been replaced by a gynæcoid worker; and (9) the female caste has differentiated into two forms. Among ants the female and worker castes have apparently advanced or retrogressed independently in their evolution.

Determination of Castes.—The castes of social insects have long puzzled students of heredity and various theories have been proposed to explain how females could transmit characters, which they do not themselves possess, to workers and soldiers, which do not reproduce and therefore do not have a chance to transmit their own characters. Certainly the male and female must have potentialities in their germ cells for all the characters that the species shows. The quantity or quality of food has often been cited as the controlling factor in the production of castes. Wheeler (1911), quoting Emery, says:

The production of the worker form is held to be the result of inadequate feeding of the larva from which it develops, directly and clearly so in the wasps and bumble bees, but indirectly and obscurely in the honey bees, ants, and termites. The disappearance of the worker phases in certain small and permanently parasitic ants like *Anergates atratulus* is explained as the overfeeding of all the female larvæ, coupled with their small size, and not as due to the uselessness of the worker caste.

Wheeler (1907) points out that in bees lack of food not only results in a retardation in the development of the gonads, but also causes the development of peculiar worker characteristics. A number of changes thus result from nutritional castration. Wheeler makes the following generalizations in regard to the Hymenoptera: (1) Except in the bees, the morphogeny of queens is probably not dependent on food. (2) Workers fed on various diets may be alike. (3) A queen starting a colony may go without food for as long as eight months, feeding her larvæ, which are very small in such cases, on saliva. (4) Withdrawal of food from larvæ by nurses or parasites produces worker castes. (5) A queen bee fed on "royal jelly" receives an unusual growth stimulus. (6) Pseudogynes result from starved female larvæ. (7) Parasitic infestation may cause peculiar forms. (8) Some castes depend more or less on seasons and food, for some species produce workers only in summer. Wheeler (1923) says that trophallaxis is of general significance among social insects as the cause of the worker caste, the differences in size being closely correlated with the amount of food assimilated.

In the present state of our knowledge we can only surmise that the differences between queen and worker castes were originally ontogenetic and determined by feeding, as they still are in wasps and bees, but that in ants the germ plasm has somehow been reached and modified, so that an heredity basis for *caste differentiation* has been established.

The late Miss Thompson did excellent work on the determination of castes in termites. She says (1917):

My final conclusion is that all termite castes are predetermined in the eggs, that some castes are distinguishable, either by external or internal characters, at the time of hatching, while others may appear considerably later in the course of development . . . An argument against the view that termite castes are mutations is the fact that the five castes are constant in their occurrence throughout the very different and widely distributed genera of three families of termites (1919).

In her final paper Miss Thompson (1922) says: "The castes of termites are regarded as segregants arising by mendelian inheritance from a heterozygous parent form."

One of Miss Thompson's captive colonies of termites lived seventeen years without the production of first-form or second-form sexually mature individuals, and the passage of periods of time such as might recur in annual successions therefore appear to be unimportant in this instance. Miss Thompson believes (1919) that termite castes are determined by intrinsic causes and are not markedly influenced by conditions of environment. There are some facts, however, which appear to indicate that the production of castes is influenced to some extent by environment. Morgan (1907) states that the presence of royal termites inhibits the production of substitutes. Pricer's (1908) observations on carpenter ants showed that kings and queens were not reared unless at least 2000 ants were present in a community. In this case the number of ants present seemed to exert a definite influence. Internal secretions, the "struggle between parts" of developing insects, and other factors have been suggested as possible influences in the production of castes. Wheeler (1907) says: "Nourishment, temperature, and other environmental factors merely furnish the conditions for the attainment of characters predetermined by heredity."

ALTERNATION OF GENERATIONS

All through the animal kingdom there are tendencies toward alternation of generations, sometimes between different types of reproductive activity among structurally similar individuals, sometimes between structurally different types of individuals. Stockard (1921) says:

Twinning or polyembryony may be considered a typical method of asexual reproduction, and its occurrence in mammals and other vertebrates makes the phenomenon of so-called "alternation of generations" universal among animals.

In the cases of polyembryony to which Stockard refers, the arrest of growth in one region may stimulate growth in others, just as the pinching off of the terminal bud of a plant shoot may lead to the development of adventitious buds which would otherwise have remained small. Darwin (1859) long ago pointed out that certain gall-fly larvæ are able to produce other larvæ asexually, and suggested that an insect of a holometabolous type really performs a similar act when a larva is transformed into a pupa, which is quite a different type of individual from its predecessor. Montgomery (1906) calls attention to the fact that a starfish larva is to be considered a separate generation from the adult starfish, which it produces by budding. The whole larva is not transformed, but collapses and dies; only a portion of it grows into a starfish. Such facts make it apparent that alternation among animals is not always a definite, clear-cut process like the alternation of the sporophyte and gametophyte among plants, but is a rather heterogeneous group of tendencies that is manifested in various ways in different branches of the animal kingdom. In all cases, however, it is essentially a modification of simple and typical modes of ontogentic development in such a way that different types of individuals alternate with more or less regularity. Montgomery (1906) classified different types of ontogenies as follows:

```
Continuous:
  Orthoplastic—Direct
  Metaplastic     ⎫
Discontinuous:    ⎬  Larval
  Metagenetic     ⎭  ⎫
  Heterogenetic      ⎬  Alternation of Generations
  Ekdytic            ⎭
```

In a continuous life cycle,

. . . every structure or part that appears at any time of somatic differentiation passes wholly over into a later structure . . . Two kinds of continuous life cycles may be distinguished, as orthoplasis and metaplasis respectively . . . Orthoplasis is the equivalent of what has generally been called direct development; . . . metaplasis is a continuous development where the ontogeny is not at all points a further direct approximation toward the adult stage. The latter is development with a free larva, but without discontinuity of structure or process.

When development becomes discontinuous there may be alternations of sexual with asexual generations (metagenesis), alternation of individuals that produce offspring from fertilized with those that produce offspring from parthenogenetic eggs (heterogenesis), or there may in ekdytic development be structures which serve for the protection, respiration, excretion, or nutrition of the immature animal and do not become part of the adult because they are thrown off at birth.

Ekdytic rightly interpreted includes both cases of intrauterine (fœtal) development, and also any development within an egg shell where special membranes are formed and become later discarded. This is a molt, ekdysis, of living parts.

Of the two types of alternation of generation that occur generally among animals, "all discontinuous larval development is metagenetic, in that the adult is formed asexually, by budding, from the larva," and all animals in which there is an alternation of amphigenetic with parthenogenetic individuals are heterogenetic. The starfish or the insect pupa that is formed as an outgrowth from the larva is to be interpreted as a separate generation from the larva. Heterogenesis is to be looked upon as the alternation of a complete sexual reproduction ending in fertilized eggs with a degredation of sexual processes in which eggs develop without fertilization. It is associated with an absence of males. "The probability of the occurrence of parthenogenesis seems to be proportioned inversely to the number of male individuals."

Metagenesis.—Metagenesis reaches a high degree of development among certain cœlenterates and is characteristic among cestodes. Brooks (1885) has given an extensive and highly philosophical discussion of the origin and development of metagenesis in hydroids. He believes that the original ancestors of hydroids were simple, solitary, floating or swimming, hydra-like animals that gradually became better adapted for swimming and thus were modified into medusæ. Later the larvæ became attached to solid objects and some species emphasized sessile life so that they lost the tendency to become medusæ, thus losing the chance of developing alternation of generations; but other species, as sessile polyps, developed the tendency to form new individuals by budding and by thus giving rise to medusæ developed metagenesis. In many species polymorphism developed in the colonies during sessile life and this greatly complicated the life history. Brooks gives many examples that illustrate specialization toward and degeneration away from complex metagenetic cycles. The following are a few examples:[1]

Æginopsis has a metaplastic development:

Egg—Planula—Medusa × Eggs

Cunia octinaria also has a metaplastic development, for all individuals produced ultimately become medusæ:

Hydra—Medusa × Eggs
×
Egg—Planula—Actinula—Medusa × Eggs
×
Hydra—Medusa × Eggs

Cunocantha parasitica shows metagenesis because the actinula does not become a medusa, but completes its life as an individual after budding off hydras:

Egg—Planula—Actinula × $\dfrac{\text{Hydra—Medusa × Eggs}}{\text{Hydra—Medusa × Eggs}}$

Turritopsis shows a secondary alternation of generations:

Egg—Planula—Root × $\dfrac{\text{Hydra} \begin{smallmatrix}\times\ \text{Medusa × Eggs}\\ \times\ \text{Medusa × Eggs}\end{smallmatrix}}{\text{Hydra} \begin{smallmatrix}\times\ \text{Medusa × Eggs}\\ \times\ \text{Medusa × Eggs}\end{smallmatrix}}$

Eutima shows secondary alternation of generations and polymorphism:

Egg—Planula—Root × $\dfrac{\begin{smallmatrix}\text{Blastostyle × Medusa × Eggs}\\ \text{Nutritive hydra × Nutritive hydra}\end{smallmatrix}}{\begin{smallmatrix}\text{Blastostyle × Medusa × Eggs}\\ \text{Nutritive hydra × Nutritive hydra}\end{smallmatrix}}$

---

[1] In the life histories × indicates that one individual gives rise to another by budding or by sexual reproduction.

Cestodarian tapeworms have simple life histories, but cestodes commonly show metagenesis, as follows:

$$\text{Proglottid} \times \text{Eggs}$$
$$\text{Egg—Onchophore—Cysticercus—Scolex} \times$$
$$\text{Proglottid} \times \text{Eggs}$$

Tœnia echinococcus shows a secondary alternation of generations

$$\text{Proglottid} \times \text{Eggs}$$
$$\text{Cysticercus—Scolex} \times$$
$$\text{Proglottid} \times \text{Eggs}$$
$$\text{Eggs—Onchopore—Cysticercus} \times$$
$$\text{Proglottid} \times \text{Eggs}$$
$$\text{Cysticercus—Scolex} \times$$
$$\text{Proglottid} \times \text{Eggs}$$

Certain annelid worms bud off sexual individuals from an anterior individual which does not become sexually mature. One anterior individual may produce several others, which are all of the same sex. Chalcid flies almost attain a secondary metagenesis, for one egg may fragment into a number of individuals.

Heterogenesis.—Heterogenesis is well developed among aphids, cladocerans, rotifers, certain nematodes, and digenetic trematodes. It more often shows variations in the periodicy of different types of individuals and appears more often to be more or less directly affected by conditions of environment than metagenesis. Some species of aphids have very complex life histories.

Baker and Turner (1916) describe that of the rosy apple aphis in Virginia as follows:

Where found	Apple	Apple	Plantain	Plantain	Apple
Stage.......	Stem mothers (wingless)	About seven generations of mothers (at first wingless; last generation nearly all winged)	Four to fourteen generations, mostly wingless	Winged males and females	Eggs
Time.......	Apr. 8–16	May 20–June 20	June–September	October	October and November

This life cycle includes a very large number of generations, all of which are produced as living young from parthogenetic females, except the stem mothers, which hatch in the spring from fertilized eggs.

Among aphids a particular individual reproduces by only one method, but the offspring of an individual may be both parthenogenetic and amphigenetic. Parthenogenesis may continue for a large number of generations if environmental conditions are favorable. Some aphids regularly alternate between certain host plants, passing particular stages on each plant, but others pass through a complex life cycle on a single plant. The grape phylloxeran, for example, alternates between the roots and leaves of its host, amphigenetic individuals passing the winter on the former and parthogenetic generations summering on the latter.

Trematodes furnish many examples of parasites that regularly alternate between definite hosts. The life history of the lung fluke, *Pargonimus ringeri*, is as follows:

Where found	Free	Water	Snail	Water	Crab or crayfish	Man
Stage.......	Egg	Miracidium	Sporocyst ×	Cercaria	Cyst	Fluke
Generation..	1	1	1	2	2	× 2

Many trematodes have a redia stage in the snail following the sporocyst.

Other Types of Alternation of Generations.—It is possible that other types of alternation of generations besides metagenesis and heterogenesis occur. Van Beneden (1876) tentatively described a nematode that had a generation of hermaphroditic alternating with one of diœcious individuals. The same may be true of *Strongyloides stercoralis* which lives in the intestine of man as a parthenogenetic female, or a hermaphrodite, and in the soil as a male or female individual. Such cases are doubtful because the sexual character of the parasitic stages is not definitely known.

Alternation of generations shows more or less correlation with environmental conditions. This is true to a greater degree of heterogenesis than of metagenesis. Hydroids pass through their metagenetic cycle as fast as the environment permits without particular regard to its conditions, except as they limit metabolic processes. Metagenesis is generally an alternation between stages that occur where an abundant food supply is available, which permits rapid multiplication by budding, and stages which are concerned with sexual reproduction and distribution. Heterogenetic life cycles usually show parthenogenetic phases when conditions (temperature, food, etc.) are favorable for rapid production of individuals and sexual phases when conditions of existence become more severe (winter, drought, etc.). In both types of alternation of generations rapid multiplication, when it occurs, usually takes place when conditions are stable and food is abundant; fertilization stages are more often associated with changing environmental conditions, particularly when such changes make the environment unfavorable for continued activity.

CHAPTER XI

INTERSPECIFIC RELATIONS

Animals of different species have varying degrees of intimacy in relations to each other, from complete indifference to such close connections as those of parasitism and symbiosis. For example, Nutting (1914) describes the animals associated with alcyonarian corals as: (1) harmless species, such as certain ophiuroids and molluscs, which do not modify the structure of the corals; (2) annelids, barnacles, crabs, and shrimps, which become overgrown more or less and thus modify the structure of the corals but do not subsist on their tissues; (3) true parasites (crustaceans, clams, annelids), which subsist wholly or in part on the corals; and (4) millepores and colonial anemones, which do not take away food, but destroy corals by growing over and smothering them. Wheeler (1923) states that myrmecophiles and termitophiles may be classified as "predators, indifferently tolerated guests, true guests, and parasites."

Wheeler describes a peculiar cœnobiotic association which he found in Arizona. Five or six organisms cooperate to form this. The oak, common in the Huachuca Mountains, was heavily infested with mistletoe. Larvæ of a beetle made borings in this, and these were tenanted by colonies of the ant *Cremastogaster arizonensis*. On the inside of the ant galleries were numerous scale insects, later described by Cockerell as *Pseudococcus phoranderi*, which slowly kill the mistletoe. Thus the ant, which fosters the scales injurious to the mistletoe, which is a serious parasite on the live oaks and other trees, may be regarded as a useful forest insect (Mann, 1913).

Caullery (1922) says:

Commensalisme, parasitisme, symbiose sont des catégories de notre esprit, qui ne sont sepàrèes dans la nature par aucune discontinuité et quie offrent des aspects diverse des mêmes lois générales.

In many cases it is not possible to say whether certain animals are related to others as commensals, symbionts, or parasites. This is often on account of lack of knowledge. Wallin (1923)

346

has proposed the term "prototaxis" to include all cases where
there is an "innate tendency to react in a definite manner to
another organism." He would include conjugants, symplasms,
symbionts, parasites, etc.

Degree of Association between Different Species.—Calvert
(1922) and others have made formulæ for computing the degree of
association that different species of animals show to each other
by using correlation in distribution as a basis. Forbes and
Richardson (1908) in discussing fishes say that there is a

. . . frequency tendency of closely allied species inhabiting the
same territory to avoid each other's company, thus to evade competition
with one another, by the choice of habitation. In consequence of this
tendency, we sometimes find widely unlike species more closely and
commonly associated in our collections than like, the ecological repul-
sion of each for its similars bringing dissimilars together in more or less
definite associate groups.

In some cases different species are commonly associated
because they seek the same habitat, and in others one or both of
the associates seeks specifically for association with the other.
Hindel (1905) found thirty-two species of insects in the willow-
cone gall: one gall maker, ten inquilines, sixteen parasites and
hyperparasites, and five transient or accidental guests. In this
instance the gall maker, guests, and inquilines seek a particular
habitat in a more general way than the parasites, which depend on
special hosts. The spiders that mimic driver ants and accompany them during their travels show a highly specialized relation
to another species. Thus animals may commonly associate with
each other for rather general or, even accidental, reasons, or for
very special reasons.

Predator and Prey.—Perhaps the relation between predator
and prey is the one most generally present between animals of
different species. One of the chief means that man has for
combating pests is through the introduction or fostering of natural enemies. Much has been written in this field. For example,
Davis (1919) has discussed the relations of the phyllophagous
beetles in great detail and gives elaborate diagrams showing
relationships to various enemies. He states that the increase of
the white grub in many localities has been due to the destruction
of enemies (skunk, etc.) which formerly kept it in check. He
also points out that the duration of various stages in the life cycle
of a June beetle are definitely related to the number of enemies

that usually attack them. The egg and pupal stages are short, well protected, and are preyed upon by very few animals. Vine (1896) published a list of predaceous and parasitic enemies of aphids. Sladen (1912) did the same by bumble bees; and Wall (1906) for snakes. Folsom (1922) gives lists of animals attacked by various predaceous insects and Ferton (1910) made similar studies of hymenopterous insects. Hudson (1922) mentions a certain year on the pampas when mice became extraordinarily abundant and ate up nearly all the bumble bees. In turn, the mice were beset by a host of enemies; owls appeared in great numbers and other predators were abundant. It is usually thus—predators increase and decrease with their prey. S. A. Forbes (1880) has discussed the interactions of animals in a very thorough manner, particularly the numerical relations between prey and predator.

Some animals do not prey upon others directly but rob food-laden individuals. H. Forbes (1885) tells how frigate-birds lurk in the lee of islands, whence they may pursue gorged noddy terns and compel them to regurgitate partly digested fish, which they skilfully catch in the air before it reaches the surface of the ocean. According to Hall (1900), the great skua gull has similar habits. Wheeler (1911) describes flies that stand beside the trails of foraging ants and capture food from individuals that are returning to their nests.

It is a general law that vegetarian or scavenger animals are more numerous than predaceous species. There must be enough of the species preyed upon to supply the predators without being exterminated. Hingston (1920) noted that predatory ants in the Himalayas were not only fewer in numbers than the harvesters on which they preyed, but differed from them in their greater swiftness and activity and in their habits of not following regular trails. Many animals have their scheme of life related primarily to escaping from enemies, and others spend their existence continually seeking for other species that they may devour. A walking-stick remains immobile for hours at a time and when it moves goes with great slowness in order that its resemblance to a twig may not be negated. Among the little bees of the genus Halictus, the male and female take turns standing guard at the entrance of their burrow in order to keep out their arch enemies, the mutillids, and other predatory insects that attempt to invade their homes (Melander and Brues, 1903).

The habits of termites in avoiding light and always building hard-walled, covered roadways for their necessary travels generally protect them from predaceous ants and other enemies.

Types of Associations between Animals of Different Species.— It is chiefly the activities of the predator seeking food and the reaction of the prey to avoid being eaten that have led to the intimate associations between animals of different species, but a few associations have apparently come about through the seeking of shelter, transportation, or other desiderata. It is difficult to classify the interspecific relations into groups because they constitute a graded series. It is unfortunate also that different usages obtain among botanists and zoölogists in regard to the terms connected with such associations. Coulter, Barnes, and Cowles (1911) use "symbiosis" to include all intimate interspecific relations, making "commensalism" and "parasitism" subdivisions under it. Zoölogists have generally used these three terms as follows:

Commensalism—an intimate association between two or more species, in which one or more may be benefited but none are injured.

Symbiosis or mutualism—an intimate association between two or more species which results beneficially to all concerned.

Parasitism—an intimate association between two or more species in which one or more (hosts) are injured and others (parasites) benefit.

COMMENSALS

The term commensal was originally used by Van Beneden (1876) in referring to animals that share the same food,[1] but has now generally come to have a broader meaning and includes all intimate associations between different species of animals which are not parasites or symbiotic. Commensals are associated and, though one may derive more or less benefit, the other member of the partnership is not essentially injured or benefited. Van Beneden looked upon commensalism as hospitality in which a large or successful species helped, or tolerated the presence of, another species without any particular sacrifice. "The messmate does not live at the expense of his host; all that he desires is a home or his friends' superfluities." Barnacles are commonly attached to whales, and some species are not found elsewhere.

[1] "Le commensal est simplement un compagnon de table."

Most of these are commensals, but some of the more specialized species work injury by causing sores in the skin, and hence are parasites.

Commensal relations are not always concerned with food but may relate to shelter migration, or other things. Sometimes commensal relations are temporary. Longley (1918) says:

Fishes of different species may establish relations with one another which persist for days. Of such partnerships one of the most interesting I observed was between a red goatfish and a small yellowtail which I saw a number of times hunting for food together.

The larger fish stirred up the mud and its companion watched nearby to snatch any small animals that escaped. Hecht (1918) tells of another type of temporary association. In this case a young amphipod (Orchestia) lived in the oral siphon of an ascidian, where it obtained food from the current, but if disturbed swam freely and left its temporary host. Essenberg (1918) states that the distribution of certain polynoids is limited by the distribution of the animals with which they live commensally.

The perfect color mimicry of commensal polynoids suggests that there is some chemical or enzymatic interaction between the messmates and the commensal producing similar color patterns in animals widely different in kind.

Clark (1921) also noted that many small commensal animals were colored like their hosts and he found that a crustacean (Alpheus) that was removed from a crinoid soon returned. He believes that symbiosis and parasitism have their origin from commensal relations.

The quotations introduced into the two preceding paragraphs show that there has been no uniformity of usage in regard to the terms "commensal," "guest," and "messmate." To the writer it seems proper to refer to all animals that have intimate relations, from which they may derive more or less benefit, with animals of other species as "commensals." It also seems proper to refer to those species which give support or shelter to commensals as "hosts."

Commensals Attached to Outsides of Hosts.—Many commensals are simply fastened to the outsides of their hosts. They thus gain attachment, perhaps some protection from the relation of the host toward certain enemies, and when the host moves are carried to situations that are favorable for respiration, the finding of food, etc. Vorticellids ride about on hydras, planarians, leeches, snails, insects, fishes, and salamanders; some species are associated with particular hosts because they require particular types of surfaces for attachment (Faure-Fremiet, 1906). The remora attaches its sucker to a shark. The shells of hermit crabs may bear actinians, hydroids, bryozoans, worms, snails, and other animals. Wheeler (1911) says:

Kneissl describes a mite that is attached to an ant's tibia by an anal secretion. It is licked and fed by ants and has an adaptation for turning from side to side without losing its hold while being licked.

Many sessile animals accidentally become attached to other living animals that have suitable exteriors; others are regularly associated with such hosts, and some cannot live without them. An animal that is attached to the outside of a favorable host may easily go further and take up symbiotic or parasitic relations.

Commensals within the Bodies or Homes of Hosts.—For commensals that invade the bodies or homes of their hosts, the development of intimate associations is perhaps much easier than among those which maintain relations from the exterior. When the Cossus beetle makes borings in tree trunks, other insects are attracted by the sap and the shelter (Joy, 1914). Dollman (1910) has reported ten species of beetles that live in moles' nests. Ainslie (1906) found the larvæ of flies (Drosophila) regularly living in the spittle masses of cercopids. There are a number of larval insects that are found in the nests of bumble bees; some of these are accidental guests and some are parasites that have hard or spiny coverings for protection (Sladen, 1912). In British Guiana, Emerson (Weese, 1922) found about fifty species of termitophiles (beetles, aphids, ants, lepismas, millipedes, etc.). Some lived with the termites, others occupied the disused portions of the nests. Snails, worms, and other animals live inside the shells of hermit crabs. Certain gall-flies, mosquitoes, and midges habitually rest on spider's webs (Knab, 1912). The driver ants (Dorylinæ) are accompanied by many myremecophiles on their travels. Wasmann (1914) groups these camp-followers under three heads: (1) symphiles, which are agreeable to the ants on account of exudations that they give off; (2) mimics, which often show remarkably close resemblances to their hosts; and (3) various animals that are protected by hard shells and are often greatly flattened. Bahr (1907) says that there are often three or four grackles' nests tucked away among the sticks of the nest of an osprey.   Fishes that live among the tentacles of actinians or corals, or actually within the bodies of their hosts, gain the protection afforded by nettling cells.   The crustaceans that live within medusæ get similar benefits and transportation as well.   There are many instances of animals that live within others: Crabs dwell in molluscs; fishes and prawns in sea-cucumbers; shrimps in actinians, sponges, salpas, cteno-phores; etc.   Cushman (1919) has described a forameniferan that lives within the shell of another, which assumes a peculiar form as a result.

Often commensals are attended to by their hosts; in other cases they remain unnoticed.   Wheeler (1911) says:

Crawley made several observations on the relations of the little isopod, *Platyarthrus hoffmanseggi*, to various ants.   He found that many species are hostile and devour or drive away these crustaceans, but that *Lazius flavus* and *L. niger* seem to be very tolerant of them.   As a rule, *L. flavus* receives *Platyarthi* from the nests of its own species and others without taking notice of them.   These small, blind woodlice pass their whole existence in ants' nests, and when they are about to molt or produce offspring, are found in small cells of earth made in the walls of the nest, where they remain for some time, finally breaking their way out.   Apparently, the cells are made by the ants, since these insects were seen carefully plastering earth around the crustaceans . . . The pseudoscorpion (*Chernes scorpioides*), found literally in thousands in *F. rufa* nests in Leichestershire, is treated with indifferences by the ants.

SYMBIONTS

Symbionts are animals, or plants and animals, of different species, that live together to the mutual advantage of each. It must be remembered, however, that botanists use the term "symbiosis" in a different sense.   McDougall (1918), for example, argues that it is a mistake to apply symbiosis to "a few cases of reciprocal parasitism," when De Bary (who first used the term) intended it to have a much broader meaning. Yet Nuttall (1923), who gives a comprehensive review of intimate relations between plants and animals, says:

The term symbiosis denotes a condition of conjoint life existing between different organisms that in a varying degree are benefited by the partnership.

The nature of symbiotic relations varies considerably. It may be concerned primarily with food, protection, other essentials, or even luxuries, of life. In some cases symbionts come together more or less by accident, in others one member of the pair may seek actively and care for the other. Many symbionts have special adaptations which distinguish them from other animals of the same type. McIndoo (Weese, 1921) has described extravagantly developed glandular knobs on the abdomens of certain staphylinid beetles that live in termites' nests in British Guiana. These give off secretions that make the beetles much sought after by the termites, which continually lick them. Many of the examples that have been cited as symbiotic will probably not stand up under careful scrutiny. A number have already been shown to be cases of commensalism or parasitism. The real question in any particular case is whether *both* species in the partnership are *benefited*. It is often not possible to come to a definite conclusion.

Wheeler (1923) says:

Social life may, indeed, be regarded as a special form of symbiosis. This term, which signifies the living together of organisms in a balanced, cooperative, reciprocally helpful manner, is commonly applied interspecifically, that is, to partners thus related belonging to different species, but there is no reason why it should not be applied to the same kind of relations between individuals of the same species, that is, intraspecifically.

Wheeler also points out that probably few animals attain to a perfectly symbiotic relation, and that symbiosis often lapses into parasitism. Van Beneden (1876) says:

When a copepod crustacean installs himself in the pantry of an ascidian, and filches from him some dainty morsel, as it passes by; when a benevolent animal renders some such service to his neighbor, either by keeping his rack clean, or removing detritus which clogs certain organs, this crustacean or this animal is no more a parasite than is he who cowers by the side of a vigilant and skilful neighbor, quietly takes his siesta, and is contented with the fragments which fall from the jaws of his companion.

Crustaceans and Cœlenterates.—The examples of symbiosis that are best and most widely known are perhaps those between crustaceans and cœlenterates. Thomson (1923) tells of a small spider crab that made its home beneath the spreading tentacles

of an anemone.   When the crab went out foraging and brought
back food, the anemone took it away and the crab appeared to
satisfy its hunger largely from the undigested fragments that the
anemone discarded.   Balss (1924) has made an extensive review
of the symbiotic relations of hermit crabs with other animals.
He lists twenty species of actinians that are more or less regularly
associated with twenty-five species of hermits; eight hydroids on
twelve hermits; sponges, bryozoans, and annelids.   Some of the
hermits, when changing to new shells, are known to transfer
their symbiotic anemones to their new dwellings.   If deprived of
their anemones some hermits will search tirelessly until they find
new individuals for their shells.   Some of the hermits do not take
food directly, but wait until it has been stung by the nematocysts
of their attached cœlenterates.   Certain little crabs (Melia)
carry anemones in their claws and use them in securing food and
for defense.   If threatened they hold the anemones out toward
the enemy.   Duerdin (1906) studied the behavior of Melias.
He states that several species of actinians are used by the crabs
and if a whole one cannot be obtained a piece is held.   The
chelipeds are not used for feeding, but the actinian secures the
food and the crab then takes it away.   He says that the actinians
can exist indefinitely without the crabs, but the crabs must have
actinians.   On the coast of Japan there are actinians and
hydroids that are commonly attached to certain fishes.

Vermin Removers.—Some small animals often associate with
larger species, keeping them free from vermin and in some cases
giving them notice of danger.   Longley (1922) observed a small
fish of this sort at Tortugas:

Thalassoma nitidus is commonly seen pecking at the surface of larger
fishes, presumably cleaning ectoparasites from them.   These larger
fishes return again and again to submit to the process of grooming and
will drive away others which interrupt the process . . . Attentions
are not merely tolerated but actually welcomed.

The imouran, a large rodent in Mongolia, is said by Ossendowski (1922) to be attended by a lark which perches on its back,
picks off parasites, flies above its host, and gives cries to give
notice of danger.   A plover is said to pick the teeth of crocodiles
(Van Beneden, 1876).   Certain birds sit on the backs of buffaloes,
cattle, rhinoceroses, and other animals.   They eat blood-sucking
insects and parasites and give warning when danger threatens.

Ant and Termite Symbionts.—Ants and termites have symbiotic relations with a considerable variety of animals and plants. Mann (1913) describes a butterfly in Java that deposits eggs on an ant plant. The caterpillars which hatch are commonly attended by ants, and those that do not receive such attention die. They give the ants a sweet secretion and are fed in return. Another caterpillar that is attended by ants displays repellant organs when it has no desirable secretions ready to be licked off by the ants.

Plants and Animals.—A number of plants are symbionts with animals. Certain termites and ants raise fungi for food, and some of the plants that they thus utilize are not found outside their nests. Other algæ and fungi live in the bodies of animals and help in the digestion or assimilation of food. Nuttall (1923) states that plants within animals assist animal metabolism or other processes in various ways, *i.e.*, decompose urates; produce enzymes that aid in sugar digestion; digest cellulose; fix free nitrogen; produce light, etc. Zoöanthellæ occur in protozoans, sponges, cœlenterates, ctenophores, turbellarians, rotifers, annelids, bryozoans, and molluscs; and bacteroids in the intestines of cockroaches, beetles, flies, butterflies, and molluscs. Some of these may be slaves or parasites, but some appear undoubtedly to be symbionts (Caullery, 1922). Certain species of termites are unable to digest wood unless they have symbiotic protozoans in their intestines (Cleveland, 1923, 1924). Perhaps the most interesting of the symbiotic fungi are the mycetomes that live in the fat bodies of a number of insects, where they contribute to the insects' metabolic processes. They give off minute spores which invade the eggs of the insects and thus the symbionts are hereditary.

Origin of Symbiosis.—Symbiosis appears in most cases to have had its origin in chance associations between animals of different species. Huxley (1912) says that scientists generally

. . . now suppose that one organism does not merely rush into a ready-made vacuum provided by the other, but that the two should conspire together to create a vacuum of their own, into which, as fast as it is created, they jointly creep. This is, in effect, what happens when two species become mutually dependent.

Wheeler (1923) describes tachigalid beetles that live in hollow petioles. Aphids wander into their dwellings and become important contributors of food to the beetles. Aphids that give food to other insects when solicited escape being eaten on account of this habit, the sweet secretions being more acceptable than the body of the producer. Balss (1924) and Brunelli (1913) who have made intensive studies of the relations between hermit crabs and their symbionts are convinced that symbiosis did not come about through modification of habits that certain crustaceans have of placing objects on their backs, but arose through accidental contacts and perhaps in some cases through the activities of the crabs. Anemones, hydroids, sponges, and other animals that are associated with hermits are commonly found attached to shells and other objects, which do not contain hermits. Kropotkin (1916), Framintzin (1907), Caullery (1922), and Wallin (1923) have stressed the importance of symbiosis as a factor in evolution, claiming that it has been important in enabling animals to attain higher levels.

Effectiveness of Symbiotic Relations.—There can be no doubt that symbiosis is useful to many animals. Balss (1924) has shown that hermit crabs that carry anemones get the benefit of the nematocysts (which sting enemies and kill prey), and protection of the shell from gradual wear and injury. In some cases the actinian takes the place of a shell and completely covers the hermit's soft abdomen. The anemones are transported from place to place, are likely to secure food because the crab continually seeks it, and are rather certain to be kept in pure, well-aerated water.

Goto (1910) described two species of hydroids that live along the Japanese coast

. . . that have the same habit of living always in symbiosis with a hermit crab, *Eupagurus constans* Stimpson, and of forming shells of their own composed of a chitinous framework, so that in most specimens there is apparent no basis of gasteropod shell, as in the case of most known species of Hydractinia.

Polimanti (1911) studied the relations between a sponge and a crab and concluded that:

It is certain that the crab takes the initiative in putting the sponge on its cephalothorax. It is also certain that the sponge affords the crab a genuine protection against the appetite of cuttlefishes.

In cases like that described by Duerdin (1906) there seems to be no doubt that an anemone is transported to food and that its transporter depends upon the anemone to secure its food. Aphids furnish food for ants and are, in turn, fed and protected. The eggs of certain species winter in the underground galleries; the young aphids are carried out by the ants in spring and placed on favorable food plants. Aphids supply honey dew to ants, moths, flies, and beetles, but are cared for only by ants (Ord, 1910). The protozoans in termites and ruminants appear to be essential for the digestive processes of their hosts and receive food and protection. The rhinoceros, by tolerating its attendant bird, is freed from ticks and warned of danger.

Reinheimer (1921) has discussed the relations of symbiosis to food. He believes that symbiosis arises when there are "a pair of opposites to be accommodated," each having something the other needs. "The presence of symbiotic systems makes on the whole for increased economy and increased security of life." Reinheimer argues for the importance of "cross-feeding" as opposed to "in-feeding," and says: "Surely the chances of fruitful, social, and mental life are therefore higher among cross-feeders than in-feeders."

PARASITES

Parasitism is an intimate relation between two animals in which one is injured. Usually the parasite takes food from its host, but parasitism is not always concerned with food relations. Parasites may do injury by occupying space within the bodies or dwellings of their hosts, by giving off poisons, and by other means. Parasites are scattered throughout the animal kingdom and, though they are most often found among protozoans, platyhelminths, nematoids, and arthropods, most other phyla have species that have taken up life as parasites.

Types of Parasites.—Ectoparasites live on the outside of their hosts and endoparasites live within, but there is no sharp line of demarcation and some species may either live on the outside or invade the interior, occupying such spaces as are furnished by buccal or branchial cavities. Some species of animals that are parasitic need not lead such a life, and hence are known as facultative parasites. On the other hand, obligate parasites cannot exist except in close association with their usual hosts. Some parasites (permanent) must be continually associated with their hosts; others (transitory) may only come in contact with their hosts at intervals or during certain stages in their life histories. Social parasites invade societies and gain a living at the expense of the community. Accidental parasites are animals that would not usually lead such a life, but through some unusual circumstances have become associated with hosts. Many parasites have attained a high degree of specialization in their host requirements. Some can live in only a single species of host; some require two or more specific hosts in order to complete their life cycle, and there is thus a regular alternation of generations and hosts. Parasites that have a simple life history and may have all stages associated with a single host are monogenetic, but those that have an alternation of generations and have relations with two or more hosts are digenetic or trigenetic. In the latter cases the primary, or definitive, host is that in which the adult or sexually mature phase of the parasite is found, and the secondary, or intermediate, host is that which contains the immature or asexual phase.

Examples of Parasitism.—An endless array of parasitic relations might be presented and the following are selected as examples of rather diverse types. Synalpheus and Typton are two shrimp-like crustaceans that live in the canals of the gigantic niggerhead sponge and, though belonging to different families, resemble each other closely in form and coloration. They eat from the walls of the canals in which they live, scraping off sponge tissues and accumulated materials (McClendon, 1910). When two individuals meet they snap their claws at each other and one or both back away. Claasen (Weese, 1921) has described a midge larva that lives in swift streams, where it lurks under the wing pads of may-fly nymphs and sucks nourishment from the bodies of its hosts. Certain parasites are associated with crinoids, stealing from the food grooves and in some cases causing galls (Clark, 1921). Calman (1911) says:

The order Isopoda includes a very large number of parasitic species. The extensive family Cymothoidæ presents a whole series of gradations in habits and structure between actively swimming predatory species and others which in the adult stage are permanently fixed to their host, usually a fish, and are incapable of movement . . . No group of Crustacea exhibits more numerous examples of parasitism than the Copepoda. Every grade of transition between a free predatory habit of life and the most complete dependence upon a host may be traced in various families of the subclass.

Though some young fishes live as symbionts among the trailing tentacles of pelagic cœlenterates, others are parasites that feed on the tentacles (Scheuring, 1915). An amphisbænian lives in the nests of leaf-cutter ants, which it eats (Bates, 1892). Certain coccinelid larvæ live in ants' nests and prey on coccids that the ants bring in (Wheeler, 1911). There is a little fly (Phora) that waits persistently at the entrances of the nests of burrowing bees (Halictus) for a moment when the doorkeeper leaves the way open so that it may dart in and lay its egg on the stored pollen mass of its host. If a laden female bee returns to the nest, the fly tries to lay an egg on her load of pollen. The halictid bees are also robbed by little ant thieves that burrow through the walls of their tunnels (Melander and Brues, 1903).

Sladen (1912) has given an interesting account of parasitic bees (Psithyrus) that live in the nests of bumble bees. Each species is quite specific in its choice of a host and is usually associated with a single species of bumble bee. The female enters a colony, stings the queen to death, and takes her place. She has a thick, hard exoskeleton, which makes it difficult to injure her. Sladen finds that bees within the genus Bombus show a tendency to parasitism, the queens of some species invading the nest of others. Many chalcids lay eggs in the eggs of other insects and the larvæ are thus able to feed on the host as it develops. Some chalcid hosts are themselves parasites on other chalcids. Wheeler (1923) describes the different types of associations of parasites with ants as follows: (1) Brigandage, by animals that snatch food from its rightful owners. (2) Thievery, by small animals that live on the walls of the nest and prey on the food stores or brood of the ants. (3) Slavery, in which one species captures the brood of another and rears workers that become a part of the colony into which they are brought. (4) Temporary social parasitism. A strange female ant invades a colony, in which the workers then kill their original queen. The new queen gradually establishes her own workers with the help of the original colony. (5) Permanent social parasites. A queen invades a strange colony, kills the original queen, and takes her place. She produces no workers, but the original workers rear her brood, which enters other colonies. (6) Ectoparasites on individual ants. (7) Endoparasites in individual ants. In another paper Wheeler (1911*a*) describes the queen ants that cannot live without the aid of another species as falling into four groups: (1) A queen enters a colony and kills the original queen, or causes the workers to do so. Her workers gradually replace the old colony. (2) A queen enters a colony, fights the original queen if she disputes the invasion, and a colony of workers of two species results. (3) Amazons, which are obligate slave makers and cannot feed themselves, enter a colony, kill the queen, and are cared for by the original workers. A mixed colony results, as new workers are captured at intervals. (4) A small, feeble queen enters a colony and is adopted in place of the original queen, which is usually killed. No workers are produced and the colony dies out after rearing the foreign aristocrats.

Origin of Parasitism.—The origin of parasitic habits is often associated with prolonged inquiline life or with attempts to secure food for the individual immediately concerned or for its offspring. Sarcophagid flies usually deposit their eggs in dead flesh, but sometimes lay them in open sores and their larvæ invade living animals. Barnacles on account of their sessile mode of life show a certain degree of degeneracy compared to many other crustaceans; certain of them (Sacculina, etc.) have apparently, after developing habits of attachment to particular animals, become parasites and now regularly depend on the absorption of nourishment from their hosts for their existence. Clark (9121), after considering many parasites among fossil animals, concludes that the assumption of sessile life by a species is often the first step toward parasitism. He also states that commensals have often become parasites. Bouvier (1922) has described an interesting series of habit relations among pompilid wasps. Some species hunt for prey and lay eggs on it; others lay eggs on spiders captured by wasps of other species; and others search over the ground for a covered nest, remove the owner's egg, deposit their own egg on the stored food, and fill the burrow again. Froggart (1915) says that blow-flies in Australia learned within twelve years to lay eggs in the soiled, damp wool of sheep. He believes that the habit arose after there was a great decrease in the amount of carrion (poisoned rabbits, etc.) available and claims that the wool-blowing habit has constantly increased. Two species of flies at first took up the habit and another adopted it later. Brues (1921) believes that many hymenopters learned to lay eggs on living hosts before they began to deposit eggs on dead animals. Haviland (1922) is of the opinion that parasitic habits among hymenopters commonly arose from former inquiline modes of life. In New Zealand, the kea formerly subsisted largely on insect larvæ, honey, fruits, berries, and roots, but now has learned to feed on sheep (Marriner, 1909). Certain individuals perch on living sheep, the largest and strongest usually being attacked, tear holes in the back of their victims, and devour the fat. Other keas flock to the feast. Marriner states that the rhinoceros bird in Africa, which used to confine its attentions to ticks, has now learned to feed on living mammals by pecking holes in them. Quite recently magpies in the western United States have been observed to attack sheep.

Ewing (1912) has given a very thorough and illuminating discussion of the development of parasitic habits in mites. He shows that parasitism has originated at least eleven times in different groups. Among zoöphagous types, parasites came from lines that were predaceous feeders, scavengers, or suckers of plant juices. Ewing believes that the assumption of parasitism by mites has been easy because of food habits and minute size.

Among our living forms we can today trace out all the stages of advancing parasitism, including the occasional or erratic parasitism, semiparasitism, facultative parasitism, even to the fixed and permanent type, and finally to endoparasitism.

Herrick (1909) has discussed the origin of parasitic habits in cuckoos, and remarks on the lack of such habits among the cuckoos of America, where the cowbirds are parasitic.

Possibly a lack of attunement of the cyclical instincts occasionally seen in all birds, and rather more frequently in these cuckoos, may have been the starting point of the parasitic habit of *Cuculus, Canorus,* and related old-world genera.

Barrett (1910) believes that cuckoos, and other birds of similar habits, began to lay eggs in the nests of other species when their own nests were not ready and they were obliged to lay at once. The cowbirds in America show various degrees of parasitism. Those of some species build a rude nest on top of the one they have appropriated; others never build a nest and commonly throw one or more of the eggs or young of their host out of the nest.

Wheeler (1923) has shown clearly that social life is favorable for the development of parasitism. Wasmann (1909, 1911) holds that interspecific parasitism among ants has usually come from previous habits of robbery and slavery—though he also recognizes development through temporary parasitism, guest relations, and sudden mutations. Wheeler (1923) points out that parasitic social wasps usually lay their eggs in the nest of closely related species. They have no worker caste, but apparently descended from forms that did. Wheeler believes that trophallaxis, or mutual feeding, is largely responsible for social parasitism among ants.

Conditions Favoring Parasitism.—There are many conditions that lead to or favor parasitism. The ideal host for a parasite is one that is tolerant and at the same time resistant. It should live and furnish nourishment or other necessary things, but not interfere with the activities of its associate. Hosts usually have various means for preventing the entrance of or eliminating parasites. Furthermore, parasites compete among themselves, and the presence of one species may inhibit the entrance of another into the same host. A parasite encounters continual difficulties in finding, entering, and remaining in hosts, and must often enter into competition after it has gained a foothold. There are also many conditions of environment that may help or hinder parasites. The writer (1924a) has been able to show that wide range, ability to invade a variety of habitats, varied food, association with vegetation, and residence in shallow water are generally associated with a greater degree of parasitic infection among freshwater fishes. Blanchard (1907) found that a marmot could not be inoculated with trypanosomes, spirochætes, or trichinæ when it was in a hibernating state. Ewing (1912) states that widely distributed species of mites are often blood suckers, and thus are able to secure a large amount of food in a short time. He also says that wide distribution among mites is usually correlated with the presence of ambulatory legs, ovoviviparity and habits of laying eggs away from hosts, and considerable resistance to variations in temperature and moisture. Ewing also points out that restricting factors are endoparasitic habits, delicate and degenerate digestive organs, specialized adhering organs, inability to live away from a host on account of climate, inability to carry on locomotion when off a host, and adaptation to a solitary or monogamous host. Van Cleave (1921) shows that all of the four species of parasites that infest the American eel are acquired in freshwater; in the European eel, seven are acquired in freshwater and two in the ocean.

Antagonism between Parasites.—As has been suggested, the presence of certain parasites may prevent those of other species from infesting hosts. Wilson (1917) states that lernæpodid crustaceans and the glochidia of clams are, as a rule, mutually exclusive when occurring on fishes, but that a light infestation with one may not be sufficient to keep off the other parasite. Plath (1922) tells of a parasitic bee which will not tolerate another individual of its own species in the same nest. Semper (1881) noted that a parasitic isopod in one branchial chamber of a shrimp prevented the entrance of a parasite of the same species on the opposite side. Animals that have homes are more susceptible to infestation by parasites such as fleas, ticks, and bird lice than are those that wander about continually.

Qualities of Hosts.—A host has certain qualities that make it desirable or undesirable for a parasite. Brues (1908) in discussing hymenopteran parasites says that a host should be large enough to furnish food, but small enough to be completely consumed when the parasite is ready to pupate. A restricted habitat, such as that of a wood borer, usually limits the number of parasites that attack the occupant. Some hosts have few parasites because they pass through a short period when they are subject to attack. Van Cleave (1918) states that the seasonal distribution of acanthocephalans depends on the extent of time necessary for the infestation of a host, length of time the larval parasite must spend in an intermediate host, and seasonal changes in food habits or migrations of final hosts. Hosts are necessary for associated parasites in various ways and at various times. The parasites of birds going north during their spring migration may be quite different from those of the same species when going south in the autumn. The European salmon sheds certain parasites when it goes into freshwater and ceases to eat. Some hymenopterous parasites destroy their hosts after they attain their growth, others destroy the larvæ or food of their hosts, and others destroy only the reproductive individual in a colony. Leiby (1922) describes a chalcid which invades a caterpillar but allows the host to live as long as possible. It feeds first on its host's fat body, then its blood, devours the muscles and other tissues, and finally pupates in the skin.

Food Relations of Parasites to Hosts.—When parasites depend on their hosts for food, it is, of course, desirable to have the host injured as little as possible during the life of the parasite. A

parasite that kills its host before it has satisfied its own needs is
in a sense maladjusted and is not highly adapted in its host
relations.   Parasites have all sorts of food relations with their
hosts.   The crab (Pinnotheres) that lives in the oyster scrapes
mucous strings from the edges of the gills of its host, thus not
injuring the body of the oyster but continually stealing food.
Graenicher (1905) described a parasite that enters the nests of
bees and lays eggs.   The egg is deposited earlier than that of the
host; the larva grows faster, first devouring the food stores and
later killing the larva of the host.   Certain chalcids mate in the
open but deposit their eggs in ants' nests (Wheeler, 1907).   The
larvæ feed upon the bodies of ant pupæ, which are not killed, but
modified so that they develop into peculiar, dwarfed forms.
Haviland (1922) describes a hyperparasite that attacks a
chalcid which is parasitic on aphids.   This waits until its host
is full fed before depositing its egg and its larva then feeds and
pupates within the aphid skin.   Body lice must have a more or
less continual supply of nourishment; some ticks can live without
food for months.   The metabolism of both these arthropods is
adapted to a parasitic mode of life, yet how different are their
relations to their essential foods.

Structural Modifications of Parasites.—Parasites perhaps
furnish the most striking examples of adaptation to be found
among animals.   Their structures, physiological qualities, feeding habits, reproduction, and behavior are often specialized to a
high degree to fit particular hosts.   Ectoparasites are commonly
flattened; their organs of locomotion are often degenerate and
organs of fixation are commonly well developed; digestive
organs are adapted to continual feeding or have developed great
storage capacity so that an animal may gorge itself and then go
for a long time without food.   There are, of course, many exceptions to such general statements.   For example, fleas are compressed and are thus able to move about readily among the hairs
of mammals; they also possess unusual ability for locomotion.
Endoparasites are not so commonly flattened and many have lost
their symmetry of bodily form completely.   In all parasites there
is a tendency toward loss of organs of vision, and often of other
sense organs also.   Endoparasites commonly show a tendency
toward the loss of enteric organs and a high degree of specialization in structures and activities associated with reproduction.
The trends of adaptation associated with parasitism are nicely

illustrated in various groups of crustaceans. The free-living copepods, in general, resemble Cyclops in form. The ectoparasitic argulids have retained their ability to swim actively, but are very flat and have appendages modified into adhesive discs and hooks for clinging to their hosts. The lernæpodids have commonly taken up life as parasites among the gill filaments of fishes. They are thus protected by the opercula of their host and are surrounded more or less by the filaments. They show various degrees of lack of metamerism and definite form and in specialized species are shapeless sacs. Isopods show similar lines of specialization: the free-living species having natatory appendages; the ectoparasitic species having flattened bodies and appendages modified for clinging; the endoparasitic species in some cases being extremely degenerate—mere membranous sacs containing reproductive products (Caullery, 1922). Among some crustaceans the effects of parasitism are the more apparent because only the females are parasitic and the males resemble non-parasitic representatives of the groups to which they belong (Van Beneden, 1876). The same is true of certain mites (Ewing, 1912).

Specificity of Parasites for Particular Hosts.—All through the animal kingdom there are trends toward dependence—toward a narrow environment (Huxley, 1912). Among parasites this is often manifested by the remarkable degree of specificity shown in host relations. Though the glochidia of some species of freshwater mussels occur on several species of fishes, a considerable number are confined to a single species of host (Howard and Anson, 1922). Many species of crustaceans (Caullery, 1922), mites (Ewing, 1912), mallophagans, myrmecophilous beetles (Wheeler, 1907), and other animals are associated with a single host species, genus, or family. The malarial parasites of the genus Plasmodium are found only in man and in anopheline mosquitoes. Chance (1922) says that an individual cuckoo usually has parasitic relations with one other species of bird. He describes one cuckoo that laid twenty-one eggs during a season, all except one in nests of the meadow pipit.

Jammes and Mandoul (1905) believe that the specificity which certain cestodes show for particular hosts depends on fluids within the host. They point out certain instances where bactericides are the same in different species of parasites that occur in the same species of host and different in a single species of parasite

that occurs in various hosts.   Bactericides constitute one means
of defense that hosts may have against invasion by parasites.
In all cases where parasites are adjusted to hosts there must be
toleration of some sort.   The fact that parasites are often associated with closely related species suggests that food and body
substances may play a rôle in toleration.   The frequent association of parasites with organs that are least vital is another
factor.   Adjustments between parasites and their hosts are, like
all other adaptations, the outcome of long interactions between
hereditary tendencies, variations, environment, and selection.

Reproduction of Parasites.—Parasites usually show a high
degree of specialization in reproduction.   There are more or less
remarkable structural, physiological, and behavioristic adaptations for multiplication, fertilization, provision for offspring,
entrance into new hosts, etc.   As among many free-living animals
(rotifers, aphids), there is among parasites a pronounced tendency when conditions of life are favorable and food is abundant
to multiply by asexual methods or parthenogenesis.   The egg of
a chalcid within the body of a host may produce many adults
through polyembryony or germinogony (Patterson, 1921;
Brues, 1921).   Cestode tapeworms show an alternation of generations, the asexual proglottids in the intestine of the primary
host budding off proglottids that in turn give rise to zygotes.
Some cestodes have introduced another generation by the
multiplication of the cysticercus in the secondary host (*Tœnia
echinococcus*).   Digenetic trematodes commonly have an alternation between parthenogenetic and amphigenetic generations,
and there is among the former a considerable tendency among
different, or even in the same, species to continue the production
of individuals without the formation of zygotes.   There are a
number of cases of extreme sexual dimorphism among parasites.
Woodruffe-Peacock (1900) discusses the reproductive peculiarities
of the cuckoo in relation to parasitism.   The female usually lays
an egg on the ground, takes it in her beak, and places it in the
nest of her host, or she may lay directly in a nest if it is favorably
situated.   The egg is small and thus well suited to the nests of
small birds.   The female cuckoo may remove the eggs of the
host.   She or her young may shove the young of the host from
their nest.   The female does not leave her young to shift entirely
for themselves.   One braconid parasite is able to fly as soon as
it leaves its cocoon (Kelly, 1908).   A female of this insect may

mate within a minute and lay eggs within four minutes after she emerges. In many ways the reproductive activities of parasites are adapted to particular hosts and particular conditions of life, which is, of course, more or less true of all adaptations.

Life Cycles of Parasites.—The life cycles of parasites are also often adapted in a high degree to peculiarities of hosts. In some cases the timing and relations of particular stages in life cycles may have been established long in the past, before one animal became a parasite on another. Two species of robber-flies have a three-year life cycle that corresponds with that of the June beetle. The larvæ of these flies can exist for long periods without food and wander through the ground in search of the white grubs of the beetle (Davis, 1919). The adult June beetles are largely nocturnal and most of their parasites are the same. Many parasitic insects that infest other insects have shorter life cycles than their hosts (Withington, 1909). According to Brues (1908), hymenopterous parasites often have easier methods of acquiring food, develop more rapidly than their hosts, and may enter another host if the first becomes unsuitable. Clausen (1923) has described a parasitic insect that lays eggs in tree buds, where they remain for about eleven months, and only those that are in dead buds survive. The larva attaches itself to a wandering ant (Camponotus) worker which carries it back to the nest. The parasitic larva then sucks blood from the larvæ and pupæ of its hosts. One hyperparasite bores through a caterpillar to find its host, but does not emerge until its host leaves the body of its caterpillar (Brues, 1921). The parasite Psithyrus winters over like its bumble bee host, but does not emerge in the spring until the host has a well-established colony; the host queen is never killed until after she has begun to lay eggs, thus insuring a certain number of workers to carry on the labor in the colony (Sladen, 1921). Even endoparasites usually have stages for distribution in their life cycles and these are usually adapted so that new host individuals are infested.

Methods by Which Parasites Establish Relations with Hosts.—Parasites have many methods of establishing relations with new individuals of their usual host species. The first step is to leave the host individual, and this is usually brought about through the production of propagative phases. The liberation of parasites may be accomplished by the death of the host (Myxosporidia), discharge from ulcers (Guinea worm), transmission to an intermediate host, passing into the eggs of the host, being taken into a blood-sucking animal, the discharge of eggs or embryos through the natural openings (anus, nostril, urethra, etc.), the eating of encysted stages in body tissues, the active migration of adult parasites, etc. After parasites have left one individual they must be able to enter another. Ransom (1906), speaking particularly of domestic animals, has given an extensive account of methods of infestation. When a mammal dies, its lice creep out to the tips of the hairs and await the passing of another host. Dourine is transmitted from one horse to another during coition. Psithyrus finds its bumble bee host by odor (Sladen, 1912). Some wasps allow themselves to be caught by tiger beetle larvæ. Then one of these wasps stings its captor to death, pokes it into its burrow, attaches an egg to it, and fills in the burrow. Withington (1909) describes an insect parasite that lays eggs on aphids. Its host runs away but, after waiting a moment, it persistently keeps up the pursuit and finally deposits its eggs. Malarial parasites are injected into man's blood in the saliva of a mosquito. Filarial worms are also carried by mosquitoes, but bore through the skin through their own efforts. Hookworm larvæ enter man from polluted soil by boring through the skin. Most trematodes enter their primary hosts with food as encysted forms, but the cercariæ of the schistosomes bore through the skin. The cysts of lung flukes (Paragonimus) commonly occur in crabs and crayfishes; those of the common liver fluke (Fasciola) are found on vegetation. Trichina and tapeworms enter man encysted in flesh. Acanthocephalans are ingested in June beetles by hogs.

Number of Parasites Occurring in Single Hosts.—The number of parasites that may infest an animal is sometimes remarkable. Practically every dogfish (Amia) supports twenty or thirty tapeworms. Sometimes portions of a fish's intestine will be actually lined with a velvety coating of small acanthocephalans. Howard and Anson (1922) found that fishes were capable of carrying from 250 to 2500 glochidia without serious injury, but usually had very much less. The number of chalcid larvæ produced by polyembryony varies in certain species according to the size of the host (Brues, 1908). Leiby (1922) found that one of these chalcids (*Copidosoma gelechiæ*) averaged 163 to a host, which was finally nothing but a shell containing pupæ in separate compartments. Thomson (1911) tells of collecting 553 Pieris caterpillars, 422 of which died from the ichneumon parasites. Every drop of blood in a man's body may contain from 200 to 300 larvæ of filarial worms; his intestine may support as many as 4000 hookworms.

Effects of Parasites on Hosts.—Parasites produce various effects on their hosts. By taking food, secreting toxins, occluding passages and in other ways they may retard growth, cause the host to live on in poor condition, become sexually impotent, assume new forms, produce galls, or die. Hosts often react to the presence of parasites by building up various defenses to combat them. The skins and the peristaltic movements in the intestines of vertebrates to a certain degree keep out or tend to pass out parasites. If the tissues of the host are infected, there may be a fibrous investment formed by the host around the parasite. Leucocytes and antibodies also serve as deterrents or preventives for parasites. A host that has enough devices to prevent a parasite from establishing or maintaining relations with it has immunity. This may be natural or acquired. The black bass becomes immune to glochidia after passing through two to five periods of infestation (Arey, 1923). Highly organized animals may take various active measures to rid themselves of parasites or prevent infestation. The beaver has a specially modified louse claw, with which it combs its fur. The kangaroo rat avoids warble-flies by strict adherence to nocturnal habits (Vorhies and Taylor, 1922), and the reindeer escapes the same parasites to some degree by frequenting wind-swept coastal barrens during the summer. The pelicans along the coast of Peru rinse the insides of their pouches with sea water to get rid of bird lice. Many birds dust their feathers at intervals to fill up the tracheal tubes of arthropodan pests.

Many of the influences exerted by parasites on hosts are rather subtle and not clearly understood. Potts (1909) claims that the parasitism of male spider crabs by Sacculina causes the assumption of female characters. Most such cases of parasitic castration merely cause the continuation of juvenile conditions, or, in other words, a failure to mature. Crickets, termites, and ants are often sterile and unusually large when parasitized. Parasites in many cases undoubtedly cause alterations in the body fluids of hosts, introducing toxins which interfere with normal activities or substances that have other effects. They may extract substances that would normally be present.

Animal Galls.—Animal galls are produced on a variety of hosts by parasites. Corals are thus modified by crustaceans, worms, and other animals. Pycnogonids cause galls on campanularian hydroids; glochidia on fishes; copepods on ophiurioids and in sea-urchins; myzostomes and other animals on crinoids.

CHAPTER XII

ECONOMIC RELATIONS OF ECOLOGY

There has long been interaction between man and other organisms on the earth. Some of these organisms have long been beneficial and others have been injurious to man. Since man has been able to carry along the ever-increasing heritage of civilization from one generation to another, he has taken a continually more dominant position. Man has transformed considerable areas of the earth's surface in order to make them more suitable to his needs. The savage gained his living in the environment without essentially changing it, but with the growth of civilization and the increasing influence of commerce and money, things that interfere with the activities of man have come to be pests and many of those that lend themselves to man's support or pleasure have been fostered and increased. Today it is the duty of man as the present dominant species to consider carefully the plant and animal populations of the earth in order that they may long continue to furnish food and other necessities for the human race. Ecology is intimately concerned with the solution of this conservation problem, which is perennial. It will never be solved completely because conditions on the earth change continually and because the interests of all individuals are not the same.

Man has two activities that are more or less antagonistic. If he increases his numbers and his dominance, there is a tendency to eliminate organisms and habitats that may be economically productive. If he conserves his natural resources, he must do so by controlling his natural instincts for destruction or by inventing new means for increasing production. Savages are few in numbers and gain their living from nearly primeval habitats. The pioneer hunts, clears away timber, breaks the sod, and raises crops or flocks. After him come railroads and cities. Man destroys and plants, changes the soil, introduces new plants and animals, changes the vegetation cover by grazing his domestic animals, and in other ways changes the environment.

371

Influence of Man on Environment in Scotland.—Ritchie (1920) has considered man's influence in Scotland very thoroughly. He discusses changes that came about through the introduction of sheep, cattle, and horses; those that came through deliberate destruction of animals for safety, food, skins, oil, the eradication of pests, and sport; those that came with the destruction of forests and the cultivation of soil; and those that were associated with the presence of new animals that resulted from commerce. Ritchie points out that, though large animals have gradually decreased, the total number of animals per acre has generally increased. He cites instances where rabbits, sheep, and goats have kept forests from developing. He also describes an interesting case where the protection of gulls on a moor led to the growth of grass and dock and a great decrease in the number of grouse. When the gulls were no longer protected, heather returned to the area and grouse again became common. Forbes and Gross (1922) have pointed out that birds are not changed to any extent by man's modification of their environment, but seek out the habitats that most nearly resemble those they occupied before. Prairie birds come to live in pastures; thicket birds turn to orchards.

Resources in the Ocean.—Ritter (1918) has discussed the probable permanence of man's natural food resources and concludes that those derived from pelagic fishes are least likely to be depleted. In the north Pacific man derives food from fishes, molluscs, turtles, birds, mammals, and algæ. He obtains important fertilizers from seaweeds, whales, fishes, and other sources. The scraps from various marine industries furnish poultry food. Clothing, furs, leather, buttons, and derivatives of algæ that serve for stiffening come from the sea. Oils are furnished by fishes, and whales. Ornaments and curios come from various animals. Algæ supply various substances, such as agar and potassium iodide. The Pacific coast of North America furnishes a billion barrels of fish annually. Aquatic habitats are especially subject to pollution by wastes resulting from the activities of man. Such contamination may not only destroy food resources, but also be inimical to the happiness and health of man.

Science and Industry.—Man's success depends on his ability to become adjusted to his environment and every variation that helps or hinders his success is of economic importance. Yet scientific knowledge and research cannot and should not be entirely devoted to or dominated by economic considerations. Howell (1921) has stressed the value of pure as well as applied science. Sumner (1910) says:

To the reader who would demand an exact economic equivalent for the labor and money here expended our answer must be a more general one. Science and industry move together. Industry is helpless without the aid of science, and the greatest industrial progress is at present being made by those countries which realize this fact most fully. But science can never prosper if forced to play the rôle of a servant. She must be free to pursue her own ends without being halted at every step by the challenge: *cui bono?* The attempt to restrict our scientific experts to problems of obvious economic importance would be equivalent to depriving ourselves of their services altogether. It is today accepted as a commonplace that all the great discoveries of practical value have resulted ultimately upon principles first brought to light to the student of nature.

Science is related to industry and economic problems, at times as a commensal, at times as a symbiont, and, it is regretfully admitted, sometimes as a parasite. Ecology, like other branches of science, should not be dominated by industry, but, on the other hand, it should not ignore industry. Environment is and will continue to be modified by man and his civilization. The world will never be primeval again and ecology must "carry on" in the world as it is and will be. It, therefore, seems appropriate to devote this chapter to a brief consideration of the economic relations of ecology.

Food Production.—Man requires a continual supply of organic food, the constituents of which have a reasonable degree of balance in chemical constitution and calorific value, and that contains an adequate supply of vitamines. Plants, directly or indirectly, are the basis for the chief foods consumed by man. Waterman (1917) has pointed out that ecology can contribute to plant production by developing general principles that may improve quality or increase productivity and by furnishing knowledge for specific crop problems. Ecologists should know the optimum conditions under which particular plants live and how such conditions may be preserved or brought about. The knowledge of the principles of production is much better for those crops that grow on land than it is for those that develop in water. Even scientific men are barely beginning to speak of aquiculture in terms of bushels or pounds per acre. With greater knowledge it will doubtless be possible to exercise more or less control over production in bodies of freshwater that are limited in extent and in favorable areas in the shallow waters of the ocean, but the great reaches of the open sea will probably long remain free from regulations of civilization, except those that relate to restrictions of fishing.

Increasing Food Resources.—The increase of food resources may be accomplished by the discovery of new foods, better methods of propagation, better ability to forecast favorable seasons or years for the gathering or producing of particular foods, the education of persons concerned in production, the limitation of the use of animals during comparatively valueless stages, which may be of greater value at other times. Ocean-ographic exploration led to the discovery of the fishing grounds for the delectable tilefish and the valuable deep-water prawn fisheries of Norway. The scientific study of the life histories and migrations of the salmon along the Pacific coast of America has made it possible to predict years when there will be heavy or light catches. The European oceanographers have been able to make similar predictions for mackerel fishermen through scientific knowledge concerning the relation of sunlight to the production of diatoms and copepods. In many countries there are laws which limit, at certain periods, the use of animals for food, when such use may be expensive because animals will be of greater value if allowed to grow to larger size or because the use of certain individuals may interfere with the normal increase of the species concerned. In aquatic habitats especially, there is need of greater knowledge of the fundamental principles of pro-duction. This is largely because many aquatic plants and animals are microscopic and reproduce rapidly. On land the approximate rate of increase of food plants and animals is rather well known, but the rate of growth and of multiplication of most aquatic organisms and the factors that control such increases are not well known. Production on land is easier to understand also because it is confined to a rather thin stratum at the surface, but aquatic habitats may be more or less productive at all depths. Increase in productiveness depends on the knowledge of the effects of fluctuations in various ecological factors. Food must be produced in an environment.

Production may be decreased through the introduction by man of influences that make the environment unfavorable for particular food animals, by depletion through the removal or destruction of too large a number of animals in a particular area, and by other acts of man. Pollution and dams have decreased the number of fishes that are taken from many streams and no other food resources compensate for such losses. The buffalo once grazed in countless herds over the prairies of North America, but can never do so again, and their place has been taken by beef cattle. These two instances illustrate the contrast between the results of the exploitation of natural food resources in terrestrial and aquatic habitats. Agriculture is developed to such a degree that it easily supplies food that is equal to or exceeds that which an area furnished under primeval conditions, but aquiculture is rarely able to do this. From another point of view, water areas for the production of human food have the advantage in their present state of development that they require little labor except that of gathering the crop. One service that ecology can perform is to point the way to more scientific methods of aquiculture. At present the human race takes natural products from aquatic habitats without much knowledge or thought of conserving and increasing production. In the oceans, the cooler parts are most productive of human foods and most difficult for navigation. All aquatic food resources are being slowly but surely depleted by overfishing. Such depletion is, of course, slower in the ocean than in freshwater.

It is possible that civilization may in time reach such a state that man will cover the whole earth with his activities; that available energy may be utilized to such a degree that food production will be entirely under control through the use of artificial light, the exploitation of domesticated plants and animals, etc. But if such a state is ever reached, it will be far in the future, and many generations must worry over the relations between food production and environment.

Environment and Health.—Huntington (1922) has made it clear that man is influenced to a considerable extent by his environment. Not only is this true of the general condition of man in regard to health, but the amount of work that man may accomplish from day to day and his attainments through successive generations are controlled more or less by climatic conditions. In other words, the type of civilization that man develops and the level that any type may attain depend on environment. Areas that have variable climates and favorable conditions of humidity have often permitted the development of a high state of culture; in arid areas with monotonous climates the human race is usually in a low state of civilization. Climate exerts influences on man through effects produced on his physiological condition, so that he may be in one locality lazy, unambitious, worried, and unproductive, and in another locality quite the opposite. Such effects are also often brought about because the environment is favorable for the propagation and spread of diseases.

The increasing recognition of the importance of knowledge concerning the environmental relations of diseases has caused great interest in the study of the ecology of parasites and other scourges of the human race. The only large unoccupied land areas that are favorable for the production of food by man are in the tropics. Parasitic diseases have long held back civilization in these beautiful and fertile regions, and an understanding of their ecology has already in many districts made conditions of living more favorable. The decline of Greek culture is assigned by many to the effects of malaria. The knowledge of the means of transmission of such diseases as malaria, yellow fever, dengue, and filariasis by mosquitoes has opened up new possibilities of living for the human race. The recognition of the importance of soil pollution as the chief factor in hookworm infestation has enabled people in great regions of the tropics to live in a better way. Knowledge of the life history of the flukes of the genus Schistosoma has made it possible for orientals to raise rice without danger of suffering and death.

There is need at present for more knowledge concerning the ecology of the organisms that cause diseases and a large number of investigators are at work. There is also a great lack of knowledge concerning the life histories and ecology of parasites in general, and this field is a promising one for research.

Water Supply and Pollution.—The bodies of freshwater from which man derives the water to supply his physiological and industrial needs and into which he discharges various wastes that result from his activities also serve as habitats for many aquatic organisms. Knowledge of the interrelations between man and the organisms in freshwater is, therefore, of prime importance. Often there is conflict between the interests of particular industries or other activities of man and those of freshwater animals. The conditions that maintain pure, healthful streams, ponds, ocean, and lake shores often conflict with those that are favorable to the cheap disposal of sewage and factory wastes and to the development of water power.

A sanitary engineer looks upon sewage disposal as a legitimate function of a river. The discharge of a large amount of organic material into a stream may act as a fertilizing agent and result in a great increase in the quantity of animal life; it may have little effect because the stream quickly exercises its powers of self-purification; or it may produce pollution. The discharge of sewage into a stream should be undertaken with forethought and knowledge of the probable effects. Forbes (1919) has made a rather extensive study of the effects of the sewage from Chicago on the Illinois River. Purdy (1923) has made similar investigations in the Ohio River, and Suter and Moore (1922) in the streams of New York. Forbes found that most species of fishes were driven downstream and the upper reaches of the river became in a sense an aquatic desert. The fishing for a time improved below the region of pollution and later decreased. Baker (1920) noted that sewage in the Genesee River caused a complete absence of snails, but the river was slowly repopulated when the amount of sewage was reduced. Jackson (1922) studied the marine fishes along the coast of New Hampshire and concluded that certain species had been exterminated. The unfavorable conditions in this instance were largely brought about by the construction of dams across rivers, and the pollution of the littoral water by wastes from a navy yard and oil-burning steamers.

Shelford (1919, 1920) has stressed the importance of the study of pollution. He suggests that many substances that now do harm as wastes and are therefore expensive to the community as a whole may, if saved, be made to pay wholly or in part for the expense involved in developing and using new methods of disposal. Suter and Moore (1922) have classified trade wastes in the following order according to their degree of toxicity to fishes:

Sawdust and treated sewage—no dilution required.

Raw sewage and fiber factory wastes—require dilution of 1:10.

Spent dyes and paper-mill wastes from 1:10 to 1:100.

Gas manufacture wastes and wastes from bleacheries—from 1:100 to 1:1000.

Caustic lime and mercuric chloride—1:1000 to 1:10,000.

Lime, strong acids, gas tar—1:10,000 to 1:100,000.

Copper sulphate, bleaching powder—greater than 1:1,000,000.

Pests.—The problems relating to the control or eradication of pests are, as a rule, ecological. The efforts of man to combat animals that cause economic losses are often of no avail because the ecology of the problem is not thoroughly understood. A struggle against an animal pest is now commonly initiated by a detailed study of behavior, habits, and life histories. The worst pests among plant lice are said to be among species that migrate readily. Sattlewait (1921) observed that billbugs injured corn in a certain field each year, but after an adjacent area of cat-tails, which harbored the pest, was plowed under, there was no more trouble. Cooper (1922) found that birds and certain plants had important relations to the control of white pine blister rust. He observed that forest birds did not feed on fruits and scatter seeds to any extent, but those that frequented open ground commonly did so. The wild gooseberry was thus planted in pastures and other cleared lands and there harbored the blister rust. Wheeler (1911) tells how ants help to increase aphids on melon vines by destroying the enemies of these pests. Barber (1925) makes the following comments on the corn borer:

Among the factors which may be held accountable for the decrease of numbers of the European corn borer in New England in 1923, the subnormal temperatures which prevailed during the oviposition season in the late summer played an important part. The probable longer periods of life of adults, caused by low temperatures, served to spread oviposition over a relatively longer period, which was favorable to the development of the egg parasite, *Trichogramma minitum* Riley, and the relatively fewer eggs deposited per female probably served to increase the importance of the parasite.

This is ecology.

Methods of Combating Pests.—Pests are commonly attacked by man during those periods in their life histories when they are more vulnerable or more easily accessible. Rats are hunted with ferrets; foxes are pursued with dogs. Against insects, parasites and predaceous enemies are commonly employed. Such allies of man as ichneumons, evanids, chalcids, tachinids, and fungi are reared and scattered about in localities where they will be of most value. The detailed knowledge of the habitats of various species of mosquitoes in regard to habitat selection and environmental conditions has been of great value in campaigns against malaria, yellow fever, and filariasis. Connor (1921) was able to free Guayaquil from yellow fever by using minnows that cost about half a cent each.

Damage by Pests.—The amount of damage done by pests is often astounding. Sometimes such damage is quite apparent, but in other cases it may remain unnoticed. The fact that ship-worms and other pile bores caused losses of $15,000,000 along the San Francisco water front during the years 1920 and 1921 attracts attention. On the other hand, grasshoppers sit in every field and, unless present in great numbers, remain unnoticed. Shull (Ruthven, 1911) found that in eastern Michigan grass-hoppers in a field of blue grass and timothy averaged 12.9 inches apart, and a single grasshopper ate 50.4 inches (127 milligrams) of grass blades in twenty-four hours. He says: "I compute that the grasshoppers in a field of 27 acres may, in a grasshopper year, devour 1 ton of cured hay per week."

Pests Due to Man's Activities.—Some animals may become pests because they are protected by man. Fishing is often restricted by law to sportmen's methods; undesirable fishes are thus not caught and increase beyond their normal numbers. Geese and ducks are protected in Alaska, where they do much damage by destroying herring eggs. Such conditions raise prob-lems that should be the subject of ecological study.

The introduction of animals into new areas is often associated with disastrous consequences to man. Familiar examples are the introduction of the rabbit into Australia, the mongoose into Hayti, and the English sparrow into the United States. The offspring of four American muskrats introduced on an estate near Prag multiplied and finally became such a pest that stringent laws were passed to limit their spread. Huey (1925) has given a graphic account of the results of the introduction of goats on Guadalupe Island by whalers.

The place proved to be a goats' paradise, for with plenty of low herb-age and not a single enemy, they had life their own sweet way. They increased by tens of hundreds, devouring everything green that was in sight and gnawing their way into the very heart of the primeval forest . . . In spite of the damage to Guadalupe Island's bird and plant life that must already have been wrought by mice, cats and goats, Dr. Edward Palmer, well-known government botanist, who visited it in 1875, described it as a "naturalist's paradise." It would seem, however, that he arrived only in the nick of time to secure a few of the vanishing birds and plants and thus preserve their memory forever in the annals of science.

In 1923, the condition of the island has well been described as that of a "biological sepulcher."

Animal Products.—Animal products that depend on the exploitation, and often also on the slaughter, of wild animals have usually decreased steadily until the supply has become so depleted that legal restrictions have been necessary. This has been the history of seal skins and other furs, shells and pearls, fishes, whales, plumes, and other natural resources. In some cases man has introduced factors into the environment that have made conditions unfavorable for the animals concerned, but most such resources have been depleted by overhunting and overfishing. Some animal products do not require the death of the animals furnishing them. According to Coker (1919) a million gannets are capable of producing about 11,400 tons of guano each year on the coast of Peru, and even more is deposited by cormorants. A large part of the revenue received by the Peruvian government is derived from the droppings of these birds, and they are carefully protected.

Domesticated Animals.—The environment of domesticated animals can often be adjusted so as to be more favorable. In general, animals do best when they are provided with room for exercise, shelter, and proper food. A ration must not only contain proteins, carbohydrates, fats, water, and minerals, but also possess a naturalness that is supplied by green foods which contain vitamines. Poultry also require light. Fox farms that are kept free from hookworms are generally most productive. In a locality where ticks are prevalent, cattle may be deficient in milk flow, flesh, and reproductive capacity. The frequent dipping of animals or the eradication of ticks by other means may transform an unfavorable environment into a favorable one. In some countries where ticks are prevalent zebus have been crossed with common cattle and a short-haired race that does not readily harbor ticks has thus been introduced. Other attempts to produce domestic animals that have greater resistance to unfavorable environmental conditions have been made by crossing yaks, buffalo, and other animals with domestic cattle. Crosses between horses and asses have produced large and sturdy draft animals. The growth of the dairy industry in New Zealand furnishes an excellent illustration of how the successful raising of domestic animals depends on environment. In many parts of the earth man has learned by experience what types of animals are best suited to local climatic conditions. Agriculture now has a considerable body of such knowledge, and more is being accumulated continually.

Soil and Soil Products.—Every farmer knows that certain soils are suited to certain crops and considerable progress has been made in the scientific study of soils. A farmer can have soil samples analyzed and receive a prescription that will enable him to apply appropriate materials to make it more productive. The study of the animals that live in the soil and the effects of these on soil productiveness is still new. Soil bacteria are rather well known; soil protozoans and nematodes have been studied somewhat, but much remains to be learned concerning the ecology of soil organisms.

One of the great injuries that man has perpetrated is the denudation of the soil. It may take long ages to build up a humus soil that can support the climax plant formation for a locality. When man removes the vegetation, the nutrition is washed away and leached out. It may take centuries to repair such damage. The loss of vegetation may also decrease the water-holding capacity of the soil, make a dearth of food and shelter for animals, and may be an important cause of disastrous floods. Recent observations indicate that the ashes resulting from forest fires may cause the death of trout in the streams that drain burned-over areas.

Conservation.—Conservation is concerned with the preservation of natural habitats, the keeping of the environment suitable for human and animal habitation, and the utilization and preservation of natural resources.

The preservation of natural habitats is important for scientists because primeval conditions are essential for certain types of ecological study. It is also often associated with the preservation of species of animals that depend upon a particular environmental complex and cannot adapt themselves to areas that have been occupied by the activities associated with civilization. In many cases forests have been wastefully cut away and swamps have been thoughtlessly drained when untouched, natural habitats would have been of more value to the human race. Natural areas have great value in relation to the pleasure, recreation, and health of men. Such tracts when wisely administered may pay dividends to many instead of furnishing a living for a few.

As the earth becomes more thickly populated, it becomes more and more necessary to keep natural habitats from being ruined by carelessness or the by-products of man's activities. Laws to prevent the introduction of plants and animals that may become pests and laws that prohibit contamination of habitats by wastes are increasingly necessary.

Obstacles to Conservation.—One of the worst obstacles to conservation is a lack of uniformity in the laws of contiguous states or countries. If a fisherman in one state is not allowed to catch fishes of a particular species that are less than 10 inches in length, while his neighbor in a state across the river can keep fishes of the same species that are 8 inches long, he naturally feels like breaking the law. If the sale of short lobsters is prohibited in one state and ignored in an adjacent state, the traffic tends to prevail in both states.

Another great obstacle to conservation is business "interests." Persons interested in making money from a particular natural resource may obtain concessions or have favorable laws passed that injure the community as a whole, and such privileges often pass unnoticed or without interest by those who are injured. In general, the sizes of fishes that may be sold has been continually made smaller in order to continue established business or to expand it. A lack of fish foods, paper pulp, and other products that might be conserved is threatened by lack of interest or thought.

It is possible that future generations may divert all the water from Niagara Falls in order to produce power. Perhaps such use of this natural resource may be for the general benefit of the human race. If such a change does come about, however, it is to be hoped that it will result from careful consideration by scientists, altruists, and business men, not as a result of privileges obtained by "special interests."

BIBLIOGRAPHY

A

AARON, S. F., 1909, Sci. Amer. Suppl., 68: 29–30.

ABBOTT, C. C., 1870, Amer. Nat., 4: 385–391.

ABBOTT, J. F., 1913, Biol. Bull., 24: 169–174.

ACKERT, J. E., 1914, J. Morphol., 25: 301–344.

ADAMS, C. C., 1901, Amer. Nat., 35: 839–852; 1902, Biol. Bull., 3: 115–158; 1904, Science, 19: 210–211; 1905, 9:53–71; 1906, Mich. Geol. Surv., Ann. Rept. (1905): 1–133; 1907, Science, 25: 897–901; 1908, Auk, 15: 109–153; 1909, An Ecological Survey of Isle Royal, Lake Superior, Lansing, xiv + 468.

ADAMS, L. E., 1908, Zoölogist, (4) 12: 9–12; 1910, M. & P. Manchester. Lit. & Philos. Soc., 54: 1–13.

ADAMSTONE, F. B., 1923, U. Toronto Stud. Biol. Sci., 22: 69–119; 1924, *Ibid.*, 24: 43–70; 1924a, *Ibid.*, 24: 73–100.

ADAMSTONE, F. B., and W. J. K. HARKNESS, 1923, *Ibid.*, 22: 121–170.

ADOLPH, E. F., 1925, Biol. Bull., 48: 327–335.

AGASSIZ, A., 1912, P. 7th Intern. Zoöl. Cong., 7: 55–59.

AINSLIE, C. N., 1906, Canad. Entom., 38: 44.

AITKEN, E. H., 1902, J. Bombay Nat. Hist. Soc., 14: 162–163.

AKEHURST, S. C., 1922, J. Roy. Micr. Soc., (1922): 341–372.

ALBERT, PRINCE OF MONACO, 1898, Nature, 58: 200–204.

ALDRICH, J. M., and L. A. TURLEY, 1899, Amer. Nat., 33: 809–812.

ALEXANDER, H. G., 1915, Brit. Birds, 8: 184–192.

ALLEE, W. C., 1912, J. Exper. Zoöl., 13: 269–344; 1919, Biol. Bull., 36: 96–104; 1920, Program, Abstracts of Papers and List of Members, Amer. Soc. Zoöl., Philadelphia, 1–75; 1921, *Ibid.*, Toronto, 1–80; 1922, *Ibid.*, Boston, 1–100; 1923, Biol. Bull., 44: 167–191; 1923, *Ibid.*, 44: 205–253; 1923c, Ecology, 4: 341–354; 1923d, Condor, 25: 129–131; 1923e, Anat. Rec., 6: 326–427; 1924, *Ibid.*, 29: 128.

ALLEN, B. M., 1912, Science, 35: 939.

ALLEN, E. J., 1909, J. Mar. Biol. Assn., Plymouth, 8: 394–406.

ALLEN, J. A., 1890, B. Amer. Mus. Nat. Hist., 3: 41–44; 1894, *Ibid.*, 6: 107–128; 1907, Smithsonian Rept., (1905): 375–402.

ALLEN, W. E., 1920, U. Cal. Publ. Zoöl., 22: 1–292; 1921, Ecology, 2: 26–31.

ALLEN, W. R., 1921, Biol. Bull., 40: 210–241; 1922, Copeia, 108; 52–54; 1922a, P. Ind. Acad. Sci., (1921): 227–238.

ALM, G., 1922, Meddel., Kungl., Lantbrukss., 236: 1–176.

ANDERSON, M. P., 1907, Science, 2: 938.

ANDREWS, R. C., 1909, Bull. Amer. Mus. Nat. Hist., 26: 213–226.

ANNANDALE, N., 1902, P. Roy. Phys. Soc. Edinburgh, 14: 439–444; 1907, Rec. Indian Mus., 1: 83.

ANTHONY, A. W., 1923, J. Mammal., 4: 60–61.
APSTEIN, C., 1910, Intern. Rev. Ges. Hydrobiol. u Hydrogr., 3: 17–33.
AREY, L. B., 1923, J. Exper. Zoöl., 38: 377–381.
AREY, L. B., and W. J. CROZIER, 1921, J. Exper. Zoöl., 32: 443–502.
ARNOLD, A. F., 1901, The Sea Beach at Ebb-tide, N. Y., xii + 429.
ARRHENIUS, O., 1921, Ecology, 2: 255–257.
ASTLEY, H. D., 1916, Ibis., (10) 4: 337–340.
ATKINS, W. R. G., 1923a, J. Mar. Biol. Assn., Plymouth, 13: 93–118;
    1923b, Ibid., 13: 119–150; 1923c, Ibid., 3: 160–163.

B

BABCOCK, S. M., 1912, U. Wis. Agr. Exp. Stat. Res. Bull., 22: 87–181.
BACOT, A., 1908, Nature, 78: 509.
BAHR, P. H., 1907, Brit. Birds, 1: 17–22, 40–43; 1907a, Ibid., 1: 202–207.
BAILEY, I. W., 1920, Ecology, 1: 174–189.
BAILEY, V., 1896, Science, 3: 250–251; 1893, U. S. Dept. Agr., Biol. Surv.
    Bull., 4: 1–69; 1893a, Ibid., 5: 1–47; Sci. Mo., 17: 66–76.
BAKER, A. C., and W. F. TURNER, 1916, J. Agr. Res., 7: 321–325.
BAKER, F. C., 1910, Bull. Ill. State Lab. Nat. Hist., 8: 441–449; 1918 Tech.
    Publ. 8, N. Y. State Col. Forestr., 1–264; 1919, Science, 49: 519–521;
    1920, Amer. Nat., 54: 152–161; 1924, T. Wis. Acad. Sci., Arts, Lett.,
    21: 109–146.
BAKER, F. S., C. F. KORSTIAN, and A. J. FETHEROLF, 1921, Ecology, 2:
    304–310.
BAKER, H. B., 1914, Rept. Mich. Acad. Sci., 15: 18–45; 1922, Occ. Pap. Mus.
    Zoöl., U. Mich., 106: 1–94.
BALES, B. R., 1907, Entom. News, 18: 402.
BALSS, H., 1924, Zeitschr., Morphol. Oekol. d. Tiere, 1: 752–792.
BANKS, N., 1902, J. N. Y. Entom. Soc., 10: 209–214.
BANTA, A. M., 1907, Publ. Carnegie Inst., Washington, 67: 1–114; 1910,
    J. Exper. Zoöl., 8: 243–310; 1912, Science, 36, 460; 1916, P. Nat.
    Acad. Sci., 2: 578–583; 1917, Anat. Rec., 11: 1–2; 1918, P. Nat. Acad.
    Sci., 4: 373–379.
BANTA, A. M., and W. L. McATEE, 1906, P. U. S. Nat. Mus., 30: 67–83.
BARBER, G. W., 1925, Ecology, 6: 39–42.
BARBER, H. G., 1913, J. N. Y. Entom. Soc., 21: 29–32.
BARBER, H. S., 1913, P. Biol. Soc. Wash., 26: 185–190.
BARKER, C. N., 1918, S. Afr. J. Nat. Hist., 1: 99–105.
BARRELL, J., 1916, Bull. Geol. Soc. Amer., 27: 40–41, 387–436; 1917, Sci.
    Mo., 4: 16–26.
BARRELL, J., C. SCHUCKERT, L. L. WOODRUFF, R. S. LULL, and E. HUNT-
    INGTON, 1918, The Evolution of the Earth and Its Inhabitants, New
    Haven, xi + 208.
BARRETT, C. L., 1910, Smithsonian Rept., (1909): 487–492.
BATCHELDER, C. H., 1915, Nautilus, 29: 43–46.
BATES, C. G. and R. ZON, 1922, U. S. Dept. Agr. Bull., 1059: 1–208.
BATES, H. W., 1892, The Naturalist on the River Amazon, London, lxxxix +
    395.

BATESON, W., 1890, Phil. T. Roy. Soc. London, 180B: 297–330; 1913, Problems of Genetics, New Haven, xii + 258.

BATHER, F. A., 1920, Science, U. S., 52: 257–264.

BAUMANN, H., 1922, Zoöl. Jahrb. Syst., 45: 501–556.

BAUMGARTNER, W. J., 1905, Science, 21: 855.

BAYLISS, W. M., 1918, Principles of General Physiology, London, xxiv + 858.

BEAL, W. J., 1900, Rept. Mich. Acad. Sci., 1: 132–133.

BEAUCHAMP, P. DE., 1907, Arch. Zoöl., (4) 7, iv–xvi.

BEAUCHAMP, P. DE, 1923, Arch. Zoöl. Exper., 61: 455–520.

BECQUEREL, P., 1915, Smithsonian Rept., (1914): 537–551.

BEDDARD, F. E., 1895, A Textbook of Zoögeography, Cambridge, viii + 246; 1900, A Book of Whales, London, xv + 320.

BEEBE, C. W., 1906, The Log of the Sun, N. Y., xii + 345; 1922, The Edge of the Jungle, N. Y., vii + 303.

BEETHAM, B., 1912, Smithsonian Rept., (1911): 433–439.

BEHRE, E. H., 1918, Biol. Bull., 35: 277–317.

BELT, C., 1874, Naturalist in Nicaragua, London, xxxiv + 306.

BERRY, E. W., 1918, Science, 47: 612–615.

BEERMAN, H., 1924, J. Exper. Zoöl., 41: 33–43.

BIANCO, S. L., 1911, M. T. Zoöl. Stat. Neapel, 20: 129–156.

BIGELOW, N. K., 1923, U. Toronto Stud., Fish Lab., 22: 41–66.

BILLUPS, A. C., 1903, Nautilus, 16: 112–114.

BIRD, H., 1921, Ecology, 2: 193–197; 1923, *Ibid.*, 4: 293–296.

BIRGE, E. A., 1897, T. Wis. Acad. Sci., Arts, Lett., 11: 274–448; 1900, Science, 11: 253–255; 1904, T. Amer. Micr. Soc., 25: 1–33; 1907, T. Amer. Fish. Soc., (1907): 223–241; 1913, Science, U. S., 38: 702-704.

BIRGE, E. A., and C. JUDAY, 1908, T. Wis. Acad. Arts, Sci., Lett., 16: 1–9; 1911, Wis. Geol. & Nat. Hist. Surv. Bull., 22, Sci, S. 7: xx + 259; 1914, U. S. Bur. Fish., 32: 525–609; 1921, *Ibid.*, 37: 209–252.

BISHOP, G. H., 1923, J. Morphol., 37: 533–553.

BLANCHARD, R., and M. BLATIN, 1907, Arch. Parasit., Paris, 11: 361–378.

BLANFORD, W. G. H., 1899, T. Entom. Soc., London, (1899): v–viii.

BLEGVAD, H., 1915, Rept. Danish Biol. Sta., 22: 41–78; 1916, *Ibid.*, 24: 17–72; 1922, P. Zoöl. Soc. London, 1: 27–32.

BLUM, H. F., 1922, U. Cal. Publ. Zoöl., 22: 349–368.

BODINE, J. H., 1923, J. Exper. Zoöl., 37: 115–125; 1923a, *Ibid.*, 37:457–476.

BOHN, G., 1911, J. An. Behav., 1:448–455.

BONSTEEL, J. A., 1912, U. S. Dept. Agr., Bur. Soils, Circ. 69:174; 1912a, *Ibid.*, Circ. 58: 1–21.

BORRADAILE, L. A., 1921, M. & P. Manchester Lit. & Phil. Soc., 55: 1–11; 1923, The Animal and Its Environment, London, vii + 399.

BOULENGER, G. A., 1899, P. Zoöl. Soc., London, (1898): 851–852; 1912, *Ibid.*, (1912): 19–22.

BOURIE, 1912, C. R. Acad. Sci., Paris T. 155: 1043–1046.

BOUVIER, E. L., 1905, Smithsonian Rept. (1904): 469–484; 1922, The Psychic Life of Insects, N. Y., xviii + 377; 1895, Ann. Sci. Nat., (7) 20: 1–30.

BOYCE, R. W., 1910, Mosquito or Man, London, xiii + 280.

BRADLEY, H. C., 1922, Wis. Medic. J., 20: 1–6; 1922a, Physiol. Rev., 2: 415–439.

BRADY, G. S., 1899, U. Durham Phil. Soc., 1: 153–164.

BRANDER, A. A. D., 1906, J. Bombay Nat. Hist. Soc., 17: 528–530.

BRANDT, K., 1901, Smithsonian Rept. (1900): 493–506.

BRANNER, J. C., 1912, Smithsonian Rept., (1911): 303–333.

BRAUN, A. F., 1908, T. Amer. Entom. Soc., 34: 269–357; 1914, J. Acad. Nat. Sci., Philadelphia, (2) 16: 105–168.

BRETSCHER, K., 1901, Biol. Centralb., 21: 538–550.

BRETZ, J. H., 1924, Sci. Mo., 18: 239–258.

BRIGGS, E. M., 1905, Cold Spr. Harb. Monogs., 4: 1–11.

BRINDLEY, H. H., 1910, Cambridge Phil. Soc., 15: 576–587.

BROCHER, F., 1909, Ann. de Biol. Lacustr., 4: 9–32, 1–6; 1910, Ibid., T. 4: 89–138; 1911, Ibid., 4: 367–379; 1919, Ibid., 9: 41–50.

BRODE, H. S., 1898, J. Morphol., 14: 141–180.

BRODIE, W., 1905, Canad. Entom., 41: 73–76.

BROOKS, W. K., 1885, M. Boston Soc. Nat. Hist., 3: 359–430; 1893, J. Hopkins Univ. Circ. Biol. Lab., 5: 129; 1894, J. Geol., 2: 455–479.

BRUES, C. T., 1903, J. N. Y. Entom. Soc., 11: 228–230; 1908, J. Econ. Entom., 1: 123–128; 1921, Amer. Nat., 51: 134–164.

BRUES, C. T., and R. W. GLASER, 1921, Biol. Bull., 40: 299–324.

BRUN, R., 1914, Die Raumorientierung der Ameisen und das Orientungs problem en allgemeinen, Jena, viii + 234.

BRUNELLI, G., 1913, Zoöl. Jahrb., Allgem. Zoöl. Physiol., 33: 1–26.

BUCHANAN, F., 1923, J. Physiol., 57: lxxvi–lxxvii.

BUCHANAN, J. W., 1922, J. Exper. Zoöl., 36: 1–48.

BUCHNER, P., 1921, Tier und Pflanze in intracellularer Symbiose, Berlin, 1–462.

BUDGETT, J. S., 1899, P. Cambridge Phil. Soc., 10: 236–240.

BULMAN, G. W., 1890, Zoölogist, (3) 14: 422–427. 1899, Nat. Sci., 14: 128–130, 250–413.

BUMPUS, H. C., 1901, U. S. Fish Com., 19: 225–230.

BURGESS, P. S., 1922, Science, 55: 647–648.

BURKE, C. V., 1911, Science, 34: 477–453.

BURREL, T. J., 1904, T. Amer. Micr. Soc., 25: 105–120.

BUXTON, P. A., 1921, Cambridge Phil. Soc., 20: 388–392; 1923, Animal Life in Deserts, London, xv + 176.

BUTTEL-REEPEN, H. VON, 1909, Arch. Rassen. Ges. Biol., 6: 289–304.

C

CALKINS, G. N., 1919, J. Exper. Zoöl., 29: 121–156.

CALMAN, W. T., 1911, The Life of Crustacea, N. Y., xvi + 289.

CALVERT, P. P., 1900–1901, Veterinarian, 73: 591–600; 1908, P. Acad. Nat. Sci. Philadelphia, 60: 486–488; 1910, Zoölogical Researches in Costa Rica, Old Penn., 9: 165–170; 1922, Ecology, 3: 163–165.

CAMERON, A. E., 1913, J. Econ. Biol., 8: 159–204; 1917, T. Roy. Soc., Edinburgh, 52: 37–77.

CARLIER, E. W., 1910, P. Birmingham Nat. Hist. Phil. Soc., 12: 1–12.
CARMICHAEL, C. D., 1921, Science, 54: 631–634.
CARPENTER, G. D. H., 1920, A Naturalist on Lake Victoria, London, xxvi + 333.
CARPENTER, G. H., 1903, Rept. Brit. Assn. Adv. Sci., 72: 657–658.
CARY, L. R., 1918, Publ. Carnegie Inst., Washington, 213: 341–362.
CASE, E. C., 1905, Bull. Wis. Nat. Hist. Soc., N. S., 43: 169–180.
CASTLE, W. E., 1911, Science, 33: 240–244.
CAUDELL, A. N., 1903, P. Entom. Soc. Wash., 5: 74–82.
CAULLERY, M., 1922, Le Parasitisme et la Symbiose, Paris, 400.
CHAMBERLAIN, T. C., and R. D. SALISBURY, 1909, Geology, N. Y., 3 vols.
CHANCE, E., 1922, The Cuckoo's Secret, London, 1–239.
CHAPMAN, R. N., 1919, Amer. J. Anat., 25: 185–219.
CHAPMAN, T. A., 1898, Entom. Mo. Mag., 9: 5.
CHENOWETH, H. E., 1917, Biol. Bull., 32: 183–201.
CHETVERIKOV, S. S., 1920, Smithsonian Rept., (1918): 441–449.
CHIDESTER, F. E., 1911, Biol. Bull., 21: 235–248; 1920, Amer. Nat., 54: 551–557; 1922, *Ibid.*, 56: 373–380; 1924, Brit. J. Exper. Biol., 2: 79–118.
CHILD, C. M., 1915, Individuality in Organisms, Chicago, x + 213; 1921, The Origin and Development of the Nervous System, Chicago, xvii + 296; 1921a, J. Exper. Zoöl., 33: 409–432.
CHITTENDEN, F. H., 1901, Bull. U. S. Dept. Agr., Div. Entom., 30: 63–75.
CHURCHILL, E. P., 1919, Bull. U. S. Bur. Fish., 36: 93–128.
CLARK, A. H., 1908, Amer. Nat., 42: 717–726; 1915, U. S. Nat. Mus. Bull., 82, 2 vols.; 1925, Sci. Mo., 20: 341–344.
CLARK, J. H., 1922, Physiol. Rev., 2: 277–291.
CLARK, J. M., 1921, Organic Dependence and Disease: Their Origin and Significance, New Haven, 1–113.
CLAUSEN, C. P., 1923, Ann. Entom. Soc. Amer., 16: 95–219.
CLEGHORN, A., 1910, Pop. Sci. Mo., 77: 356–364; 1911, Science, 34: 513–514.
CLEMENS, W. A., et al., 1923a, *Ibid.*, 22: 171–188; 1924, U. Toronto Stud., 24: 1–12.
CLEMENS, W. A. and L. S., 1921, Contr. Canad. Biol., (1918–1920): 69–83; 1922, Science, 55: 445–446; 1917, U. Toronto Biol. Ser., 17: 43; 1923, U. Toronto Stud., Fish. Lab., 22: 1–31.
CLEMENS, W. A., and N. K. BIGELOW, 1922, *Ibid.*, 20: 39–53.
CLEMENTS, F. E., 1905, Research Methods in Ecology, Lincoln, xvii + 334; 1923, Carnegie Inst., Washington, Publ. 336: vii + 274.
CLEVELAND, L. R., 1923, P. Nat. Acad. Sci., 9: 424–428; 1924, Biol. Bull., 46: 177–225.
COBB, J. N., 1921, Rept., U. S. Fish. Com., (1921): 1–268.
COBB, N. A., 1914, T. Amer. Micr. Soc., 33: 69–134; 1915, Yrbk. U. S. Dept. Agr., 1914: iii + 457–490; 1918, Waverly Press, Baltimore: 189–212.
COCHRAN, M. E., 1911, Biol. Bull., 20: 332–349.
COCKAYNE, E. A., 1911, T. Entom. Soc. London, (1911): 168.
COCKERELL, T. D. A., 1916, Canad. Entom. 48: 76–80.
COKER, R. E., 1911, Arch. Ges. Hydrobiol. u. Hydrogr., 4: 174–182; 1915, Pop. Sci. Mo., 9: 90–99; 1918, Sci. Mo., 12: 120–129; 1919, P. U. S.

Nat. Mus., 56: 449–511; 1925, Ecology, 6: 52–65.

COLE, A. E., 1921, J. Exper. Zoöl., 33: 293–320.

COLE, L. J., 1901, Biol. Bull., 2: 195–207.

COLLINS, E. T., 1922, Arboreal Life and the Evolution of the Human Eye, Philadelphia, 1–108.

COLLINS, P., 1913, Sci. Amer., 109: 459.

COLTON, H. S., 1908, P. Acad. Nat. Sci., Philadelphia, (1908): 410–448; 1918, Biol. Bull., 35: 48–49; 1922, Ecology, 3: 146–157.

COMSTOCK, A. B., 1904, Science, 20: 923–924.

CONNOLLY, C. J., 1925, Biol. Bull., 48: 56–77.

CONNOR, M. E., 1921, Nat. Hist., 21: 279–281.

COOK, M. T., 1911, Science, 34: 683–684; 1923, *Ibid.*, 57: 6–14.

COOK, W. C., 1920, 18 Rept. State Entom. Minn., 43–56.

COOKE, W. W., 1911, Nat. Geog. Mag., 22: 346–365; 1913, Auk, 30: 205–221.

COOPER, W. S., 1922, Ecology, 3: 7–16.

COPE, E. D., 1885, Amer. Nat., 19: 1226–1227.

CORNISH, V., 1910, Waves of the Sea and Other Water Waves, London, 1–374; 1914, Waves of Sand and Snow and the Eddies Which Make Them, Chicago, 1–383.

COULTER, J. M., C. R. BARNES, and H. C. COWLES, 1911, A Textbook of Botany for Colleges and Universities, vol. 2, Ecology, x + 485–981.

COUPIN, H., 1900, Rev. Sci., (4) 14: 780–784; 1903, *Ibid.*, (4) 20: 274–277; 1910, Rev. Sci. Ann. 48, Sem. 2: 838–840.

COVILLE, F. V., 1914, Smithsonian Rept. (1913): 333–343.

COWARD, T. A., 1912, The Migration of Birds, N. Y., ix + 137.

COWLES, H. C., 1901, Bot. Gaz., 31: 73–108; 1901, Bull. Geog. Soc. Chicago, 2: 76; 1901, Bot. Gaz., 31: 73–108; 145–182; 1902, School Rev., 10: 48–49; 1909, Amer. Nat., 43: 356–368; 1911, Bot. Gaz., 51: 161–183.

COWLES, R. P., 1913, Philippine J. Sci., 8: 119–126; 1915, *Ibid.*, (D) 10: 11–16.

COWLES, R. P. and A. M. SCHWITALLA, 1923, Ecology, 4: 402–416.

CRAIG, T., 1897, Amer. Mo. Mich. J., 18: 253–256.

CRAIG, W., 1918, J. An. Behav., 7: 444–448.

CRAWFORD, D. R., and W. J. J. SMIDT, 1922, Bull. U. S. Bur. Fish., 38: 281–310.

CRAMPTON, G. C., 1912, Science, 35: 634–635.

CRIDDLE, N., 1911, Ann. Roy. Entom. Soc. Ontario, 41: 60–61.

CROZIER, W. J., 1916, J. Exper. Zoöl., 20: 297–356; 1917, Zoöl. Jahrb., 35: 233–297; 1918, J. Exper. Zoöl., 26: 379–389; 1920, Amer. Nat., 54: 88–91; 1920a, Biol. Bull., 39: 116–129; 1921, *Ibid.*, 41: 98–101; 1923, P. Soc. Exper. Biol. & Med., 21: 58.

CUENOT, L., 1898, Bull. Soc. Zoöl. France, 23: 37–58; 1922, Smithsonian Rept. (1921): 335–345.

CULVER, D. E., 1914, Auk, 31: F95–397.

CUMMINGS, B. F., 1908, Brit. Birds, 2: 119–124; 1910, Zoölogist, (4) 14: 161–175, 211–222, 272; 1911, J. An. Behav., 1: 305–306.

CUNNINGHAM, A., 1914, Centralb. Bokt. Parasit., (2) 42: 8–27.

CUNNINGTON, W. A., 1920, P. Zoöl. Soc. London, (1920): 507–622.

D

DACHNOWSKI, A., 1912, Geol. Surv., Ohio, (4): 16.

DAHL, F., 1896, Sets.-Ber. Acad. Wiss. Berlin, (1896): 705–714, (1898): 102–118; 1898, Verh. deutsch. Zoöl. Ges., 8: 121–131; 1901, Biol. Centralb., 21: 275–281; 1921, Grundlagen einer Okologischen Tiergeographie, Jena, viii + 118.

DAKIN, W. J., 1912, Inter. Rev. d. Ges. Hydrobiol. u. Hydrog., 5: 53–80.

DAMANT, G. C. C., 1924, J. Physiol., 59: 345–356.

DANOIS, E. C., 1924, Ann. l'Inst. Oceanogr., 1: 1–52.

DARWIN, C., 1875, Origin of Species, London, 6 ed., xxi + 441; 1881, The Formation of Vegetable Mould through the Action of Worms, London, 1: 8–31; 1920, Journal of the Researches into the Geology and Natural History of the Various Countries Visited during the Voyage of H. M. S. Beagle Around the World, London, xvi + 496.

DAVENPORT, C. B., 1903, U. Chicago, Decen. Publ., (1) 10: 157–176; 1903, Cold Spr. Harb. Monogrs., 2: 1–32; 1908, Exper. Morphol., N. Y., xvii + 508.

DAVIDSON, A., 1905, Entom. News, 16: 233–234.

DAVIDSON, J., 1924, Science, 59: 364.

DAVIS, D. W., 1919, J. Exper. Zoöl., 28: 161–263.

DAVIS, J. J., 1907, Entom. News, 18: 269–275; 1919, Bull. Ill. Nat. Hist. Surv., 13: 1–138.

DAVIS, W. M., 1915, Science N. S., 41: 455–458.

DEAN, B., 1912, P. Zoöl Soc. London, (1912): 607–612.

DE LA TORRE BUENO, J. R., 1903, Canad. Entom., 35: 235–237.

DENNYS, F. O. B., and F. C. SELOUS, 1906, J. Bombay Nat. Hist. Soc. 17: 245–247.

DEWAR, J. M., 1924, The Bird as a Diver, London, xii + 173.

DEXLER, H., and L. FREUND, 1906, Amer. Nat., 40: 49–72.

DICE, L. R., 1920, U. Mich. Occ. Pap. Mus. Zöol., 85: 1–24; 1920a, Ibid., 86: 1–20; Science, 55: 1–4; 1922, Ibid., 55: 335–338; 1922a, Ecology, 3: 29–46; 1923, Ibid., 4: 40–53; 1923a, Ibid., 4: 247–260; 1923b, J. Mammal., 4: 39–47.

DICE, L. R., and H. B. SHERMAN, 1920, U. Mich. Occ. Pap. Mus. Zöol., 109: 1–46: 1922.

DI CESNOLA, A. P., 1904, Biomtrika, 3: 58–59.

DISTANT, W. L., 1905, Zoölogist, (4) 9: 281–292; 332–345; 1907, Ibid., 11: 401–414.

DIXEY, F. A., 1908, T. Entom. Soc., London, (1908): lxxviii; 1908a, Ibid., 559–583.

DIXON, C., 1899, The Migration of Birds, London, xvi + 300; 1897, Curiosities of Bird Life, London, 1–334.

DIXON, J., 1922, J. Mammal., 3: 136–146.

DIXON, R., 1914, The Human Side of Plants, N. Y., 1–288.

D'ORBAIN, E. A., 1906, Emu, 5: 185–189.

DODD, F. O., 1902, Entomologist, 35: 16–17.

DODDS, G. S., 1917, P. U. S. Nat. Mus., 54: 59–87; 1920, Biol. Bull., 39: 89–107.

Dodds, G. S., and F. L. Hisaw, 1924, Ecology, 5: 137–148; 1924a, Ibid., 5: 262–271.

Doflein, F., 1907, Spolia Zeylanica, 3: 203–209; 1910, Zeitschr. 70 Gebuststag R. Hertwigs, 3: 215–292.

Dolley, W. L., Jr., 1917, J. Exper. Zoöl., 23: 507–518.

Dollman, H. C., 1910, Entom. Rec. J. Var., 22: 36.

Domogalla, B. P., C. Juday, E. B. Fred, and W. H. Peterson, 1925, J. Biol. Chem., 63: 269–295.

Donisthorpe, H. St. J., K., 1901, Entom. Rec. J. Var., 13: 51–56; 1922, Biol. Bull., 42: 173–184.

Dore, W. H., and R. C. Miller, 1923, U. Cal. Publ. Zoöl., 22: 383–400.

Douglas, S. R., 1917, P. Zoöl. Soc. London, (1917) 2: 159–165.

Drew, G. A., 1907, Biol. Bull., 12: 127–140.

Duerden, J. E., 1906, P. Zoöl. Soc. London, 11: 494–511.

Dugmore, A. R., 1914, The Romance of the Beaver, Philadelphia, xv + 225.

Düring, H., 1897, Prometheus, 9: 103–107.

Durnford, C. D., 1906, Amer. Nat., 40: 1–11.

E

East, E. M., and R. W. Glaser, 1914, Psyche, 21: 27–30.

Eaton, A. E., 1876, P. Roy. Soc., 23: 351–355.

Edmonson, C. H., 1912, Science, 35: 938–939; 1920, T. Amer. Micr. Soc., 39: 167–198.

Eigenmann, C. H., 1895, T. Ind. Acad. Sci., (1895): 204–296; 1898, Ibid., (1897): 229–230; 1909, Cave Vertebrates of America, Carnegie Inst., Washington, ix + 241; 1911, M. Carnegie Mus., 5: xxii + 578.

Eigenmann, C. H., and W. A. Denny, 1900, Biol. Bull., 2: 33–41.

Ekman, S., 1915, Intern. Rev. Ges. Hydiobiol. u. Hydrog., 7: 146–204, 275–425; 1919, Ibid., 25: 477–528; 1920, Ibid., 8: 543–589; 1920a, Festschr. f. Zschokke, 2: 1–12.

Eltringham, H., 1910, African Mimetic Butterflies, Oxford, 1–136.

Embody, G. C., 1912, Inter. Rev. Ges. Hydrobiol., 3: 1–32; 1922, A Study of the Fish-producing Waters of Tompkins County, N. Y. Conserv. Com., 1–43.

Emery, C., 1880, Fauna u. Flora des Golfes von Neapel, 2: 1–76.

English, P. F., 1923, J. Mammal., 4: 1–9.

Essenberg, C., 1918, U. Cal. Publ. Zoöl., 18: 171–238; 1922, Ecology, 3: 55–64.

Esterly, C. O., 1912, Science, U. S. 35: 192–193; 1914, U. Cal. Publ. Zoöl., 13: 21–38; 1914a, Ibid., 13: 123–145; 1916, Ibid., 16: 171–184; 1919, Ibid., 19: 1–83.

Evans, P. N., 1911, Science, 34: 562–563.

Evans, T. J., 1910, Ann. Mag. Nat. Hist., (8) 6: 284–291.

Evers, J., 1910, Zeitschr. Wiss. Insekten Biol., 6: 401.

Ewald, W. E., 1910, Biol. Centralb., 30: 1–16, 49–63, 379–384, 385, 399; 1912, J. Exper. Zoöl., 13: 591–611.

Ewing, H. E., 1912, T. Acad. Sci. St. Louis, 21: 1–70.

EYCLESHYMER, A. C., 1915, Amer. Nat., 49: 504–517.
EYDEN, D., 1923, P. Cambridge Phil. Soc., Biol. Sci., 1: 49–55.

F

FABRE, H., 1914, Eng. Rev., (1914): 152–167.
FARQUHARSON, C. O., 1922, T. Entom. Soc. London, (1921): 319–448.
FARREN, W., 1907, Brit. Birds, 1: 301–308.
FASTEN, N., 1912, Bull. Wis. Nat. Hist. Soc., 10: 61–80.
FAURE-FREMIET, E., 1906, C. R. Soc. Biol. Paris, 61: 456–458.
FELT, E. P., 1906, Mem. 8, N. Y. State Mus., 2 vols.; 1910, J. Econ. Entom.,
    3: 347–356; 1911, *Ibid.*, 4: 451–475.
FERRONNIÈRE, G., 1901, Bull. Soc. Sci. Nat. Ouest Nantes, 11: 1–456.
FERTON, C., 1910, Ann. Soc. Entom., 79: 145–178.
FIEBRIG, K., 1912, Jena Zeitschr. Nat., 48: 315–364.
FIELD, I. A., 1922, Bull. U. S. Bur. Fish., 38: 125–259.
FINN, F., 1902, Nature, 65: 534.
FISCHER, H., 1924, Inter. Rev. Sci & Prac. Agr., 2: 822–830.
FISHER, W. K., 1903, Auk, 20: 384–397; 1904, *Ibid.*, 21: 8–20.
FLATHER, M. D., 1919, Biol. Bull., 36: 54–62.
FLATTELY, F. W., 1920, Sci. Progr., 14: 418–426; 1921, *Ibid.*, 16: 251–257.
FLATTELY, F. W., and C. L. WALTON, 1922, The Biology of the Seashore,
    N. Y., xvi + 336.
FLETCHER, T. B., T. Entom. Soc. London, (1909): xlvi.
FLOERSHEIM, C., 1910, Entom. Rev. & J. Var., 22: 203–204.
FLORENTIN, R., 1899, Ann. Sci. Nat., (8) 10: 209–346.
FORBES, A. C., 1910, Irish Nat., 19: 89–91.
FORBES, H., 1880 Wanderings of a Naturalist in the Malay Archipelago,
    London, xix + 536.
FORBES, S. A., 1878, Bull. Ill. State Lab. Nat. Hist., 2: 71–89; 1880, *Ibid.*,
    1: 3–17; 1883, *Ibid.*, 6: 65–94; 1888, *Ibid.*, 12 (8): 433–473; 1914, *Ibid.*,
    1–19; 1919, *Ibid.*, 13: 139–156.
FORBES, S. A., and A. O. GROSS, 1922, Bull. Ill. Nat. Hist. Surv. Div.,
    14: 187–218.
FORBES, S. A., and R. E. RICHARDSON, 1908, The Fishes of Illinois, Nat.
    Hist. Surv. Ill., 3, Icthiology, cxxi + 357.
FORD, E., 1923, J. Mar. Biol. Assn., Plymouth, 13: 164–224.
FOREL, F. A., 1869, Bull. Soc. Vaud. Sci. Nat., 383–391; 1874–1879, *Ibid.*,
    13; 1–164; 14: 97–164, 201–364; 15: 497–535; 16: 149–394; 1892–1904,
    Le Leman, Lausanne, 3 vols.
FOSTER, B. E., 1924, J. Mammal., 5: 266–268.
FOWLER, W. W., 1918, Entom. Mo. Mag., 54: 92.
FRAMINTZIN, A., 1907, Biol. Centralb., 27: 353–364.
FRANCÉ, R. H., 1911, Centralbl. Bakt. Paras. Infsk., (2) 32: 1–7.
FRANZ, V., 1911, Arch. Hydrobiol. Planktonkde., 7: 493–499; 1913, Monat-
    schr. Nat. Unter., 6: 161–178.
FRANZ, V., and E. STECHOW, 1908, Zoöl. Anz., 32: 752–754.
FRED, E. B., F. C. WILSON, and A. DAVENPORT, 1924, Ecology, 5: 322–339.
FRIEND, H., 1912, Zoölogist, (4) 16: 246–249.

FRIERSON, L. S., 1899, Nautilus, 12: 139–140.

FRISCH, K. von, 1912, Zoöl. Jahrb., Zoöl. Physiol., 33: 151–164; 1920, *Ibid.*, 37:1–238; 1923, Zoöl., Jahrb., Allgem. Zoöl. & Physiol., 40: 1–186; 1923*a*, Naturwiss, 24: 470–476.

FROGGATT, W., 1915, Rept. 84 Meet. Brit. Assn. Adv. Sci., 422–424.

FROHAWK, F. W., 1914, Entomologist, 47: 212–213.

FULTON, J. F., 1921, J. Exper. Zoöl., 33: 353–364; 1922, Q. J. Micr. Sci., 66: 339–396.

FYLES, T. W., 1908, Ann. Rept. Entom. Soc. Ontario, 38: 31–35

G

GADOW, H., 1913, The Wanderings of Animals, Cambridge, viii + 150.

GAGE, S. H., 1891, Amer. Nat., 25: 1084–1110.

GAIN, L., 1913, Smithsonian Rept., (1912): 475–482.

GALLOWAY, T. W., 1908, School Sci. & Math., (1908): 1–5.

GALLOWAY, T. W., and P. S. WELCH, 1921, T. Amer. Micr. Soc., 30: 13–39.

GALTSOFF, P. S., 1924, Ecology, 5: 1–5.

GANDOLFI HORNYOLD, A., 1912, Amer. Biol. Lacustre, 5: 131–135.

GARDNER, M. W., 1918, Rept. Mich. Acad. Sci., 20: 357–423.

GARMAN, H., 1888, Bull. Ill. State Lab. Nat. Hist., 8: 123–184.

GARSTANG, W., 1896, Rept. Brit. Assn. Adv. Sci., Liverpool, 1–2; 1898, Q. J. Micr. Sci., 40: 211–232, 1922, J. Linn. Soc. London, 35: 81–102.

GATES, B. N., 1914, Bull. U. S. Dept. Agr., Bur. Entom., 96: 1–29.

GAYLOR, D., 1922, Ind. Acad. Sci., (1922): 239–250.

GEDDES, P., and J. A. THOMSON, 1914, Sex, N. Y., 1–256.

GEISER, S. W., 1923, Amer. Midl. Nat., 8: 153–163.

GEROULD, J. H., 1921, J. Exper. Zoöl., 34: 385–417.

GERRETSEN, F. C., 1922, Biol. Centralb., 42: 1–9.

GIARD, A., 1898, C. R. Soc. Biol. Paris, 50: 1013–1015; 1903, *Ibid.*, 55: 1144–1147, 1185–1188, 1261–1262.

GIBSON, A., 1903, 33 Rept. Amer. Entom. Soc. Ontario, 74–78; 1904, Ann. Rept. Ontario Entoml. Soc., 34: 50–61.

GILBERT, C. H., 1922, Bull. U. S. Bur. Fish., 38: 317–350.

GILL, T. N., 1903, Smithsonian Misc. Coll., 45: 295–305; 1904, 8th Intern. Geog. Cong., Washington, D. C., (1904): 617; 1905, Smithsonian Misc. Coll., 47: 348–359; 1905*a*, Smithsonian Rept., (1904): 495–515; 1907, *Ibid.*, (1905): 403–531; 1909, *Ibid.*, (1908): 565–615; 1909, Smithsonian Misc. Coll., 52: 277–286; 1909*b*, *Ibid.*, 52: 155–180.

GIVLER, J. P., 1922, J. Elisha Mitchell Soc., 37: 130–137.

GLEASON, H. A., 1909, Adam's Ecol. Surv. Isl. R., 57–78.

GODFREY, R., 1897, Sci. Gossip, 3: 294–295.

GOLDSCHMIDT, R., 1923, The Mechanism and Physiology of Sex Determination, London, viii + 259.

GOLDSMITH, W. M., 1918, Ind. Acad. Sci., (1916–1917): 447–455.

GOODEY, T., 1911, P. Roy. Soc., London, 84B: 165–180; 1915, *Ibid.*, 88B: 437–456.

GORNITZ, K., 1923, J. Ornithol., 71: 456–511.

GOTO, S., 1910, J. Exper. Zoöl., 9: 469–496.

GOUDIE, J. C., 1905, Victorian Nat., 22: 75–76.

GOULD, H. N., 1917, J. Exper. Zoöl., 23: 225–250.

GRAENICHER, S., 1902, Bull. Wis. Nat. Hist. Soc., 2: 29–38; 1905, *Ibid.*, 3: 153–167; 1907, *Ibid.*, 5: 14–45, 84–95; 1910, *Ibid.*, 8: 91–101; 1911, Bull. Publ. Mus. Milwaukee, 1: 221–249.

GRAF, A., 1896, T. N. Y. Acad. Sci., 15: 67–69.

GRAHAM, S. A., 1920, Rept. State Entom. Minn., 18: 26–42; 1922, *Ibid.*, 19: 22–40.

GRAVE, B. H., 1922, Biol. Bull., 42: 234–256.

GRAVIER, C., 1907, C. R. Acad. Sci., Paris, 144: 1462–1464.

GREELEY, A. W., 1901, J. Physiol., 6: 122–128.

GREEN, W. R., 1919, Biol. Bull., 37: 49–95.

GREENE, C. W., 1911, Bull. U. S. Bur. Fish., 29: 129–148; 1914, *Ibid.*, 33: 73–138.

GREENE, E., 1912, Spolia Zeylanica, 8: 71–72.

GRINNELL, J., 1922, Auk, 39: 373–380; 1924, Ecology, 5: 225–229.

GROOS, K., 1911, The Play of Animals, N. Y., xxii + 341.

GUDGER, E. W., 1910, Bull. U. S. Bur. Fish., 28: 1069–1109; 1912, Science, 35: 192; 1915, Zoölogica, N. Y. Zoöl. Soc., 1: 349–389; 1918, Carnegie Inst., Washington, 252: 53–108.

GULLIVER, F. P., 1899, P. Ann. Acad. Arts Sci., 34: 149–258.

GURNEY, J. H., 1899, Ibis, 5: 19–42; 1900, Zoölogist, (4) 4: 358–374, 422, 478, 479.

GUILBEAU, B. H., 1908, Amer. Nat., 42: 783–798.

GURLEY, R. R., 1902, Amer. J. Psychol., 13: 408–425.

H

HADWEN, S., and L. G. PALMER, 1922, Bull. U. S. Dept. Agr., 1089: 1–74.

HAEBERLI, A., 1918, Rev. Suisse Zoöl., 26: 147–231.

HAECKER, V., 1908, Valdivia Exped., 14.

HAEMPEL, O., 1918, Rev. Ges. Hydrobiol. u. Hydrogr., 8: 225–306.

HAHN, W. L., 1908, Biol. Bull., 15: 165–193.

HALL, F. G., 1922, Biol. Bull., 41: 31–51; 1924, *Ibid.*, 47: 79–127.

HALL, G. B., 1922, Ecology, 3: 93–121.

HALL, R., 1900, Victorian Nat., 17: 101–104.

HAMILTON, S. H., 1903, Nautilus, 16: 138.

HANCOCK, J. L., 1905, Amer. Nat., 39: 1–11; 1911, Nature Sketches in Temperate America, Chicago, xviii + 451.

HANKIN, E. H., 1915, Animal Flight, London, x + 412.

HANKINSON, T. L., 1908, Biol. Surv. Mich. Geol. Surv. Rept., (1907): 155–288; 1910, T. Ill. State Acad. Sci., 3: 23–31; 1922, Mich. Acad. Sci., Arts, Lett., 22: 197–205.

HARGITT, C. W., 1912, J. An. Behav., 2: 51–78; 1915, *Ibid.*, 5: 250–257.

HARKNESS, W. J. K., 1924, U. Toronto Stud. Biol. Sci., 24: 13–42.

HARPER, R. M., 1918, Science, 48: 208–211.

HARRINGTON, N. R., 1899, Amer. Nat., 33: 721–728.

HARRIS, J. A., 1903, Kans. U. Sci. Bull., 2: 51–187; 1913, Science, 38: 402–403.

HARSHBERGER, J. W., 1923, Ecology, 4: 297–306.

HARTMAN, C., 1905, T. Tex. Acad. Sci., 7: 15–85; 1913, J. An. Behav., 3: 353–360.

HARTRIDGE, H., 1920, J. Physiol., 54: 54–57.

HARVEY, E. N., 1920, The Nature of Animal Light, Philadelphia, x + 182.

HARVEY, L. H., 1903, U. Maine Studies, 5: 1–56.

HARVEY, M., 1893, T. Roy. Soc. Canad., 10 (4): 17–37.

HASEMAN, J. D., 1911, Biol. Bull., 21: 113–121.

HAUPT, H., 1915, Copeia, 20: 18–19.

HAUSMAN, L. A., 1920, Biol. Bull., 37: 363–371.

HAVILAND, G. D., 1902, Smithsonian Rept., (1901): 667–678.

HAVILAND, M. D., 1922, Q. J. Micr. Sci., 66: 321–338.

HAWKINS, C. J., 1920, Smithsonian Rept., (1918): 461–473.

HEADLEE, T. J., 1906, Amer. Nat., 40: 875–885; 1906, Biol. Bull., 11: 305–318.

HEATH, H., 1902, Biol. Bull., 4: 44–63; 1907, Ibid., 13: 161–164; 1910, Ibid., 19: 73–78.

HECHT, S., 1918, J. Exper. Zoöl., 25: 237.

HEGNER, R. W., 1919, J. Exper. Zoöl., 30: 1–95; 1919a, Ibid., 29: 427–441; 1919b, Genetics, 4: 95–150.

HEILPRIN, A., 1887, The Geographical Distribution and Geological Distribution of Animals, N. Y., xii + 435.

HEIM, 1898, Smithsonian Rept. (1896): 411–455.

HEIMBURGER, H. V., 1924, Ecology, 5: 276–282.

HEINDEL, R. L., 1905, Amer. Nat., 39: 859–873.

HELLAND-HANSEN, B., 1912, Inter. Rev. Ges. Hydrobiol. u. Hydrogr., Suppl., 1: 1–84; 1923, Ibid., 11: 393–496.

HELLAND-HANSEN, B., and F. NANSEN, 1909, Rept. Norwegian Fishery & Mar. Investig. 2.

HEMPEL, A., 1898, Bull. Ill. State Lab. Nat. Hist., 5: 301–388.

HENDERSON, J. B., JR., 1905, Nautilus, 18: 109–110.

HENDERSON, L. J., 1914, Science, 39: 524–527; 1917, The Order of Nature, N. Y., v + 234; 1922, Sci. Mo., 15: 405–416.

HENSEN, V., 1906, Arch. Hydrobiol. Planktonkde., 11: 360–377.

HENSHAW, H. W., 1911, Smithsonian Rept. (1910): 545–559.

HERBERT, F. A., 1908, Brit. Birds, 2: 92.

HERDMAN, W. A., 1907, T. Liverpool Biol. Soc., 21: 1–23; 1909, Science, 30: 240–749.

HERMS, W. B., 1907, J. Exper. Zoöl., 4: 45–84.

HERRICK, F. H., 1902, The Home Life of Wild Birds; A New Method of the Study of Photography of Birds, N. Y., 1–148; 1909, Science, 29: 431; 1919, W. Reserve U. Bull., 22: 41–49.

HERTER, C. A., 1906, Science, 24: 859–861.

HERWERDEN, M. A., VON, 1914, Biol. Centralb., 34: 213–216.

HESS, C., Pflüger's Archiv., 155: 421–436; 1921, Farbenlehre, Egrebn. Physiol., 20: 1–107.

HESS, W. N., 1920, Biol. Bull., 38: 39–76.

HESSE, R., 1913, Die Ökologischen Grundlagen der Tier Verbreitung, Geog. Zeitschr., 19: 241–259; 335–345; 445–460; 498–513; 1917, Aus der Nat.,

(1917); 257–267: 1920, Die Anpassung der Meerestiere an das Leben in Susswasser, Bonn, 1–6; 1922, Naturw. Abth. d. Niederrh. zu. Bonn, (1920–1922): 1–4.

HESSE, R., and F. DOFLEIN, 1910, Tierbau und Tierleben in ihrem Zuzammenhang betrachtet, Leipzig, Berlin, xvii + 789; 1914, *Ibid.*, Bd. 2, xv + 960.

HICKSON, S. J., 1894, The Fauna of the Deep Sea, N. Y., xvi + 169.

HINGSTON, R. W. G., 1920, A Naturalist in Himalaya, London, xii + 300.

HINTZE, A. L., 1925, Ann. Entom. Soc. Amer., 18: 31–34.

HIRSCH, E., 1915, Arch. Hydrobiol. Planktonkde., 10: 273–286.

HISAW, F. L., 1923, J. Mammal, 4: 9–20.

HJORT, J., 1911, Inter. Rev. Ges. Hydrobiol. u. Hydrogr., 4: 152–173.

HOBSON, A. D., and L. H. MATHEWS, 1923, Ann. Mag. Nat. Hist., (9) 11: 240–245.

HOFMANN, J. V., 1923, Sci. Mo., 16: 280–283.

HOLMES, S. J., 1911, The Evolution of Animal Intelligence, N. Y., v + 296; 1911a, J. An. Behav., 1: 393–400; 1913, *Ibid.*, 3: 389–400; 1922, J. Comp. Psychol., 2: 173–186.

HOOKER, H. D., 1917, Science, 46: 197–204.

HOPKINS, A. D., 1898, Canad. Entom., 30: 21–29.

HOPKINS, H. S., 1921, J. Exper. Zoöl., 34: 339–384.

HOWARD, A. D., 1919, Prog. Ecol. Soc. Amer., (1919): 3–4.

HOWARD, A. D., and B. J. ANSON, 1922, J. Parasitol., 9: 68–82.

HOWARD, H. E., 1920, Territory in Bird Life, London, xiii + 308.

HOWARD, L. O., 1895, Insect Life, 7: 413–414; 1901, Yrbk. U. S. Dept. Agr., (1900): 79–106.

HOWE, M. A., 1912, Science, 35: 837–842.

HOWELL, G. C. L., 1921, Ocean Research and the Great Fisheries, Oxford, 1–220.

HOY, P. R., 1873, Ann. Mag. Nat. Hist., (4) 11: 319–320.

HUBBARD, H. G., 1896, P. Entom. Soc. Washington, 3: 314–316.

HUBBS, C. L., 1920, Amer. Nat., 54: 380–384; 1921, Ecology, 2: 262–276; 1921a, T. Ill. Acad. Sci., 11: 147–151; 1922, Amer. Nat., 56: 360–372.

HUBER, J., 1907, Smithsonian Rept., (1906): 355–367.

HUDSON, G. V., 1913, Entom. Mo. Mag., (2) 23: 269–275.

HUDSON, P., 1906, J. Bombay Nat. Hist. Soc., 17: 518.

HUDSON, W. H., 1922, The Naturalist in La Plata, London, x + 394.

HUEY, L. M., 1925, Science, 61: 405–407.

HUIE, L. H., 1902, P. Scott. Micr. Soc., 3: 213–216.

HUNCKE, E., 1906, Arch. Rassenbiol., Berlin, 3: 646–673.

HUNGERFORD, H. B., and F. X. WILLIAMS, 1912, Entom. News, 23: 241–260.

HUNTINGTON, E., 1922, Principles of Human Geography, xiv + 430.

HUNTSMAN, A. G., 1918, Canad. Fisherman, (May): 1–5; 1918a, T. Roy. Soc. Canad., 11: 53–60; 1918b, *Ibid.*, 12: 61–67; 1920, Amer. Fish. Soc., 50: 326–333.

HURD, W. E., 1920, U. S. Mo. Weather Rev., 48: 94–98.

HUTCHINS, C. B., 1920, Canad. Entom., 52: 241–245.

HUXLEY, F. M., 1913, J. Exper. Physiol., 6: 183–196.

HUXLEY, J. S., 1912, P. Zoöl. Soc. London, (1912): 647–655; 1912a, The Individual in the Animal Kingdom, Cambridge, xi + 167; 1923, J. Linn. Soc. London, 35: 253–292.

I

IDRAC, P., 1920, Comptes Rendus, 170: 269–272; 1921, *Ibid.*, 172: 1161–1164.
IHERING, H. VON, 1897, Ann. Mag. Nat. Hist., (6) 19: 133–137; 1904, Auk, 21: 313–322.
ILTIS, H., 1913, Biol. Centralb., 33: 685–700.
ISGROVE, A., 1909, T. Liverpool Biol. Soc., 23: 469–573.

J

JACKSON, C. F., 1922, Ecology, 3: 48–54.
JACKSON, C. M., 1923, Science, 57: 537–546.
JACKSON, H. H. T., 1914, Bull. Wis. Nat. Hist. Soc., 12: 4–54.
JACOBS, M. H., 1912, J. Exper. Zoöl., 12: 519–542; 1919, *Ibid.*, 27: 427–442.
JACOBSON, E., 1907, Victorian Nat., 24: 36–38.
JAMBUNATHAN, N. S., 1905, Smithsonian Misc. Coll., 47: 365–372.
JAMMES, L., and Q. MANDOUL, 1905, C. R. Soc. Biol. Paris, 59: 104–106.
JARDINE, J. T., and C. L. FOSLING, 1922, U. S. Dept. Agr. Bull. 1031.
JENNINGS, H. S., 1906, Behavior of the Lower Organisms, N. Y., xvi + 366; 1911, Science, 33: 927–932; 1911, *Ibid.*, 34: 902–910; 1917, J. Wash. Acad. Sci., 7: 281–301.
JENSEN, A. C., 1918, Biol. Bull., 34: 18–25.
JEWELL, M. E., 1920, J. Exper. Zoöl., 30: 461–506; 1922, Ecology, 3: 22–28; 1924, Anat. Rec., 29: 127.
JOHANSEN, F., 1921, Rept. Canad. Arct. Exped., 3: 1k–61k; 1922, *Ibid.*, 7N: 1–31.
JOHNSTONE, J., 1908, Conditions of Life in the Sea, Cambridge, xiv + 332; 1921, The Mechanism of Life in Relation to Modern Physical Theory, London, xii + 248.
JOICEY, J. J., and L. B. PROUT, 1922, T. Entom. Soc. London, (1922): xii–xcii.
JONES, F. M., 1904, Entom. News, 15: 14–17; 1907, *Ibid.*, 18: 413–420.
JOURDAIN, F. C. R., 1913, Brit. Birds, 6: 234–245.
JOY, N. H., 1904, Entom. Rec. J. Var., 16: 89–90; 1910, T. Entom. Soc. London, (1910): 379–385.
JUDAY, C., 1902, T. Ind. Acad. Sci., (1902): 120–133; 1904, T. Wis. Acad. Sci., 14: 534–568; 1907, Bull. U. S. Bur. Fish., 26: 147–178; 1907, T. Wis. Sci. Acad. Arts, Lett., 15: 782–793; 1908, T. Wis. Acad. Sci., 16: 10–16; 1912, Inter. Rev. Ges. Hydrobiol. u. Hydrogr., 5: 449–460; 1913, Science, 38: 546–547; 1919, Biol. Bull., 36: 92–95; 1921, *Ibid.*, 40: 271–286; 1922, T. Wis. Acad. Sci., Arts., Lett., 20: 461–493; 1924, Inter. Rev. Ges. Hydrobiol. u. Hydrogr., 12: 1–12.
JUDAY, C., and G. WAGNER. 1908, T. Wis. Acad. Sci., Arts, Lett., 16: 17–22.

JUDAY, C., E. B. FRED, and F. C. WILSON, 1924a, T. Amer. Micr. Soc., (1924); 177–190.

JUDD, S. D., 1899, Amer. Nat., 33: 461–484.

K

KAMMERER, P., 1913, Smithsonian Rept., (1912): 421–440.

KEEBLE, F. W., and F. W. GAMBLE, 1900, Q. J. Micr. Soc., 43: 559–698; 1904, Phil. T. London, (B) 196: 295–388.

KEILHACK, K., 1896, Prometheus Jahrg., 7: 577–583, 595–598, 611–615.

KEILIN, D., 1921, Ann. Mag. Nat. Hist., (9) 8: 601–608.

KELLY, E. O. G., 1909, P. Entom. Soc. Washington, 11: 64–66.

KELLY, H. M., 1899, Bull. Ill. State Lab. Nat. Hist., 5: 399–418.

KELLOGG, V. L., 1905, American Insects, N. Y., ix + 674; 1907, Entom. News, 18: 426–429; 1914, Science, 39: 360–361.

KENNEDY, C. H., 1922, Ecology, 3: 325–336.

KENOYER, L. A., 1917, P. Iowa Acad. Sci., 23: 483–487.

KENYON, F. C., 1898, Science, 8: 551–554.

KEPNER, W. A., 1911, Biol. Bull., 20: 266–280.

KEPNER, W. A., and J. G. EDWARDS, 1917, J. Exper. Zoöl., 24: 381–408.

KEPNER, W. A., and A. M. FOSHEE, 1917, J. Exper. Zoöl., 23: 519–532.

KEPNER, W. A., and B. D. REYNOLDS, 1923, Biol. Bull., 44: 22–47.

KERN, F. D., 1921, Ecology, 2: 211–214.

KERNER, A. (Oliver F. W.), 1895, Natural History of Plants, N. Y., 4 vols.

KERR, H. W., 1912, P. Zoöl. Soc. London, (1912): 379–392.

KERR, J. G., 1898, P. Zoöl. Soc. London, (1898): 41–44; 1912, P. Roy. Phys. Soc., 18: 241–243.

KIDD, W., 1902, P. Zoöl. Soc. London, 2: 145–158.

KINCER, J. B., 1922, Ecology, 3: 127–133.

KING, L. A. L., 1914, Mar. Biol. Assn. W. Scotland Ann. Rept., (1913): 1–125; 1914, P. Roy. Phys. Soc. Edinburgh, 19: 129–141.

KING, L. A. L., and E. S. RUSSELL, 1909, P. Roy. Phys. Soc., Edinburgh, 17: 225–253.

KLINGKSIEGK, P., and I. VALETTE, 1908, Code des couleurs, Paris, 86.

KLUGH, A. B., 1923, Ecology, 4: 366–377; 1924, *Ibid.*, 5: 192–196.

KNAB, F., 1912, Science, 35: 662–663, 1912a, J. N. Y. Entom. Soc., 20:143–146.

KNAUER, F., 1908, Himmel und Erde, 20: 49–68.

KNUTH, P., 1898, Illustr. Zeitsche. Entom., 3: 71–72.

KOBELT, Z. H., 1902, Die Verbreitung der Tierwelt, Leipzig.

KOCH, G. P., 1915, J. Agr. Res., 4: 511–559.

KOETTLITZ, R., 1900, P. Roy. Phys. Soc. Edinburgh, 14 (2): 266–277.

KOFOID, C. A., 1899, Amer. Nat., 33: 439; 1900, Amer. Micr. Soc., 21: 113–126; 1903, Bull. Ill. State Lab. Nat. Hist., 6: i–xviii, 95–629; 1908, *Ibid.*, 8: i–xviii, 1–361; 1907, Amer. Nat., 41: 242–251.

KOLKWITZ, R., and M. MARSEN, 1909, Intern. Rev. Ges. Hydrobiol. u. Hydrogr., 2: 126–152.

KRIBS, H. G., 1910, J. Exper. Zoöl., 8: 43–75.

KROGH, A., 1914, Zeitschr. Allgem. Physiol., 16: 163–177; 1914a, *Ibid.*, 16: 178–190.

KROPOTKIN, P., 1916, Mutual Aid, a Factor of Evolution, N. Y., vii + 240; 1920, Smithsonian Rept., (1918): 409–427.

KRUGER, L., 1899, Insectenwanderungen zwischen Deutschland und den Vereinigten Staaten von Nordamerika, Stettin, viii + 174.

L

LALOY, L., 1906, Parasitisme et Mutualisme dans la Nature, Bibl. Sci. Intern., Paris, 1–184.

LAMEERE, A., 1922, Smithsonian Rept., (1920): 511–522.

LATTER, O. H., 1906, Nature, 74: 200.

LAURENS, H., 1917, J. Exper. Zoöl., 23: 195–206.

LAUTERBORN, R., and E. WOLF, 1909, Zoöl. Anzeig., 34: 130–136.

LE SOUËF, D., 1899, Ibis., 5: 9–19.

LEATHERS, A. L., 1922, Bull. U. S. Bur. Fish., 38: 1–61.

LEBOUR, M. V., 1923, J. Mar. Biol. Assn., Plymouth, 13: 70–92.

LEIBY, R. W., 1922, J. Morphol., 37: 195–286.

LENG, C. W., 1913, J. N. Y. Entom. Soc., 21: 33–42.

LEOPOLD, N. F., 1923, Auk, 40: 409–414.

LEVICK, G. M., 1914, Antarctic Penguins, London, x + 140.

LILLIE, R. S., 1922, Sci. Mo., 14: 113–130.

LINDER, C., 1904, Rev. Suisse Zoöl., 12: 149–258.

LINDINGER, L., 1906, Ann. Mag. Nat. Hist., (7) 17: 426–432.

LINTON, E., 1907, Amer. Nat., 41: 1–4; 1921, Rept. U. S. Fish. Com., (1921): 3–14.

LINVILLE, H. B., 1902, Ann. N. Y. Acad. Sci., 14: 160–161.

LITTLEHALES, G. W., 1911, Science, 34: 874.

LIVINGSTON, B. E., 1909, Amer. Nat., 43: 369–378.

LLOYD, J. T., 1914, J. N. Y. Entom. Soc., 22: 145–152; 1915, Psyche, 22: 17–21.

LOCHHEAD, W., 1918, Rept. Entom. Soc. Ontario, 48: 85–91.

LODGE, R. B., 1908, Zoölogist, (4) 12: 401–206.

LOEB, J., 1911, Science, 34: 653–665.

LOEB, L., 1921, Biol. Bull., 40: 143–180.

LOHMANN, H., 1911, Intern. Rev. Ges. Hydrobiol. u. Hydrogr., 4: 1–38; 1912, Inst. Meereskunde, Geog. Naturwess. R., 1: 1–92.

LOHNIS, F., and E. B. FRED, 1923, Textbook of Agricultural Bacteriology, N. Y., ix + 283.

LONGLEY, W. H., 1916, P. Nat. Acad. Soc., 2: 733–737; 1917, Amer. Nat., 51: 250–256; 1917a, J. Exper. Zoöl., 23: 533–601; 1917b, Amer. Nat., 51: 257–285; 1918, Amer. Mus. J., 18: 79–88; 1922, Anat. Rec., 23: 131.

LONGSTAFF, G. B., 1906, T. Entom. Soc. London, (1906): 97–118, xxvi–xxix; 1912, Butterfly Hunting in Many Lands: Notes of a Field Naturalist, London, xviii + 724.

LOVELL, J. H., 1909, Amer. Nat., 43: 338–349; 1912, Pop. Sci. Mo., 81: 198–203; 1914, J. An. Behav., 4: 147–175; 1914a, Entom. News, 25: 315–321.

LOWE, H. J., 1921, Nature, 107: 684.

LOWE, J. N., 1917, J. Exper. Zoöl., 23: 147–194.

LOWIE, R. H., 1920, Primitive Society, N. Y., viii + 463.

LUBBOCK, J., 1885, Ants, Bees, and Wasps, 7 ed., London, xix + 448.

LUCAS, T. P., 1897, P. Roy. Soc. Queensland, 12: 49–53.

LULL, R. S., 1906, Amer. Nat., 40: 537–566.

LUND, E. J., 1911, J. Exper. Zoöl., 11: 415–468.

LUTZ, F. E., 1902, Canad. Entom., 34: 64–66; 1911, Amer. Nat., 45: 190–192; 1913, J. N. Y. Entom. Soc., 21: 1–4; 1924, Ann. N. Y. Acad. Sci., 29: 181–283.

LYON, E. P., 1904, Amer. J. Physiol., 12: 149–161.

LYON, M. B., 1915, Entom. News, 26: 1–15.

M

MCATEE, W. L., 1907, Science, 26: 447–449; 1908, Entom. News, 19: 488–491; 1922, Smithsonian Rept., (1920): 411–438.

MACBRIDE, E. W., 1914, Ann. Rept. Mar. Biol. Assn. W. Scotland, (1913): 72–99.

MACCAUGHEY, V., 1917, Bot. Gaz., 64: 89–114; 1917a, Amer. J. Bot., 4: 561–603; 1918, Amer. Nat., 52: 409–438.

MCCOLLOCH, J. W., and W. P. HAYES, 1922, Ecology, 3: 288–299; 1923a, Ecology, 4: 29–36.

MCCOOK, H. C., 1879, The Natural History of the Agricultural Ant of Texas, Philadelphia, 1–311; 1882, The Honey Ants of the Garden of the Gods and the Occident Ants of the American Plains, Philadelphia, 1–188; 1889–93, American Spiders and Their Spinningwork, Philadelphia, 3 vols.

MCCLENDON, J. F., 1910, Publ. Carnegie Inst., 132: 57–62; 1917, Physical Chemistry of Vital Phenomena, Princeton, viii + 240; 1918, Dept. Mar. Biol., Carnegie Inst., 12: 213–258.

MCCREARY, O., 1906, Mich. Geol. Surv., 1905, 56–67.

M'CURDY, J. G., 1902, Sci. Amer., 87: 175.

MCDERMOTT, F. A., 1912, Smithsonian Rept., (1911): 345–362.

MCDOUGALL, W. B., 1918, Plant World, 21: 250–256.

MCEWEN, G. F., 1919, Bull. Scripps Inst. Biol. Res. U. Cal., 9: 58–64.

MACFIE, J. W. S., 1912, Bull. Entom. Res., 3: 223–224.

MCGEE, W. J., 1896, Science, 3: 493–505.

MCGREGOR, R. C., 1920, Philippine J. Sci., 16: 361–437.

MCINDOO, N. E., 1910, Biol. Bull., 19: 303–323; 1922, Smithsonian Rept., (1920): 461–484.

MCINTOSH, W. C., 1900, Brit. Assn. Adv. Sci., Bradford, 70: 785.

M'KINTOSH, 1904, Ann. Mag. Nat. Hist., 13 (7): 117–130.

MAAS, O., 1907, Lebensbedingungen und Verbreitungen der Tiere, Leipzig, v + 138.

MACE, H., 1912, Nature, 89: 62–65.

MANDERS, N., 1911, P. Zoöl. Soc., 1911 (3): 696–749; 1915, T. Entom. Soc. London, (1915): xxiii–xxxii.

MANN, F. C., and D. DRIPS, 1917, J. Exper. Zoöl., 23: 277–286.

MANN, W. M., 1911, Psyche, 19: 98–100; 1913, J. An. Behav., 3: 429–445.
MARAIS, E. N., 1915, Smithsonian Rept., (1914): 511–522.
MARMER, H. A., 1922, Sci. Mo., 14: 209–222.
MARRINER, G. W., 1909, The Kea: A New Zealand Problem, 1–151.
MARSH, C. D., 1901, Wis. Acad. Sci., Arts, Lett., 13: 163–187; 1903, Wis. Nat. Hist. Surv. Bull., 12: vi+194.
MARSH, H. O., 1910, U. S. Dept. Agr., Bur. Entom., 82: 59–66.
MARSH, M. C., 1910, Bull. U. S. Bur. Fish., (1908): 893–906.
MARSHALL, G. A. K., 1908, P. Zoöl. Soc. London, 1 (1908): 93–142; 1909, T. Entom. Soc. London, (1908): 20–21.
MARSHALL, G. A. K., and E. B. POULTON, 1902, T. Entom. Soc. London, (1902): 287–541.
MARTIN, G. W., 1922, Sci. Mo., 15: 455–467; 1923, Rept. N. J. Exper. Sta., 317–320.
MAST, S. O., 1911, Light and the Behavior of Organisms, N. Y., xi + 410; 1912, Science, 36: 871–873; 1912a, J. An. Behav., 2: 256–272; 1916, Bull. U. S. Bur. Fish., 34: 173–276; 1917a, J. Exper. Zoöl., 23: 335–360; 1917b, J. Exper. Zoöl., 22: 471–528.
MAST, S. O., and Y. IBARA, 1923, Biol. Bull., 45: 105–112.
MASTERMAN, A. T., 1897, Brit. Assn. Adv. Sci., 66: 837; 1897a, Nat. Sci., 10: 382–392.
MAUCK, A. V., 1901, Amer. Nat., 35: 477–478.
MAUREL, E., 1900, C. R. Soc. Biol. Paris, 52: 822–824.
MAYER, A. G., 1906, Carnegie Inst., Washington, Publ., 7: 1–62; 1912, Science, 35: 465; 1917, U. S. Nat. Mus. Bull., 100: iii, 175–233; 1922, Dept. Mar. Biol. Carnegie Inst., 18: 61–85.
MAYER, A. G., and C. G. SOULE, 1906, J. Exper. Zoöl., 3: 415–433.
MEADE-WALDO, G., 1910, T. Entom. Soc. London, (1910): L–L11.
MEEK, A., 1916, The Migrations of Fish, London, xiv + 427.
MÉGNIN, P., 1896, Bull. Mus. Hist. Nat., Paris, 2: 187–190.
MEINERTZHAGEN, R., 1921, Smithsonian Rept., (1919): 339–348; 1922, Smithsonian Rept., (1921): 365–372.
MEISSNER, V., 1909, Zs. Insektenbiol., 5: 319–320.
MELANDER, A. L., and C. T. BRUES, 1903, Biol. Bull., 5: 1–27; 1906, Bull. Wis. Nat. His. Soc., 4: 22–36.
MELROSE, J. A., 1921, Psychol. Rev., 28: 189–221.
MENZEL, H., 1913, Zoöl. Jahrb., Allgem. Zoöl. u. Physiol., 33: 235–258.
MERRIAM, C. H., 1890, N. A. Fauna, 3: 1–136; 1898, U. S. Dept. Agr., Biol. Surv. Bull., 10: 1–79; 1899, U. S. Dept. Agr. N. A. Fauna, 16: 1–179.
METCALF, Z. P., 1924, Ecology, 5: 171–174.
MIALL, L. C., 1893, Smithsonian Rept., (1891): 349–364.
MICHAEL, E. L., 1916, U. Cal. Publ. Zoöl., 15: i–xxiii; *Ibid.*, 18: 239–298; 1919, Bull. Scripps Inst. Biol. Res., U. Cal., 9: 51–57.
MILL, J. S., 1848, Principles of Political Economy, Boston, 2 vols.
MILLER, A. R., 1902, Science, 16: 514–515.
MILLER, W. J. C., 1897, Nature Notes, 8: 181–188.
MILLS, W., 1903, Pop. Sci. Mo., 62: 344–347.
MITCHELL, E. G., 1905, Canad. Entom., 37–332.
MOFFATT, C. B., 1904, Irish Nat., 13: 81–87; 1905, *Ibid.*, 14: 97–108.

MONARD, A., 1918, Rev. Suisse Zoöl., 26: 341–359.

MONTGOMERY, T. H., 1906, The Analysis of Racial Descent in Animals, N. Y., xi + 311; 1910, Amer. Nat., 44: 151–177.

MOORE, B., Science, 51: 66–68; 1922, Ecology, 3: 65–83.

MOORE, B., and G. A. HERDMAN, 1914, T. Liverpool Biol. Soc., 28: 411–419.

MOORE, B., E. S., EDDIE, and E. WHITLEY, 1914; *Ibid.*, 28: 387–410.

MOORE, E., 1922, N. Y. Conserv. Com., 52–63.

MOORE, H. F., 1919, Smithsonian Rept., (1917): 595–608.

MOORE, J. E. S., 1907, Rept. Meet. Brit. Assn. Adv. Sci., 76: 601.

MOORE, J. P., 1899, P. Acad. Nat. Sci., Philadelphia, (1899): 125–144; 1922, Rept. U. S. Fish. Com., (1922): 1–60.

MORGAN, A. H., 1913, Ann. Entom. Soc. Amer., 6: 371–413.

MORGAN, C. L., 1891, Habit and Instinct, London, 1–351; 1900, Animal Behavior, London, viii + 344.

MORGAN, T. H., 1907, Experimental Zoölogy, N. Y., xii + 454.

MORGAN, T. H., and A. F. SHULL, 1910, Ann. Entom. Soc. Amer., 3: 144–146.

MORGULIS, S., 1923, Sci. Mo., 16: 54–65.

MORLEY, C., 1907, Entom. Mo. Mag., (2) 18: 45–51.

MORSE, A. P., 1904, Publ. 18, Carnegie Inst., Washington, 1–55; 1906, Rept. Mich. Geol. Surv., (1905): 68–72; 1907, Bull. Carnegie Inst., 1–54.

MOTTRAM, J. C., 1914, Controlled Natural Selection and Value Marking, N. Y., 130; 1918, J. Linn. Soc., 34: 47–63.

MOUSLEY, H., 1921, Auk, 38: 321–328.

MRÁZEK, A., 1913, Biol. Centr., 33: 658–666.

MÜLLER, R. T., 1918, Rev. Suisse Zoöl., 26: 361–408.

MURPHY, R. C., 1923, Geog. Rev., 13: 64–85.

MURRAY, J., 1895, Challenger Repts.: 1431–1464; 1896, C. R. 3 Cong. Intern. Zoöl., Leyden: 99–111; 1897, Nature, 55: 500–501; 1897a, Geol. Mag., (4)4: 227–229; 1897b, Sci. Prog., 6: 379–396; 1898, Smithsonian Rept., (1896): 397–409.

MURRAY, J., and J. HJORT, 1912, The Depths of the Ocean, London, xv + 812; 1914, The Ocean, a General Account of the Science of the Sea, London, iv + 256; 1914a, P. Roy. Inst. Gt. Brit., 20: 625–630.

MUTTKOWSKI, R. A., 1918, Wis. Acad. Sci., Arts, Lett., 19: 374–482; 1920, Bull. Brooklyn Entom. Soc., 15: 89–96; 131–141; 1921, Ann. Entom. Soc. Amer., 16: 150–156; 1921a, Science, 53: 453–454; 1921b, T. Amer. Micr. Soc., 40: 144–157.

N

NATZMER, G., 1913, Biol. Centralb., 33: 666–667.

NEEDHAM, J. G., 1900, Amer. Nat., 34: 361–386; 1901, N. Y. State Mus. Bull., 47: 383–612; 1902, Science, 16: 347–348.

NEEDHAM, J. G., and H. V. WILLIAMSON, 1907, Amer. Nat., 41: 477–494.

NEEDHAM, J. G., and J. T. LLOYD, 1916, The Life of Inland Waters, Ithaca, 1–438.

NEEDHAM, J. G., C. JUDAY, C. K. SIBLEY, and J. O. TITCOMB, 1922, A Biological Survey of Lake George, N. Y., State Conserv. Com., 1–78.

NELSON, E. W., 1921, Nat. Acad. Sci., 16.

NELSON, T. C., 1917, Rept. Dept. Biol. N. J. Exper. Sta., (1916): 399–430; 1921, *Ibid.*, (1920): 319–349; 1922, N. J. Agr. Exper. Sta. Circ., 130: 1–15; 1923, P. Soc. Exper. Biol. & Med., (1923): 90–91; 1923a, R. N. J. Agr. Exper. Sta., (1922): 321–343.

NEWBIGIN, M. I., 1898, Colour in Nature, London, xii + 344.

NEWSTEAD, R., and B. F. CUMMINGS, 1913, Ann. Mag. Nat. Hist., 11: 306–308.

NICHOLS, J. T., 1918, Science, 48: 168–170.

NOBLE, G. K., 1925, J. Morphol. & Physiol., 40: 341–416.

NORMAND, H., 1918, Bull. Soc. Entom. France, (1918): 76–79.

NOVAKOVSKY, S., 1922, Ecology, 3: 275–283.

NOYES, A. A., 1914, Ann. Entom. Soc. Amer., 7: 251–275.

NUTTALL, G. C., 1907, Knowledge, 4: 223–224.

NUTTALL, G. H. F., 1923, Amer. Nat., 77: 449–475.

NUTTING, C. C., 1898, Amer. Nat., 33: 662; 1899, *Ibid.*, 33: 793–799; 1914, Science, 39: 366.

O

OBERHOLSER, H. C., 1921, Smithsonian Rept., (1919): 355–366.

OLMSTED, J. M. D., 1917, J. Exper. Zoöl. 24: 223–236; 1917a, *Ibid.*, 24: 333–380.

OLSEN, C., 1921, Science, 54: 539–541.

O'MALLEY, H. W., and W. H. RICH, 1919, Rept. U. S. Fish., Com. (1918): 1–38.

ORD, G. W., 1900, T. Nat. Hist. Soc. Glasgow, 5: 355–366.

ORTMANN, A. E., 1896, Grundzuge der Marinen Tier Geographie, Jena; 1899, Amer. Nat., 33: 583–591; 1902, P. Amer. Phil. Soc., 41: 267–400; 1902a, Amer. Nat., 36: 157–159; 1920, P. Amer. Phil. Soc., 59: 269–312.

ORTON, J. H., 1920, J. Mar. Biol. Assn., Plymouth, 12: 339–366; 1921, Nature, 106: 533–534.

OSBORN, H., 1909, Pop. Sci. Mo., 73: 85–91.

OSBORN, H. F., 1902, Amer. Nat., 36: 353–363; 1917, The Origin and Evolution of Life, N. Y., xxi + 322.

OSBORN, R. C., 1913, J. N. Y. Entom. Soc., 21: 9–11.

OSSENDOWSKI, F., 1922, Beasts, Men and Gods, N. Y., xiii + 325.

OSTERHOUT, J. Q. V., 1912, Science, 35: 112–115.

OSTWALD, W., 1902, Biol. Centralb., 59: 22–65; 1903, Zoöl. Jahrb., Abt. Syst., 18: 1–62.

P

PACKARD, A. S., 1904, P. Amer. Phil. Soc., 43: 393–450.

PACKARD, E. L., 1918, U. Cal. Publ. Zoöl., 18: 299–336.

PALMER, W., 1909, Auk, 26: 23–36; 1900, Auk, 17: 216–242.

PAPANICOLAOU, G. N., 1923, Anat., Rec., 25: 285–292.

PARKER, G. H., 1913, Amer. Nat., 47: 83–89; 1917, Sci. Mo., 4: 387–409; 1917, J. Exper. Zoöl., 24: 139–148; 1917a, *Ibid.*, 24: 303–332; 1917b, *Ibid.*, 22: 193–230; 1919, *Ibid.*, 27: 499–507; 1922, J. Mammal, 3: 127 –135; 1920, J. Exper. Zoöl., 31: 343–365; 1920a, *Ibid.*, 31: 475–514; 1922, J. Gen. Physiol., 5: 45–64.

PATCH, E. M., 1908, Entom. News, 19: 484–488.

PATTEN, C. J., 1900, Irish Nat., 9: 187–209.

PATTEN, B. M., 1917, J. Exper. Zoöl., 23: 251–276.

PATTERSON, A. H., 1909, Zoölogist, (4) 13: 208–212.

PATTERSON, J. H., 1921, J. Morphol., 36: 40–69.

PAUSE, J., 1918, Zoöl. Jahrb., Allgem. Physiol., 36: 339–452.

PAYNE, F., 1907, Biol. Bull., 13: 317–323; 1911, *Ibid.*, 21: 297–301.

PEARL, R., 1901, R. Mich. Acad. Sci., 3: 75–76; 1914, J. An. Behav., 4: 266–288.

PEARL, R., and S. L. PARKER, 1922, P. Nat. Acad. Sci., 8: 212–219.

PEARSE, A. S., 1911, J. An. Behav., 1: 79–110; 1914, Bull. Wis. Nat. Hist. Soc., 11: 8–34; 12: 72–80; 1914a, Smithsonian Rept., (1913); 415–428; 1915, P. U. S. Nat. Mus., 49: 531–556; 1918, Bull. U. S. Bur. Fish., 35: 245–292; 1919, *Ibid.*, (1918): 1–16; 1920, U. Wis. Stud. Sci., 1: 1–51; 1921, U. Wis. Stud. Sci., 3: 1–61; 1921a, Bull. U. S. Bur. Fish., 37: 255–272; 1921b, *Ibid.*, 49: 1–8; 1923, Ecology, 4: 24–28; 1924, *Ibid.*, 5: 254–258; 1924a, T. Wis. Acad., 21: 161–194; 1925, Ecology, 6: 7–16.

PEARSE, A. S., and H. ACHTENBERG, 1920, Bull. U. S. Bur. Fish., 36: 293–366.

PELSENEER, P., 1906, Revue du mois, Paris, 2: 413–425.

PENNINGTON, L. H., 1906, Rept. Mich. Acad. Sci., 8: 54– 63.

PEPOON, H. S., 1909, School Sci. & Math., 9: 441–446, 522–527.

PETERSEN, W., 1924, Anat. Rec., 29: 131.

PETERSON, C. G. J., 1918, Rept. Danish Biol. Sta., 1–62.

PETERSON, C. G. J., and P. BOYSEN, 1911, J. Roy. Micr. Soc., (1911): 741.

PETRUCCI, R., 1906, Origine polyphyletique homotypie et non-comparabilitie directe des Societes Animales, Brussels, viii + 126.

PFEFFER, G., 1901, Ann. Mag. Nat. Hist., (7) 7: 301–322.

PHILLIPS, J. C., Auk, 30: 205–221.

PICADO, C., 1913, Bull. Sci. France Belg., 7 (47): 215–360.

PICTET, A., 1913, Mem. Cor. Faculti Sci. Geneve, (1911): 111–278.

PIERCE, W. D., 1916, J. Agr. Res., 5: 1183–1191.

PIÉRON, H., 1908, C. R. Soc. Biol., Paris, 64: 955–957; 1909, *Ibid.*, 148: 530–532.

PIKE, F. H., 1923, Ecology, 4: 129–134.

PIKE, F. H., and E. L. SCOTT, 1915, Amer. Nat., 49: 321–359.

PING, C., 1921, Cornell Agr. Exper. Sta., Mem. 49: 555–616.

PLATH, O. E., 1922, Biol. Bull., 43: 23–44.

PLOUGH, H. H., 1917, J. Exper. Zoöl., 24: 147–192.

POCOCK, R. J., 1901, Nature, 63: 466; 1910, P. Zoöl. Soc. London, (1910): 837–840; 1911, Ann. Mag. Nat. Hist., 8: 750–757.

POCOCK, R. J., and E. B. POULTON, 1911, P. Zoöl., Soc. London, (1911) 2: 804–868.

POLIMANTI, O., 1911, Zoöl. Jahrb. Allgem. Zoöl. u. Physiol., 30: 359–376; 1914, J. An. Behav., 4: 289–292.

POND, R. H., 1905, U. S. Fish. Com. Rept., (1903); 483–526.

POTTS, F. A., 1909, Parasitology, 2: 42–56; 1914, P. Cambridge Phil. Soc., 17: 460–465.

POULTON, E. B., 1888, T. Roy. Soc. London, 178B: 311–441; 1890, The Colours of Animals, London, xvi + 360; 1913, Entom. Mo. Mag., (1913): 177–180; 1921, T. Entom. Soc. London, (1921): xcix–c.

POUND, R., and F. E. CLEMENTS, 1898, Bot. Gaz., 25: 370–372.

POWERS, E. B., 1921, Publ. Puget Sound Biol. Sta., 3: 1–22; 1923, Ecology, 4: 307–312.

PRATT, E., 1901, M. & P. Manchester Lit. Phil. Soc., 45: 1–5.

PRATT, F. C., 1912, Canad. Entom., 44: 180–184.

PRICER, J. L., 1908, Biol. Bull., 14: 177–218.

PRZIBRAM, H., 1911, J. Exper. Zoöl., 10: 255–264.

PUNNETT, R. C., 1915, Mimicry in Butterflies, Cambridge, viii + 188.

PURDY, W. C., 1923, U. S. Pub. Health Bull., 131: i–v, 1–78.

PUSCHAREW, B. M., 1913, Arch. Protistenk, 28: 323–362.

PÜTTER, A., 1907, Zeitsch. Allgem. Physiol., 7: 283–320; 1907a, *Ibid.*, 7: 321–368; 1923, Pflüger's Arch. Ges. Physiol., 201; 501–536; 1924, Arch. Hydriobiol., 15: 70–117.

PYCRAFT, W. P., 1913, The Infancy of Animals, N. Y., xiv + 272.

R

RACOVITZA, E. G., 1904, Smithsonian Rept., (1903): 627–645; 1907, Arch. Zoöl. Paris, (4) 6: 372–488.

RANSOM, B. H., 1906, Yrbk. U. S. Dept. Agr., (1905): 139–166.

RASMUSSEN, A., 1923, J. Morphol., 38: 147–205.

RASPAIL, X., 1901, Bull. Soc. Zoöl. France, 26: 53–61.

RATHBUN, M. J., 1905, P. Acad. Nat. Sci. Philadelphia, 57: 371–372.

RAU, P. and N., 1916, J. An. Behav., 6: 27–63.

REDFIELD, E. S. P., 1917, J. Exper. Zoöl., 22: 231–240.

REED, H. S., 1901, Rept. Mich. Acad. Sci., 3: 43–45.

REEKER, H., 1896, Zoöl. Anzeig, 19: 3–5.

REGIS, J., 1905, Naturaliste, Paris, Ann., 27: 26–27, 50–52, 61–62, 74–75, 99–100, 256, 268.

REGNAULT, F., 1915, Smithsonian Rept., (1914): 593–597.

REIGHARD, J., 1894, Bull. Mich. Fish. Com., 4: 1–61; 1903, Mark Ann. Vol.: 57–109; 1908, Pap. Tortugas Lab. Carnegie Inst., Washington, 2: 257–325; 1910, Bull. U. S. Bur. Fish., 28: 1112–11B6.

REINHEIMER, H., 1921, Sci. Prog., 16: 258–284.

REYNAUD, G., 1899, Smithsonian Rept., (1898): 481–498.

REYNOLDS, W. E., 1920, Sci. Prog., 15: 250–264.

RHODE, C., 1912, Deutsch. Ent. Zeitschr., (1912): 203–223, 386.

RICH, W. H., 1920, Bull. U. S. Bur. Fish., 37: 1–73; 1921, Cal. Fish. & Game, 7: 7–8.

RICHARDSON, C. H., 1914, Psyche, 21: 136–137.

RICHARDSON, R. E., 1921, Ill. Nat. Hist. Surv., 13: 363–522; 1921, *Ibid.*, 13: 359–522.

RICKETT, H. W., 1920, Science, 52: 641–642; 1922, T. Wis. Acad. Sci., 20: 501–527; 1924, *Ibid.*, 21: 381–414.

RIDGWAY, R., 1922, Smithsonian Rept., (1921): 303–324.

RIDLEY, H. N., 1899, J. Straits Brit. Roy. Asiat. Soc., 32: 185–210; 1910, Ann. Bot. London, 24: 457–483.

RIDSDALE, E. L. J., 1896, Nature, 54: 248, 573, 621–622.

RILEY, C. V., 1892, 3 Ann. Rept. Mo. Bot. Garden, (1891): 99–158; 1893, P. Biol. Soc. Washington, 7: 81–104.

RITCHIE, J., 1920, The Influence of Man on Animal Life in Scotland, Cambridge, xvi + 550.

RITTER, W. E., 1909, U. Cal. Publ. Zoöl., 6: 65–114; 1918, Bull. Scripps Inst. Biol. Res., 5: 20; 1921, Condor, 23: 3–14; 1922, *Ibid.*, 24: 109–122.

RITTER, W. E., and B. M. DAVIS, 1903, U. Cal. Publ. Zoöl., 1: 171–210.

ROBERTSON, A., 1921, T. Amer. Fish. Soc., 51: 87–90; 1921*a*, *Ibid.*, 51: 91–96.

ROBERTSON, C., 1895, Amer. Nat., 29: 99–117; 1896–1899, Bot. Gaz., 21: 72–81, 266–274; 22: 154–165; 25: 229–245; 28: 27–45; T. Acad. Sci. St. Louis, 151–179; 1897, Bot. Gaz., 23: 288–289; 1906, Science, 23: 307–310; 1922, Ecology, 3: 17–21; 1922*a*, Sci. Mo., 201–203; 1922, Bot. Gaz., 73: 148–153; 1923, Psyche, 30: 93–111; 1924, Ecology, 5: 393–407; 1924*a*, Psyche, 31: 93–111.

ROGERS, C. G., 1906, Biol. Bull., 10: 165–170.

ROGERS, K. S., 1913, T. Entom. Soc. London, (1912): xcvii–xcix.

ROMANES, J., 1911, P. Cambridge Phil. Soc., 16: 121–123.

ROTHSCHILD, N. C., 1917, T. Entom. Soc. London, (1916): cxli–clvi.

ROUBAUD, E., 1911, C. R. Acad. Sci. Paris, 153: 476–480.

ROULE, L., 1912, C. R. Soc. Biol. Paris, 72: 758–759; 1913, C. R. Assn. Franc. Adv. Sci. Sess., 41: 413–415; 1913*a*, C. R. Acad. Sci. Paris, 157: 1545–1547.

ROWNTREE, L. G., 1922, Physiol. Rev., 2: 116–169.

RUDEMANN, R., 1922, Amer. Nat., 56: 256–272.

RUTHVEN, A. G., 1906, Mich. Geol. Surv. Ann. Rept., (1905): 17–55; 1907, Amer. Mus. Nat. Hist. Bull., 23: 483–604; 1908, Amer. Nat., 2: 388–393; 1908, U. S. Nat. Mus. Bull., 61: 1–201; 1911, Mich. Geol. & Biol. Surv. Publ. 4, Biol. S., 2: 1–347; 1922, U. Mich., Mus. Zoöl., Misc. Publ., 8: 1–69.

RYDER, J. A., 1886, Amer. Nat., 20: 823–824.

S

SAFFORD, W. E., 1923, Smithsonian Rept., (1921): 381–394.

SALISBURY, R. D., 1919, Physiography, N. Y., xv + 676.

SAMPSON, L. V., 1900, Amer. Nat., 34: 687–715.

SANDERS, N. J., and V. E. SHELFORD, 1922, Ecology, 3: 306–320

SASAKI, M., 1923, Annat. Zoöl. Japan, 10: 209–213.

SATTERTHWAIT, A. F., 1921, Ecology, 2: 198–210.

SAUNDERS, A. A., 1914, Auk, 31: 200–210; 1924, Carnegie Inst. Yrbk., (1923): 163–169; 1923, Syracuse U. Bull., 22: 239–354.

SAVILLE-KENT, W., 1897, Nature, 57: 81–82.

SCHAEFFER, A. A., 1910, J. Exper. Zoöl., 8: 75–132.

SCHANTZ, H. L., 1907, T. Amer. Micr. Soc., 27: 75–98.

SCHARFF, R. F., 1907, European Animals; Their Geological History and Geographic Distribution, London, xiv + 258; 1912, Distribution and Origin of Life in America, N. Y., xvi + 497.

SCHEFFER, T. H., 1905, Kans. U. Sci. Bull., 3: 85–114.

SCHLESINGER, G., 1911, Zoöl. Jahrb. Syst., 31: 469–480.

SCHEURING, L., 1915, Biol. Centralb., 35: 181–190.

SCHIMPER, A. F. W., 1903, Plant Geography upon a Physiological Basis, Pt., Oxford, 1–256.

SCHMIDT, P., 1919, Smithsonian Rept., (1917): 501–505.

SCHNEIDER, G. H., 1909, Vorlesungen uber Tierpsychologie, Leipzig, xii + 310.

SCHOENICHEN, W., 1903, Der Scheintod als Schutzmittel des Lebens. Odenkirchen, ii + 107; 1906, Aus der Wiege des Lebens, Osterwieck, 1–130.

SCHRADER, W., 1909, Entom. News, 20: 351–352.

SCHREINER, S. C. C., 1897, Zoölogist, 1: 97–120, 167–168; 1897a, Nature, 55: 546–547.

SCHUCHERT, C., 1910, Bull. Geol. Soc. N. Am., 20: 427–606.

SCHUETTE, H. A., 1918, T. Wis. Acad. Sci., Arts, Lett., 19: 594–613.

SCHUETTE, H. A., and A. E. HOFFMAN, 1922, *Ibid.*, 20: 529–531.

SCHULTZ, E., 1912, Aufsatz. u. Entw.-mech. d. Organ., 14: 1–26.

SCHWARZ, E. A., 1905, P. Entom. Soc. Washington, 7: 5–9.

SCOTT, H., 1912, Ann. Mag. Nat. Hist., (8) 10: 424–438.

SCOTT, W., 1909, Biol. Bull., 17: 386–407; 1910, Ind. Acad. Sci., (1910): 1–48.

SCOTT, W. E. D., 1902, Science, 16: 70–71.

SCOURFIELD, D. J., 1894, J. Linn. Soc., 25: 1–19; 1899, J. Quekett Micr. Club, (1900): 395–404; 1900, *Ibid.*, (2) 7: 309–312; 1900a, *Ibid.*, (2) 10: 357–366; 1901, *Ibid.*, 11: 137–142.

SEKERA, E., 1907, Arch. Hydrobiol., 2: 342–354.

SELL, H., 1907, *Ibid.*, 3: 179–188.

SELOUS, E., 1908, Zoölogist, (4) 12: 333–341.

SELOUS, F. C., 1908, African Nature Notes and Reminiscences, London, xxx + 356.

SEMPER, C., 1881, Animal Life as Affected by the Natural Conditions of Existence, N. Y., xvi + 472.

SETCHELL, W. A., 1920, Amer. Nat., 54: 385–397; 1922, Science, 56: 575–577.

SETON, E. T., 1909, Life Histories of Northern Animals, N. Y., xxx + 673; xii + 677–1267; 1911, The Arctic Prairies, Y. N., xvi + 415; 1920, J. Mammal, 1: 53–57.

SEVERIN, H. P. and H. C., 1911, J. Econ. Entom., 4: 307–320; 1911, Behav. Monogr., 1: 1–44.

SEYSTER, E. W., 1919, Biol. Bull., 37: 168–182.

SHACKLETON, E., 1910, Smithsonian Rept., (1909): 355–368.

SHANTZ, H. L., 1906, Bot. Gaz., 42: 179–207; 1907, T. Amer. Micr. Soc., 27: 75–98.

SHARP, D., 1896, Entomologist, 29: 325–327; 1899, P. Cambridge Phil. Soc., 10: 236–240.

SHAW, W. T., 1921, Ecology, 2: 189–192; 1925, *Ibid.*, 6: 75–81.

SHELFORD, R. W. C., and E. B. POULTON, 1916, A Naturalist in Borneo, London, xviii + 319.

SHELFORD, V. E., 1907, Biol. Bull., 14: 9–14; 1908, J. Linn. Soc., Zoöl., 30: 157–184; 1911, J. Morphol., 22: 551–618; 1911a, Biol. Bull., 21: 11–35; 1911b, *Ibid.*, 21: 127–151; 1911c, *Ibid.*, 22: 1–38; 1912, *Ibid.*, 23: 59–99; 1912a, *Ibid.*, 23: 331–370; 1913, Animal Communities in Temperate America, Chicago, xiii + 362; 1914, Biol. Bull., 25: 79–120; 1914a, *Ibid.*, 26: 294–315; 1914b, J. An. Behav., 4: 31–49; 1915, Biol. Bull., 28: 315–334; 1915a, J. Ecol., 3: 1–23; 1916, Puget Sound Mar. Sta. Publ., 1: 157–176; 1917, Ill. Biol. Monogr., 3: 1–137; 1917a, Bull. Ill. State Lab. Nat. Hist., 11: 337–410; 1918, Amer. Nat., 32: 129–154; 1918a, Science, 48: 225–230; 1918b, 1918c, Bull. Ill. Nat. Hist. Surv., 13: 25–42; 1919, Sci. Mo., 7: 97–124; 1920, Geog. Rev., 9: 250–263.

SHELFORD, V. E., and W. C. ALEE, 1912, Science, 36: 76–77.

SHELFORD, V. E., and F. W. GAIL, 1922, Publ. Puget Sound Biol. Sta., 3: 141–176.

SHERMAN, A. R., 1910, Wilson Bull., 22: 117–118.

SHREVE, F., 1919, Prog., Ecol. Soc. Amer. St. Louis, 1–10; 1924, Ecology, 5: 128–136.

SHULL, A. F., 1914, Amer. Nat., 48: 161–176, 236–247; 1917, Genetics, 2: 480–488; 1917a, Amer. Nat., 51: 361–370; 1918, Biol. Bull., 34: 335–350; 1918a, Amer. Nat., 52: 507–520; 1923, Eugen., Genet. & Fam., 1: 138–141.

SHULL, A. F., G. R. LA RUE, and A. G. RUTHVEN, 1920, Principles of Animal Biology, N. Y., xv + 441.

SIMROTH, H., 1908, Rept. 77 Brit. Assn. Adv. Sci., Leicester, (1907): 544–545.

SIMSOM, C. C., 1907, Ibis, (9) 1: 380–387.

SJÖSTEDT, Y., 1916, Smithsonian Rept., (1915): 341–347.

SKORIKOV, A., 1906, Bull. Acad. Sci., St. Petersburg, 24: 53–64.

SLADEN, F. W. L., 1912, The Humble Bee, London, xiii + 283

SLEIGHT, C. E., 1913, J. N. Y. Entom. Soc., 21: 4–8.

SLONAKER, J. R., 1901, P. Ind. Acad. Sci., (1900): 167–170.

SLOSSOM, A. T., 1905, Entom. News, 16: 67–71.

SMALLWOOD, W. M., 1916, Biol. Bull., 31: 453–464.

SMITH, B. G., 1907, Science, 25: 784–785.

SMITH, E., 1912, Science, 35: 891–892.

SMITH, H. E., 1915, U. S. Dept. Agr., Bull., 293: 1–12.

SMITH, H. H., 1913, Brit. Birds, 6: 334–336.

SMITH, J. B., 1910, Entom. News, 21: 437–441.

SMYTH, B. B., 1909, T. Kans. Acad. Sci., 22: 384–385.

SNODGRASS, R. E., 1921, Smithsonian Rept., (1919): 381–409; 1922, *Ibid.*, (1920): 485–510.

SNOW, L. M., 1902, Amer. Nat., 36: 855–864.

SNYDER, C. D., 1904, School Sci. & Math., 4: 90–92.

SNYDER, J. O., 1922, Cal. Fish. & Game, 8: 102–107.

SNYDER, J. O., and E. C. SCOFIELD, 1924, Cal. Fish. & Game, 10: 9–17.

SOLOKOWSKY, A., 1910, Aus dem Seelenleben hoherer Tiere, Leipzig, 1–74; 1919, J. Roy. Micr. Soc., (1921): 33.

SOULE, C. G., 1900, Psyche, 9: 7–8.

SOUTHWELL, I., 1905, T. Norfolk Norwich Nat. Soc., 8: 15–21.

SPARROW, C. M., 1923, Science, 57: 488–490.

SPENCER, H., 1924, J. Morphol. & Physiol., 39: 543–551.

STAHL, E., 1888, Pflanzen und Schnecken, Jena, vii + 126.

STARR, I., 1921, Biol. Bull., 40: 134–142.

STEAD, D., 1900, Zoölogist, (4) 4: 345–357.

STEBBING, E. P., 1902, Nature, 66: 407.

STECHOW, E., 1921, Zoöl. Anz., 53: 221–223.

STEEL, D., 1913, Amer. Nat., 47: 429–433.

STEFANSSON, V., 1921, The Friendly Arctic, N. Y., xxxi + 784.

STEINER, A., 1924, Zeitschr. Allgem. Physiol., 2: 23–56.

STEINMANN, P., 1908, Arch. Hydrobiol. Planktonkde., 3: 266–273.

STEPHENSEN, K., 1916, Meddelseler om Grønland, 53: 229–378.

STEUER, A., 1910, Planktonkunde, Leipzig, xv + 723.

STEWART, A., 1915, Plant World, 18: 192–200.

STIASNY, G., 1910, Zoöl. Anz., 35: 561–565, 633.

STIEDLECKI, M., 1909, Biol. Centralb., 29: 704–714, 715–737.

STIMPSON, W., 1870, Amer. Nat., 4: 403–405.

STOCKARD, C. R., 1908, Publ. Carnegie Inst., Washington, Tortugas Lab., 2: 43–59; 1921, Amer. Anat., 28: 115–277.

STRECKER, J. K., 1908, P. Biol. Soc. Washington, 21: 199–206.

STRONG, R. M., 1915, Smithsonian Rept., (1914): 479–509.

STUBBS, F. J., 1912, Zoölogist, (4) 16: 441–449.

SUMNER, F. B., 1910, Bull. U. S. Bur. Fish., 28: 1225–1263; 1911, Science, 34: 928–931; 1911a, J. Exper. Zoöl., 10: 409–505; 1921, J. Mammal., 2: 75–86; 1921a, Bull. Scripps Inst. Biol. Res., 10: 1–12; 1922, Sci. Mo., 14: 223–233; 1922a, Biol. Bull., 43: 123–165.

SUMNER, F. B., and H. S. SWARTH, 1924, J. Mammal., 5: 81–113.

SUTER, R., 1923, N. Y. Conserv. Com., 1–50.

SUTER, R., and E. MOORE, 1922, N. Y. Conserv. Com., 1–34.

SVEC, F., 1897, Bull. Internat. de L'Acad. Sci. Bohême, (1897): 1–19.

SWINGLE, W. W., 1922, Science, 56: 720–721; 1922a, J. Exper. Zoöl., 37: 219–257; 1923, Biol. Bull., 45: 229–253.

SWYNNERTON, C. F. M., 1915, T. Entom. Soc. London, (1915): xxxii–xliv; 1918, J. Nat. Hist., 1: 69–73.

SYMONS, C. T., 1912, Spoila Zeylandica, 8: 65–66.

T

TAYLOR, A. M., 1914, Rept. Meet. Brit. Assn. Adv. Sci., 83: 778.

TAYLOR, W. P., 1922, Ecology, 3: 214–236.

TEPPER, J. G. O., 1913, J. Econ. Entom., 6: 359–361.

TERAO, A., 1917, Annat. Zoöl. Japan, 9: 299–316.

THAYER, A. H., 1912, Sci. Amer., 106: 566, 573, 574.

THAYER, G. H., 1909, Concealing-coloration in the Animal Kingdom, N. Y., xix + 260.

THOMAS, R. H., 1902, Nature, 65: 233.

THOMPSON, C. B., 1917, J. Morphol., 30: 83–154; 1919, Biol. Bull., 36: 379–398; 1922, J. Morphol., 36: 495–537.

THOMPSON, C. B., and T. E. SNYDER, 1919, Biol. Bull., 36: 115–132; 1920, J. Morphol., 34: 591–633.

THOMPSON, D' A. W., 1917, On Growth and Form, Cambridge, xvi + 793.

THOMPSON, D. L., 1923, J. Mar. Biol. Assn., Plymouth, 13: 243–244.

THOMPSON, I. C., 1903, Rept. Southport Soc. Nat. Sci., 8: 19–29.

THOMPSON, M. T., 1907, Psyche, 14: 71–74.

THOMPSON, W. F. and J. B., 1919, Cal. Fish. & Game Com., Fish. Bull., 3: 1–27.

THOMSON, J. A., 1901, Rept. Meet. Brit. Assn. Adv. Sci., Glasgow, 71; 378–382; 1911, The Biology of the Seasons, N. Y., xii + 384.

THORNDIKE, E. L., 1911, Animal Intelligence, N. Y., viii + 297.

THORNTON, H. G., and G. SMITH, 1915, P. Roy. Soc. London, 88B: 151–165.

TILLYARD, R. J., 1911, P. Linn. Soc. N. So. Wales, 35: 666–676; 1917, The Biology of Dragonflies, Cambridge, xii + 396.

TOLLINGER, A., 1911, Zoöl. Jahrb. Syst., 30: 1–302.

TOWER, W. L., 1907, Publ. Carnegie Inst., 48.

TOWNSEND, C. H. C., 1924, Ecology, 5: 14–25.

TOWNSEND, C. W., 1909, Auk, 26: 109–116; 1909, Auk, 26: 234–248.

TRANSEAU, E. N., 1903, Bot. Gaz., 36: 401–420; 1905, *Ibid.*, 40: 351–375, 418–448, 41: 17–42; 1905, Amer. Nat., 39: 875–889.

TREADWELL, A. L., 1915, Science, 41: 438.

TROLLEOPE, C., 1899, Zoölogist, (4) 3: 403–406.

TROUESSART, E., 1901, Bull. Soc. Zoöl. France, 26: 10–20.

TURNER, C. E., 1918, Sci. Mo., 7: 34–45.

TURNER, C. H., 1911, J. An. Behav., 1: 401–412; 1911, Biol. Bull., 21: 249–264; 1913, J. An. Behav., 3: 401–428; 1922, Biol. Bull., 42: 153–172.

TURNER, E. L., and P. H. BAHR, 1907, The Home Life of Some Marsh-birds, Brit. Birds, 1 Suppl.: 1–62.

TUTT, J. W., 1902, Migration and Dispersal of Insects, London, ii + 132.

U

UEXKULL, J. VON, 1909, Umwelt und Innenwelt der Tiere, Berlin, iv + 260.

UHLENHUTH, E., 1915, Biol. Bull., 29: 138–147.

UICHANCO, L. B., 1919, Philippine J. Sci., 15: 59–65.

ULRICH, J. L., 1921, J. Comp. Psychol., 1: 1–95, 155–199, 221–286.

UVAROV, B. P., 1921, Bull. Entom. Res., 12: 135–163.

V

VAN BENEDEN, P. J., 1876, Animal Parasites and Messmates, London, xxvii + 274.

VAN CLEAVE, H. J., 1916, J. Parasitol., 2: 106–110; 1920 T., Ill. Acad. Sci., 13: 280–292; 1921, T. Amer. Micr. Soc., 49: 1–13.

VAN DER HEYDE, H. C., 1921, Biol. Bull., 41: 249–255; 1922, *Ibid.*, 42: 95–98; 1922, J. Exper. Zoöl., 35: 335–352.

VAN NAME, W. G., 1921, Bull. Amer. Mus. Nat. Hist., 44: 275–282; 1921*a*. *Ibid.*, 44: 283–494.

VAUGHN, T. W., 1919, Smithsonian Rept., (1917): 189–276.

VERRILL, A. E., 1873, Invertebrate Animals of Vineyard Sound, Rept. U. S. Fish., Com., (1871–1872): 295–538.

VESTAL, A. G., 1913, Biol. Bull., 25: 141–180; 1913, Ill. State Lab. Nat. Hist., 10: 1–96; 1914, Amer. Nat., 48: 413–445; 1917, Bot. Gaz., 64: 353–385.

VINE, H. C. A., 1896, Inter. J. Micr. Nat. Sci., 15: 35–45, 157–178, 249–263, 369–375.

VIRÉ, A., 1904, C. R. Acad. Sci. Paris, 139: 992–995.

VISCOSA, P., JR., 1923, Copeia, (1923): 35–44.

VISHER, S. S., 1923, Ecology, 4: 1–10.

VORHIES, C. T., 1917, Amer. Nat., 51: 494–499.

VORHIES, C. T., and W. P. TAYLOR, 1922, U. S. Dept. Agr., Bull., 1091: 1–40.

W

WAGNER, F. VON, 1906, Zoöl., Jahrb.; Syst., 23: 295–318.

WAKSMAN, S. A., 1924, Ecology, 5: 54–59.

WALL, F., 1907, J. Bombay Nat. Hist. Soc., 17: 375–395.

WALLACE, A. R., 1876, The Geographical Distribution of Animals, London, xxiv + 503, xi + 607; 1878, Tropical Nature and Other Essays, London, xiv + 356; 1880, Island Life, London, xviii + 526; Natural Selection and Tropical Nature, London, xii + 492; 1902, Island Life, London, xx + 563; 1905, Darwinism, London, x + 494; 1912, Darwinism, London, xx + 494.

WALLER, A. E., 1918, J. Amer. Soc. Agron., 10: 49–83.

WALLIN, I. E., 1923, J. Anat. Rec., 25: 65–73.

WALTER, H. E., 1908, School Sci. & Math., 8: 1–16.

WARBURTON, C., 1902, J. Linn. Soc. London, Zoöl., 28: 366–378.

WARD, H. B., 1909, 7 Intern. Zoöl. Cong., Boston, 1–12; 1921, Ecology, 2: 236–254.

WARD, H. B., and G. C. WHIPPLE, 1918, Freshwater Biology, N. .Y., ix + 1111.

WARMING, E., 1909, Oecology of Plants, Oxford, xi + 422.

WARREN, E., 1900, Q. J. Micr. Sci., 43: 199–224.

WASHBURN, M. F., 1911, J. An. Behav., 1: 456–460.

WASMANN, E., 1909, Biol. Centralb., 29: 683–703; 1912, Zoöl., Anzeig., 39: 473–481; 1913, Smithsonian Rept., (1912): 455–471.

WATSON, A. T., 1903, Brit. Assn. Adv. Sci., Belfast, 72: 652; 1907, Brit. Assn. Adv. Sci., 76: 599.

WATSON, J. B., 1911, J. An. Behav., 1: 430–464.

WATSON, J. B., and K. S. LASHLEY, 1913, J. An. Behav., 3: 446–462; 1915, Pap. Dept. Mar. Biol. Carnegie Inst., Washington, 7: 1–60; 1915, *Ibid.*, 61–83.

WEAVER, J. E., and A. F. THIEL, 1917, Bot. Surv. Nebr., 1: 1–60.
WEBSTER, F. M., 1903, Amer. Nat., 36: 795–801.
WEDDERBURN, E. M., 1911, Rev. Hydrobiol. u. Hydrogr., 4: 55–63.
WEESE, A. O., 1921, Prog. Ecol. Soc. Amer. (1921) 1–20; 1922, *Ibid.*, 4: 1–16.
WEISS, H. B., 1913, Canad. Entom., 45: 135–137; 1913a, *Ibid.*, 45: 302–304.
WEISS, H. B., and E. WEST, 1922, J. N. Y. Entom. Soc., 30: 170–190; 1924, Ecology, 5: 241–253.
WEITH, R. J., 1902, Entom. News, 13: 90.
WELCH, P. S., 1919, Ann. Entom. Soc. Amer., 12: 213–226.
WELCH, P. S., and H. A. Loomis, 1924, T. Amer. Micr. Soc., 43: 203–235.
WELCH, P. S., and L. P. WEHRLE, 1919, T. Amer. Micr. Soc., 37: 141–176.
WELLS, M. M., 1913, Biol. Bull., 25: 323–347.
WESENBERG-LUND, C., 1901, Biol. Centralbl., 20: 606–619, 644–656, 1905, P. Roy. Soc. Edinburgh, 25: 401–448; 1908, Science, 30: 345–346; 1908a, Intern. Rev., Hydrobiol. u. Planktonkde, 1: 574–609; 1911, Intern. Rev. Hydrobiol. Hydrogr., (Biol. Suppl)., (III), 5: 1–64; 1911, *Ibid.*, 4: 65–91; 1923, Selsk. Skrifter, Naturvidensk, og. Mathem, (8) 4: 191–345.
WEYMOUTH, F. W., 1918, Brit. Columb. Fish. Dept., (1917): 81–90.
WHEELER, W. M., 1887, P. Nat. Hist. Soc. Wis., 1: 132–140; 1902, Science, 15: 971–976; 1904, Bull. Amer. Mus. Nat. Hist., 20: 139–158; 1907, *Ibid.*, 23: 1–94; 669–808; 1911, J. An. Behav., 1: 413–429; 1911a, J. Morphol., 22: 307–325; 1911b, J. N. Y. Entom. Soc., 19: 169–174; 1913, J. An. Behav., 3: 374–387; 1916, *Ibid.*, 6: 70–73; 1921, J. Abnorm. Psychol., (1920): 295–318; 1922, Biol. Bull., 42; 185–201; 1923, Social Life among the Insects, N. Y., vii + 375; 1923a, Science, 57: 61–71.
WHERRY, E. T., 1922, *Ibid.*, 55: 568–570; 1922a, Smithsonian, Rept., (1920): 247–268; 1924, Ecology, 5: 309.
WHIPPLE, G. C., 1896, N. E. Water Works Assn., 11: 1–26; 1898, Amer. Nat., 32: 25–33.
WHIPPLE, G. C., and H. N. PARKER, 1902, T. Amer. Micr. Soc., 23: 103–144.
WHITEHOUSE, R. H., 1914, Irish Nat., 23: 41–47.
WHITFORD, H. N., 1901, Bot. Gaz., 31: 289–325.
WHITMAN, C. O., 1899, Animal Behavior, Biol. Lect. Mar. Biol. Lab., Woods Hole, 1–338.
WHITNEY, D. D., 1907, Arch. Entw. Mech., 24: 524– 537; 1908, Amer. Nat., 42: 665–671; 1917, J. Exper. Zoöl., 24: 101–138.
WHITNEY, M., 1922, Science, 56: 216–218.
WHITTLE, C. L., 1923, Auk, 40: 224–240.
WIDMAN, O., 1896, Osprey, 1: 304.
WILCOX, M. A., 1905, Amer. Nat., 39: 325–333.
WILDER, H. H., 1901, *Ibid.*, 35: 183–186.
WILLEY, A., 1902, Zoöl. Results, 6: 691–826; 1920, T. Amer. Fish. Soc., 50: 320–325; 1920a, P. Zoöl. Soc. London, (1920): 649–651.
WILLIAMS, F. X., 1909, Entom. News, 20: 58–62.
WILLIAMS, S. R., 1900, Amer. Nat., 34: 95–108.
WILLIAMSON, H. C., 1917, J. Zoöl. Res., 2: 100–110.
WILLIS, J. C., 1913, Nature, 91: 425.

WILLISTON, S. W., 1914, Water Reptiles of the Past and Present, Chicago, vii + 251.

WILSON, C. B., 1901, Biol. Bull., 2: 332–333; 1917, Bull. U. S. Bur. Fish., 34: 331–374.

WILSON, W. P., 1890, P. Acad. Nat. Sci. Philadelphia, (1889): 67–69.

WILSON-BARKER, D., 1899, Nature, 61: 128.

WINCHILL, C. A., 1896, Zoölogist, (3) 20: 77.

WINN, A. F., 1901, Canad. Entom., 33: 330–331; 1902, Ann. Roy. Entom., Soc. Ontario, 32: 82–84.

WITHINGTON, C. H., 1909, T. Kans. Acad. Sci., 22: 314–322.

WODSEDALEK, J. E., 1911, Biol. Bull., 21: 265–271; 1912, J. An. Behav., 2: 1–19.

WOLTERECK, R., 1909, Verhandl. Deutsch. Zoöl. Gesell., (1909): 110–172; 1911, Intern. Rev. Hydrobiol. u. Hydrogr., 4: 91–128.

WOODRUFF, C. E., 1910, Science, 31: 618–620.

WOODRUFF, L. L., 1908, Amer. Nat., 42: 520–526; 1909, Biol. Bull., 17: 287–308; 1911, *Ibid.*, 22: 60–65.

WOODRUFF, L. L., and E. L., MOORE, 1924, P. Nat. Acad. Sci., 10: 183–186.

WOODRUFFE-PEACOCK, E. A., 1900, Naturalist, (1900): 99–108, 114, 156, 192.

WOODWORTH, J. B., 1894, Amer. Geol., 14: 209–235.

WOLCOTT, G. N., 1918, Science, 47: 371–374.

WRIGHT, A. H., 1908, Biol. Bull., 14: 284–289.

Y

YATSU, N., 1902, Annat. Zoöl. Japan, 4: 61–67.

Z

ZACHARIAS, O., 1906, Arch. Hydrobiol., 1: 247–344; 1906, *Ibid.*, 2: 235–238; 1906a, *Ibid.*, 2: 498–575.

ZELENY, C., 1923, Biol. Bull., 44: 105–112.

INDEX